Noise and Vibration Control in the Built Environment

Special Issue Editor
Jian Kang

Special Issue Editor
Jian Kang
University of Sheffield
UK

Editorial Office
MDPI AG
St. Alban-Anlage 66
Basel, Switzerland

This edition is a reprint of the Special Issue published online in the open access journal *Applied Sciences* (ISSN 2076-3417) from 2016–2017 (available at: http://www.mdpi.com/journal/applsci/special_issues/vibration_control).

For citation purposes, cite each article independently as indicated on the article page online and as indicated below:

Author 1; Author 2; Author 3 etc. Article title. *Journal Name*. **Year**. Article number/page range.

ISBN 978-3-03842-420-8 (Pbk)
ISBN 978-3-03842-421-5 (PDF)

Table of Contents

Chapter 1: Urban Sound Environment and Soundscape

Chapter 2: Building Acoustics and Room Acoustics

About the Guest Editor

Jian Kang obtained his first MSc from Tsinghua University and PhD from University of Cambridge. He has been Professor of Acoustics at the University of Sheffield since 2003, and a Professor at the Harbin Institute of Technology since 2005. He was also a Humboldt Fellow at the Fraunhofer Institute of Building Physics in Germany. His field is Environmental and Architectural Acoustics, with over 80 research projects, over 800 publications, and over 90 engineering/consultancy projects. He is a Fellow of the UK Institute of Acoustics (IOA), Acoustical Society of America, and International Institute of Acoustics and Vibration, and an Editor for Acta Acustica united with Acustica. He chairs the Technical Committee for Noise of the European Acoustics Association, and EU COST on Soundscape of European Cities and Landscapes. He was awarded the IOA Tyndall Medal 2008, Peter Lord Award 2014, and the Noise Abatement Society's Lifetime Achievement Award 2014.

Preface to "Noise and Vibration Control in the Built Environment"

Sustainable Urban Sound Environment

Shuo Xian Wu

State Key Laboratory of Subtropical Building Science of China;
Faculty of Architecture, South China University of Technology

Abstract: This paper demonstrates from many ancient Chinese references that for a very long time, before mankind invented letters and hence could pass on culture, thinking and knowledge by reading, hearing historically had the responsibility for handing down cultural heritage and information exchange. This suggests that ancient Chinese people were aware of the importance of soundscape. It is also suggested that regardless of the size, an urban area has to be divided as a bustling quarter, an alleviating quarter and a quiet quarter according to the function and topography of the district to construct a sustainable urban sound environment.

Keywords: Hearing; soundscape; urban noise control

1. Introduction

The importance of sight is well known, but the importance of hearing is not so well understood. To construct a sustainable sound environment, architects, planners and the public have to pay more attention to the role of hearing in our life. Music and language were both invented long before letters and both music and speech are emitted by the mouth and received by the ears. Therefore, before mankind invented letters and hence could pass on culture, thinking and knowledge by reading, hearing was historically responsible for handing down cultural heritage and information exchange. In this paper, a range of ancient Chinese literature was collected to show that the ancient Chinese people were aware of the importance of hearing and soundscape. It is also suggested that, in order to construct a sustainable urban sound environment, regardless of size, the urban area has to be divided into a bustling quarter, an alleviating quarter and a quiet quarter according to the function and topography of the district and we have to put emphasis on the soundscape construction.

2. The Importance of Hearing

People have five sensory organs: eyes, ears, nose, mouth (tongue) and skin. They have visual, auditory, gustatory, olfactory and somatic sensations respectively. Among them, eyes and ears are the most important organs by which people exchange information with the outside world. The importance of seeing is well known by people. Here, the author highlights the importance of sound and hearing, because this is often overlooked.

Sound is related with the two aforementioned sensory organs: one is the mouth with the tongue as a sound emitting organ, the other is the ears as a hearing organ. Mankind has a long history of nearly 2.5 million years. During this period, mankind has used letters (through seeing) as the main medium for cultural heredity for only the last few hundreds of years. For a very long time, before mankind invented letters and hence could pass on culture, thinking and knowledge by reading, hearing was historically responsible for handing down cultural heritage and information exchange.

In ancient China, saint was written as "shèng" which combines both characters of ear (ěr) and mouth (kǒu). This demonstrates that ancient Chinese people paid more attention to the importance of hearing. In Chinese phrases that relate to ears and eyes, and sound and color at the same time, the order is always such that, "ear" is mentioned before "eye" and sound is placed ahead of color. For example, "cōng míng" （cleaver）, "ěr mù" (ear and eye), shēng sè" (sound and color), "ěr mù yī xīn" (find everything fresh and new), and so forth.

Confucius said that when a person reaches sixty years of age, he/she will be pleasing to hear. This demonstrates that he was conscious of the importance of hearing morality. Confucius always conversed with his students and did not write. He passed on his thinking only by talking. His book 《 lún yǔ》 （discourse） is about his recorded utterances collected by his students according to his talking.

Indeed, hearing has some advantages over seeing. Firstly, hearing can occur in a dark environment. The ancient Chinese clearly knew this. 《shuō wén》 (characters explication) said that the "word for referring to oneself, "míng", combines both characters for mouth "kǒu" and evening "xī"; "xī" means dark. In dark environments, people cannot recognize each other, therefore they use names to facilitate recognition". In Chinese language, many words are pronounced like "Yin" "yīn" (musical sound) and usually have the meaning of "dark", such as "dark" (àn) and "àn" (gloomy). Moreover, sound waves have strong penetrating power and can diffract around some objects. Therefore, it is more difficult to avoid sound than it is to avoid light. The ancient Chinese said "You may hear one's sound before seeing him (bú jiàn qí rén, xiān wén qí shēng), "Walls have ears—beware of eavesdroppers!" (gé qiáng yǒu ěr). These idioms illustrate this truth. Furthermore, in comparison with writing, talking is more natural, more immediate and easier. This is the reason why, nowadays, a lot of people prefer calling instead of writing letters. Lastly, it is easier to learn by heart and retain information that is received audially. Famous ancient scholar Zhu Xi said, "Sound is always penetrating the heart" (shēng rù xīn tōng). Talking also has the benefit of two-way exchange; therefore, education is still fundamentally based on teaching orally.

Here, the relationship between hearing and thinking is illustrated. Thinking is mainly based on language. One's stream of consciousness mainly denotes a stream of speech that is read silently in one's mind. Hence, thinking has to be undertaken in a quiet environment. "Tranquility can let thinking go further" （"níng jìng zhì yuǎn"） , "In a quiet night, people can think more deeply" ("jìng yè sī"). All these phrases illustrate the same fact: outside noise can disturb the internal monologue and affect our thinking. Therefore, the construction of a good urban acoustic environment by implementing noise control is very important.

However, sound was not easily recorded, copied and transmitted over long distances until the invention of the gramophone and telephone. Nowadays, new sound techniques such as recording, multi-media, mobile phones, telephones, networks, hi-fi and sound cards are popularized, so that both auralization and visualization have become the most important technologies for advancing the information revolution.

3. Urban Environmental Noise Control

An ancient poet said "To construct a living house in a city, the prerequisite is to avoid noise from carts and horses." But for a long time, in the urban planning for many cities, the planners often failed to take acoustic planning into consideration, so quiet places are scarce in many cities.

Regardless of size, the urban area has to be divided into a bustling quarter, alleviating quarter and quiet quarter according to the function and topography of the district. Green earth dykes, sound screens and special green belts can be used for protection from noise. For example, in the center of New York City, there is a big park which has become a peaceful place for people to escape the noisy business quarter. Both banks of the Seine river of Paris are also designed as peaceful paths where people can easily walk to avoid busy roads.

Nowadays, there are some environmental noise prediction software packages such as CADNA and SOUNDPLAN, etc. By taking measurements and using these software packages, urban planners can predict the noise levels for different places according to the intensity and distribution of noise sources including point, linear or surface sources. In addition, urban noise maps can also be drawn to check the noise levels for different sectors or buildings. The noise map can combine a GIS

(Geographical Information System) system, remote sensing and network technology to promote further analysis and noise planning.

4. Soundscape

The ancient Chinese were aware of the importance of soundscape. Among the ten famous landscapes of West Lake in Hangzhou, three belong to a soundscape such as "liǔ làng wén yīng" (Orioles sing under the willow shade）, "nán píng wǎn zhōng" (Later bell sound emitted from the Nanping temple) and "qǔ yuàn fēng hé" (Lotus leaves swing and swish in the wind by the circuitous courtyard). In the traditional gardens of Suzhou, there are many soundscape places such as "tīng sōng fēng chù" (Place to hear pine wind), "liú tīng gé" (Pavilion to stay and listen) "tīng yǔ xuān" （Hall for enjoying the rain sound）and "wú zhú yōu jū" (Tranquil house for listening to the phoenix and bamboo sound). These places are built especially for enjoying the natural sound of the effect of wind and rain on pine, lotus, phoenix or bamboo.

In the ancient poem or ci works, many sentences illustrate the concept of soundscape, such as "cháng ān yī piàn yuè, wàn hù dǎo yī shēng" (Under the cover of moon light, in Changan city you can hear the beating clothes sound from thousands of families) "xiǎo lóu yī yè tīng chūn yǔ, shēn xiàng míng zhāo mài xìng huā"(Living in a low-rise building to hear the sound of spring rainfall for a whole night, and you can also hear the yell of apricot flowers being sold from the deep alley in the morning).

In traditional acoustics, the physical properties of sound waves such as frequency, intensity, wavelength and the propagation characteristics of sound in the air or other elastic media are usually studied. However, when dealing with the human responses to sound and the acoustic environment, relative parameters are more complicated. Not only the physical properties of sound, but also the information carried by the sound and the social, historical as well as geographical status of the listeners are all important factors. Therefore, the concept of soundscape opens up research areas for traditional architectural and environmental acoustics; thus, it investigates the human acoustic environment with a more holistic approach and by combining other disciplines such as sociology, environmental psychology, art and ecology.

Soundscape research investigates the acoustic characteristics of different geographical areas and different architectural spaces (such as garden, park or inhabitant quarters) in different historical periods. Soundscape also investigates the methods of describing, recording and evaluating soundscape and the techniques and skills for constructing a special soundscape. One of the purposes of soundscape research is to find and preserve valuable and typical soundscapes.

In the long evolutionary history of mankind, people have enjoyed natural sounds such as tides, water flowing and water falling, wind and rain, birds singing and insects crying as well as the sounds of pine and bamboo, etc. Manmade sounds such as the bell or drum, chimes and musical sounds emitted from stringed or wind instruments have also been enjoyed. This behavior is deeply rooted in our genetics and blood. This forms the base for people to notice, enjoy and need soundscape. Therefore, the improvement of the urban sound environment has to include the construction of soundscape.

The preservation and construction of urban soundscape fulfils the requirement of urban ecological construction, environmental protection and sustainable development; because, only in a good urban ecological environment, can the natural animal, vegetation and climatic sound sources such as birds or insects, pine or bamboo and wind or rain etc., be offered in abundance.

5. Conclusions

Music and language were both invented long before letters and both music and speech are emitted by the mouth and received by the ears; therefore, for a very long time—before mankind invented letters and hence could pass on culture, thinking and knowledge by reading—hearing was historically responsible for handing down cultural heritage and information exchange. The ancient Chinese people were aware of the importance of hearing and soundscape. To construct a sustainable urban sound environment, regardless of size, the urban area has to be divided into a bustling quarter, alleviating quarter and quiet quarter according to the function and topography of the district and people have to emphasize the importance of soundscape construction.

References

1. Yuan, X.; Wu, S. Construction of soundscape in traditional Chinese gardens. *J. Archit.* **2007**, *5*, 70–72 (in Chinese).

Chapter 1:
Sustainable Urban Sound Environment and Soundscape

Article

An Experimental Study on the Influence of Soundscapes on People's Behaviour in an Open Public Space

Francesco Aletta [1], Federica Lepore [2], Eirini Kostara-Konstantinou [2], Jian Kang [1,*]
and Arianna Astolfi [2]

[1]   School of Architecture, University of Sheffield, Sheffield S102TN, UK; f.aletta@sheffield.ac.uk
[2]   Department of Energy, Politecnico di Torino, Torino 10129, Italy; federica.lepore@studenti.polito.it (F.L.);
       eirini.kostarakonstantinou@studenti.polito.it (E.K.-K.); arianna.astolfi@polito.it (A.A.)
*   Correspondence: j.kang@sheffield.ac.uk; Tel.: +44-114-222-0325

Academic Editor: Gino Iannace
Received: 25 July 2016; Accepted: 20 September 2016; Published: 27 September 2016

Abstract: Several studies have investigated how environmental sounds and music can modulate people's behaviours, particularly in marketing research. However, there are relatively few examples of research about such relationships with a focus on the management of urban public spaces. The current study investigated an open public space used mainly as a pedestrian crossing to analyse the relationship between the audio stimuli and peoples' behaviours. An experiment relying on covert behavioural observation was performed. During the experiment, three different music stimuli and a control condition (i.e., no music) were reproduced in order to find out firstly whether music compared to no music could elicit an increase in the number of people stopping in the investigated area, and secondly whether music is associated with a longer duration of stay for those who stop. Results showed that the presence of music had no effect on the number of people stopping in the area, but it had a statistically significant effect on the duration of stay for those who stopped. The above findings support the idea that people felt more invited to stay in the area with music rather than with no music, and suggest that the acoustical manipulation of the existing sound environment could provide soundscape strategies capable of promoting social cohesion in public spaces.

Keywords: soundscape; music stimuli; environmental noise; people's behaviour

1. Introduction

Since the 1970s, soundscape started to emerge as a new science and research field. Schafer and his colleagues defined this concept as "an environment of sound (or sonic environment) with emphasis on the way it is perceived and understood by the individual or a society" [1]. The International Organization for Standardization [2] released a standard in 2014 where soundscape is defined as the "acoustic environment as perceived or experienced and/or understood by a person or people, in context". The number of studies in the field is increasing over time, and there is more and more research interest on the relationships between sonic environments, people, and contexts.

Over the last decades, several studies have investigated the influence of environmental sounds and music on peoples' behaviour, especially in terms of the pace of some activities or performance, mainly with a commercial or business perspective. These studies considered the effects of sound on individuals' mood, music perception, and behaviours through a wide range of parameters, such as productivity in the workplace, pace of shopping, and time and money spent in aggregation places (e.g., restaurants and shopping malls). Regarding product choice, Areni and Kim [3] showed that classical music played in a wine shop resulted in consumers choosing more expensive wines. Generally, the results supported the idea that a good perceived match between music and context improves persuasion. Subsequently, Yalch and Spangenberg [4] focused their research on time spent in a retail context, and suggested that more familiar background music (vs. less familiar) decreased consumers' actual shopping time, and, conversely, unfamiliar music triggered consumers' attention.

Previously, Milliman [5] investigated the relationship between pace of shopping, sales, and tempo. His research suggested that slower music is related to a slower pace of peoples' movement in a retail environment, and, as a result, more time and money spent there; while fast musical tempo reproduced in a restaurant caused a shorter duration of eating time [6]. Focusing more on the effect of music tempo, Kampfe, Sedlmeier, and Renkewitz [7] asserted that hearing background music characterized by a fast tempo leads to an increase in the pace of certain behaviours, such as drawing, reading, walking and running, and eating and drinking. In general, there are two fundamental hypotheses for these effects; the first is the synchronization of the movements to the musical beat, while the second is the increase in the arousal found with fast-tempo music [8].

Even if several studies explored the effect of sound environment on consumers' behaviour (mainly observed in indoor contexts), there have been limited studies investigating its effects regarding the management of public urban spaces. There is an increasing interest about the effects of background sounds on listeners' behaviour, focusing on the effectiveness of soundscape strategies on the sustainable development of cities and the improvement of the health and the quality of life [9]. Witchel et al. [10] managed to improve crowd behaviour and to decrease anti-social behaviours through the manipulation of the outdoor acoustic environment with sounds and music played onto the main street of the city's busiest clubbing and entertainment district in Brighton and Hove (UK). Sayin et al. [6] reported a significant effect of human sounds and music on the perceived safety of individuals in public places that are characterized by people's reluctance and avoidance, such as car parks, metro stations, and many green areas. Finally, Thomas Schafer et al. [11] assessed the relationship between the processing of music and the experience of safety and danger and found that music scenarios are experienced as less stressful and dangerous than silent scenarios. In particular, silence or very repetitive and monotonous auditory stimuli representing absence of information about the surroundings might be expected to evoke feelings of stress or danger. While the study by Schafer et al. relied on a laboratory experiment, raising some issues about its ecological validity, it does show that music can modulate human perception and behaviours.

All of the above-mentioned research focusing on public spaces explored the potential of sound to decrease anti-social behaviour and negative feelings such as anxiety and lack of safety in public areas. According to Brown et al. [12], safety and sense of control are some of the outcomes included in the philosophy of soundscape. Communication, enjoyment, and comfort are other aspects underpinning the final soundscape construct. However, there is a current lack of research focusing on these latter aspects, and overall on the potential of the acoustic environment to support social cohesion in public spaces. The "safer, cleaner, greener" UK policy on "live-ability" [13] for well-designed and well-planned urban places was discussed by Dempsey [14], who investigated the relationship between a good-quality built environment and social cohesion through the identification of features capable of providing quality in the built environment. Accessibility, inclusiveness, connectedness, and permeability were some of the analysed features, contextualized within a neighbourhood.

The current research focused on the area under the Concourse Bridge, the improvement of which is one of the key projects of the long-term Masterplan proposed by the University of Sheffield and built upon the University Estates Strategy 2010–2015. The intention is to reinforce the link between the connected spaces and upgrade the quality of the area through a combination of traditional urban renewal practises based on visual aspects (e.g., light, greenery) [15]. In addition to this, the rationale for the current study was to test whether the sound—as a feature of the physical environment—would influence peoples' perception of a public place with no particular aesthetic and social dimension, through the introduction of music in order to create a more "desirable" public space and lead the end users to a satisfying experience without any kind of intervention on the existing buildings.

In particular, the main aims of the study were: (1) to test whether there is an effect of added music sounds on the number of persons stopping in the selected public urban space; (2) to test whether there is an effect of added music sounds on people's duration of stay in the selected public urban space.

For this purpose, covert behavioural observations were performed under the Concourse Bridge, an open public space at the University of Sheffield (UK), mainly used for connection between different buildings within the University campus. Three different music excerpts and a control condition (no music) were cyclically reproduced over a term week at different times, and video-recording data were gathered and processed for behavioural observations [10]. To the knowledge of the authors, this is one of the first attempts in soundscape studies to manipulate an actual acoustic environment in an open public space, collecting data in a systematic way through a covert observational protocol.

2. Materials and Methods

This study relies on non-participant covert observations, during which the users—not aware of the experiment—were video-recorded, and the final subconscious and spontaneous responses constituted the database used for later behavioural analysis. Indeed, there is still no clear agreement on what is the optimal method for data collection in soundscape studies. In most cases, data collection is participative and participants are required to have an attentive listening style. According to Aletta et al. [16], this raises a question about whether being "aware" of taking part in a soundscape study might actually affect the responses people give. The study received ethic approval through the Ethics Committee procedure of the School of Architecture, University of Sheffield (ref: 002442, January 2015). Cameras were set to a low resolution in order to avoid the identification of peoples' faces.

2.1. Study Area

The analysed public space is inside the University campus, and serves as the connection between different Departments' facilities and the central building where services and administration offices, as well as bars, restaurants, and shops are located. It is a pedestrian area below a raised vehicular bridge, an important crossroad for pedestrians coming from Weston park area, the Alfred Denny Building, the Arts Tower, and the Western Bank Library toward the Hicks building, Students' Union, and the Octagon centre, and it has not undergone any particular design interventions over the past 15 years. Since then, different attempts have been made to substantially improve the public space and enhance the public dimension underneath the Concourse Bridge, which is made of raw concrete, mainly in dim light during the day and poorly lit at night, and hosts the highest pedestrian affluence across campus. The Concourse Bridge is a key student space providing an important link beneath Western Bank, offering space for shelter and gatherings [15]. It constitutes a node where people usually stop for a break between various activities within the campus. Given the centrality of the area, the space—divided by pylons into two branches—presents low solid parapets along the edges used like benches in order to facilitate people's stay. The main sound sources are human voices and the traffic coming from the upper arterial road of Western Bank. Figure 1 shows the location of the site, as well as the observation area and the location of the cameras, which will be better described in the following section.

Figure 1. Plan of the site (**left**); the green area shows the observation area (underneath the Concourse Bridge); the red dot shows the location of the cameras used for video recordings in the Students' Union building (**right**)—See also details in Section 2.2.

2.2. Equipment and Procedure

The experiment was performed during five consecutive working days in February 2015. The equipment used for the experiment was: a laptop with the driver software of the audio card for outputs regulation; a professional audio card (RME Babyface); two loudspeakers (Genelec 8030B); and two cameras (Sony handycam DCR-DVD115) for video recording.

The nature of a non-participant observational study implies that no interaction between the research team and the participants would happen. In fact, the two cameras were placed at the first floor of the Students' Union building in order to cover the investigated area, and were hidden from people's sight (as shown in Figure 1).

In order to characterise the acoustic environment of the observation area, a set of ten simultaneous ten-minute background noise level measurements were carried out, using ten 1/8" microphones (B&K) connected to a portable recorder (Edirol), placed along the direction of walking at two-meter distance intervals. At the same time, a computation of the sound propagation in the area was made using two reference omnidirectional sound sources with a sound power of 100 dB (white noise spectrum) to simulate the loudspeakers to be installed for the experiment. The simulation of the sound propagation reported in Figure 2 shows a relatively homogeneous sound pressure levels (SPL) distribution in the observation area. If this information is compared with the background noise level profile, it can be reasonably assumed that people in the observation area would be approximately exposed to the same sound field, regardless of their location.

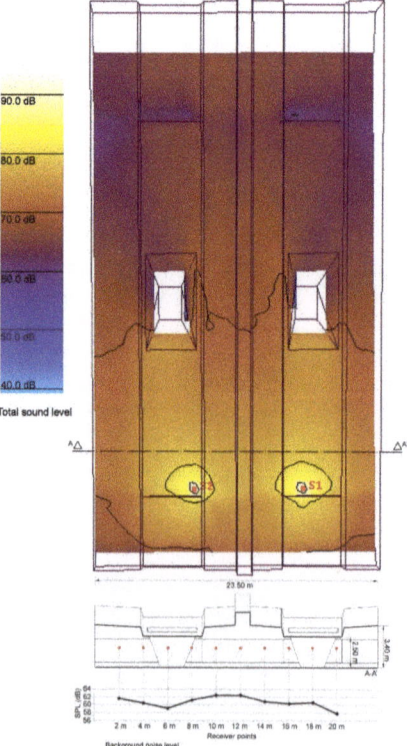

Figure 2. Sound pressure level (SPL) distribution simulation with location of the hypothetical sound sources (loudspeakers) and section with location of the microphones and corresponding background noise levels.

2.3. Signal Analysis

During the experiment, a playlist of three music excerpts and a control condition (no music) was cyclically reproduced. Following the protocol of a previous experiment carried out by Witchel and colleagues [10], three instrumental pieces of music from contrasting genres (namely classical, jazz, and ambient electronic music) were used to ensure a high level of inclusiveness, involving different social groups in terms of age and gender [17]. It has been affirmed that conventional acoustic parameters for noise measurement—e.g., weighted sound pressure levels (SPLs)—are not sufficient for the adequate measurement of soundscape [18–22].

Since soundscape is a perceptual construct and music is known to trigger emotions and affect perception, soundscape and music are closely related; thus, the psychoacoustic parameters that have previously been applied mainly in music perception may also be applicable in soundscape research [23]. However, for the purpose of this study, it was decided to rely on pitch-related parameters for the selection of the stimuli to be used in the experiment. The pitch features are particularly significant in the field of environmental sounds and their perception [18]. Pitch maybe defined as "that attribute of auditory sensation in terms of which sounds maybe ordered on a musical scale from high to low", and is generally assigned by the frequency of a pure tone having the same subjective pitch as the considered sound [24,25]. Another additional parameter defining other pitch sensations is the pitch strength (PA, a-dimensional), corresponding to the assessment of the sound along a scale from faint to distinct. It has been asserted that high pitch could be associated with feelings like strong activation, excitement, surprise, happiness. Low pitch instead could be associated with low activation, calmness, and quietness [26–28]. According to Yang [21], the values of the most prominent pitches among environmental sounds are 4000 Hz for bird songs, 1000 Hz for fountain sounds, and no pitch perceived for river, sea waves, traffic, and wind. Western music generally refers to the 440 Hz pitch [29]. Therefore, the rationale for selecting the stimuli was having music excerpts with a relatively broad range of pitch features. These were selected amid those used in Witchel's experiment in Brighton [10]: Classical (*Waltz of the Flowers*) Pitch 148 Hz, PA 9.3, Ambient (*Cirrus*) Pitch 577 Hz, PA 10.9, Jazz (*Creole Jazz*) Pitch 736 Hz, PA 5.3.

The average background noise level in the observation area was found to be 60.7 dB, so the loudspeakers' gain was set accordingly, with the overall aim to exceed the background noise by at least 10 dB approximately in the whole observation area, as per the simulation in Section 2.2, so as to provide a reasonably homogeneous signal-to-noise ratio. Figure 3 shows the spectrum of the background noise level recorded on site, compared to the spectra of the three music excerpts, calibrated as if they had an overall sound pressure level of 75 dB. The spectra suggest that the music should be clearly audible over the background noise.

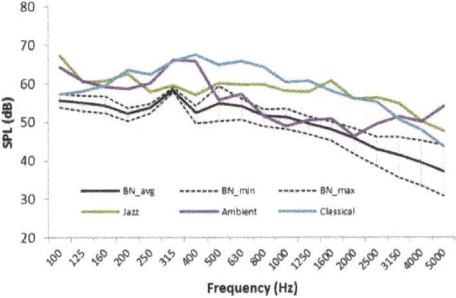

Figure 3. One-third octave band spectrum of the background noise (BN) level (black line) averaged over the ten recording points reported in Figure 2, with minimum and maximum values (dashed lines), compared with the spectra of the three music excerpts (hypothetical broadband sound pressure level of 75 dB).

The music excerpts (reproduced in loop) and the control were cycled repeatedly between 10:00 am and 1:00 pm (or between 11:00 a.m. and 2:00 p.m.) in one-hour slots. The experimental design consisted of 180 min of exposure for each of the four conditions (i.e., three music excerpts and the control), distributed during the five days of observation. A rotation of the stimuli was set across the week and the daily time slots, in order to obtain the widest range of observations for the same music excerpts in different days and times.

The video recordings were used to investigate peoples' behaviour in response to sound. Direct observational assessment of people behaviours was performed by means of the *Behavioural Observation Research Interactive Software* (BORIS, v. 2.95, University of Torino, Torino, Italy) [30]. In each BORIS project, information related to a set of observations (such as Behaviours and Participants) are manually annotated through computer vision and respectively inserted in the Ethogram and Subjects table. Ethograms consist of a list of behaviours exhibited by an individual or a group, with corresponding definitions of each using descriptive terms and phrases [31,32]. The ethogram reported in Figure 4 shows the duration of stay (in seconds) of all stopping subjects for a corresponding observation period. For each stopping subject, three more attributes were annotated, namely: (1) Activity (Chatting/Eating-Drinking/Loitering/Smoking/Talking on the phone), related to the main activity carried out by the subjects during their stay; (2) Group (alone/group) related to whether the subjects were staying alone or in group; and (3) Posture (sitting/standing), related to whether the subjects were sitting or standing. Furthermore, the number of passers-by under the bridge was registered in terms of point behaviours (no duration) to examine the total number of subjects passed during the corresponding stimulus condition.

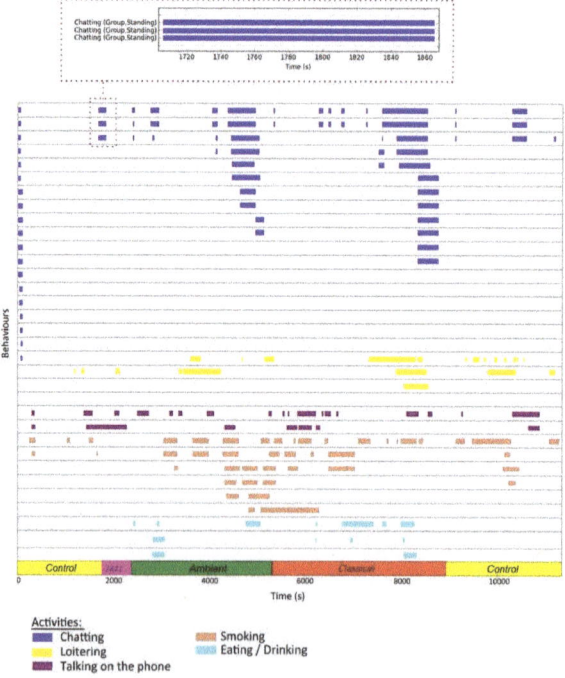

Figure 4. Example of the ethogram obtained from the Behavioural Observation Research Interactive Software (BORIS) exportation. The graph shows the results of a typical daily observation, recording the duration of stay of the subjects during the different excerpts' exposure time and the additional information annotated for each event.

3. Results

3.1. Effect of Music on Ratio of People Stopping By

One of the main aims of this research was to investigate whether there is an effect of added music sounds on the number of people stopping by the investigated public area. To address this purpose, two different variables were defined. The fist variable was the Stimulus, consisting of four levels, Classical, Ambient, Jazz music, and Control (No music) condition; while the second variable was defined as the ratio between the number of stoppers by the area and the total number of passers in a given reference time slot; this was defined as a numerical variable, namely the Ratio Stoppers–Passers (RSP). During the experiment, the total exposure time for each Stimulus condition was 180 min. Each of the four overall periods was divided in 18 slots, lasting approximately 10 min (180 min/18 = 10 min), finally obtaining 72 video excerpts (18 × 4 stimuli, including the control). Afterwards, the RSP was calculated and the Stimulus variable was defined for each of the 72 recording slots. Table 1 reports the total number of observations of passers-by and stoppers-by for each stimulus condition.

Table 1. Number of observations according to the different stimuli conditions averaged over the 72 video excerpts. RSP: Ratio of Stoppers–Passers.

Stimulus	Number of Passers-by	Number of Stoppers-by	Mean *RSP*	Std. Dev. *RSP*
Classical	4107	181	4.4%	2.5%
Ambient	2921	161	5.5%	3.8%
Jazz	2989	135	4.5%	2.9%
Control (No Music)	2765	119	4.3%	3.5%

The 72 RSP values corresponding to the 72 video excerpts were used for the statistical analysis. Since the distributions of the RSP values across the four stimuli were non-normal, a nonparametric test was used. A Kruskal–Wallis H test was run to determine if there were differences in RSP score between the four conditions. Distributions of RSP scores were not similar for all groups, as assessed by visual inspection of a boxplot. The mean rank of RSP scores was not statistically significantly different between groups, $\chi^2(3) = 0.24$, $p = 0.971$. Thus, there was no detected effect of the different stimuli on the number of subjects who stopped by the area, nor a significant difference between the RSP values recorded during the music excerpts exposure with respect to the control condition.

3.2. Effect of Music on Duration of Stay

Although no significant effect of the added music on the number of people stopping was found, its influence on people's duration of stay was further investigated, and a continuous variable was defined accordingly. Preliminary results reported in Table 2 showed that during the reproduction of the music stimuli, people's duration of stay was longer than in the absence of music. Starting from this point, the influence of three other potential co-variants was explored in order to examine whether people's mean duration of stay was affected by the stimulus variable or other effects.

Table 2. Descriptive statistics of the duration of stay for each stimulus condition.

Stimulus	Mean Duration of Stay (s)	Bootstrap (10,000 Bootstrap Samples)			
		Bias	Std. Error	95% Confidence Interval	
				Lower	Upper
Classical	320.57	0.30	24.01	274.94	368.74
Ambient	274.69	−0.18	21.74	233.42	318.60
Jazz	257.56	−0.02	21.27	217.20	299.75
Control (No Music)	132.18	0.09	11.93	109.89	156.58

3.2.1. Analysis of Covariant Attributes on Duration of Stay

The three attributes described in Section 2.3 (i.e., Activity, Group, and Posture) were considered to be potential covariant factors of influence on the duration of stay. Thus, three corresponding variables were defined. Activity was defined as a categorical variable with five levels: Chatting, Eating–Drinking, Loitering, Smoking, and Talking on the phone. Group was defined as a dichotomous variable: No (Alone) or Yes (Two or more people). Posture was defined as a dichotomous variable: Standing or Sitting.

Since the distribution of duration of stay scores was positively skewed, a log transform (natural logarithm) was performed to normalise the data, and this resulted in an approximately normal distribution of scores. Thus, from now on, the Duration of stay variable will refer to the log-transformed dataset.

A one-way Welch ANOVA was carried out to investigate whether the different activities carried out affected people's mean duration of stay. Homogeneity of variances was violated, as assessed by Levene's Test of Homogeneity of Variance ($p = 0.018$). Duration of stay score was statistically significantly different between different activities groups, Welch's $F(4, 143.522) = 14.821$, $p = 0.001$, partial $\eta^2 = 0.030$. However, Games–Howell post hoc analysis revealed that only the duration of Talking on the phone events (M = 4.66, SD = 1.06) had a statistically significant difference with respect to Smoking events (M = 5.26, SD = 0.96), $p = 0.04$, and Eating/Drinking events (M = 5.38, SD = 1.14), $p = 0.04$. It seems likely to assert that the occurrence of Talking on the phone events implies a shorter mean duration of stay than the one detectable during the other four activities. A second critical inspection of the recordings revealed that in most cases, the duration of the Talking on the phones event was mainly related to the actual duration of the call (i.e., people would stay in the observation area only for the time necessary for the call, being uninterested in the music). No significant difference was observed between the duration of stay recorded during Chatting, Eating/Drinking, Loitering, and Smoking events, so no other relative effect could be stated according to the Activities variable.

Furthermore, a one-way Welch ANOVA was carried out to investigate whether the being alone or in group could affect people's mean duration of stay. Homogeneity of variances was not violated in this case, as assessed by Levene's Test of Homogeneity of Variance ($p = 0.050$), but the difference between the two levels of the Group variable was not statistically significant, Welch's $F(1, 577.373) = 0.070$, $p = 0.791$. Eventually, a one-way Welch ANOVA was carried out for the Posture variable, to investigate whether standing or sitting could affect people's mean duration of stay. Homogeneity of variances was violated, as assessed by Levene's Test of Homogeneity of Variance ($p = 0.004$). The difference between the two levels of the Posture variable was statistically significant, Welch's $F(1, 469.457) = 136.946$, $p < 0.001$, partial $\eta^2 = 0.183$.

Thus, the Activity and Group variables were excluded from further analysis, as their influence on the duration of stay values was not significant. Only the effects of Posture and Stimulus on the Duration of stay variable will be explored in the following section.

3.2.2. Combined Effect of Posture and Music on Duration of Stay

A two-way ANOVA was conducted to examine the effects of Posture and Stimulus on Duration of stay. Homogeneity of variances was assessed by Levene's test, and it was violated ($p < 0.001$); however, there is an overall consensus in the literature to carry on regardless when the ratio of the largest to the smallest group variance is less than three (a condition that is met in this study), since the test is reasonably robust to heterogeneity of variance in these cases [33].

The interaction effect between Posture and Stimulus was not statistically significant for Duration of stay scores, $F(3, 574) = 1.197$, $p = 0.310$, partial $\eta^2 = 0.006$. Therefore, an analysis of the main effect for Stimulus was performed, which indicated that the main effect was statistically significant, $F(3, 574) = 3.781$, $p = 0.010$, partial $\eta^2 = 0.019$. All pairwise comparisons were run, where reported 95% confidence intervals and p-values were Bonferroni-adjusted. The unweighted marginal means of Duration of stay scores for Classical, Ambient, Jazz, and Control (No music) were 5.29 ± 0.072,

5.25 ± 0.079, 5.17 ± 0.087, and 4.83 ± 0.120, respectively. These point scores of the log-transformed duration variable correspond to mean Duration of Stay of 198 seconds (Classical), 190 s (Ambient), 176 s (Jazz), and 125 s (Control). Figure 5 shows the estimated marginal means of the ANOVA model for the log-transformed version of Duration of stay. The Control condition was associated with a mean Duration of stay score 0.45 points lower than Classical ($p = 0.007$), 0.42 points lower than Ambient ($p = 0.021$), and 0.34 points lower than Jazz, but the latter difference was not statistically significant ($p = 0.124$). For the sake of clarity, Figure 6 reports the mean Duration of stay scores (as observed) during the on-site campaign).

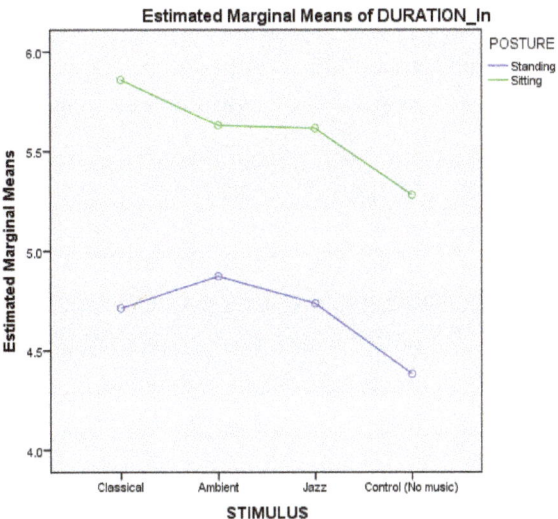

Figure 5. Mean Duration of stay (log-transformed) as a function of the Stimulus variable, when controlling for the Posture variable.

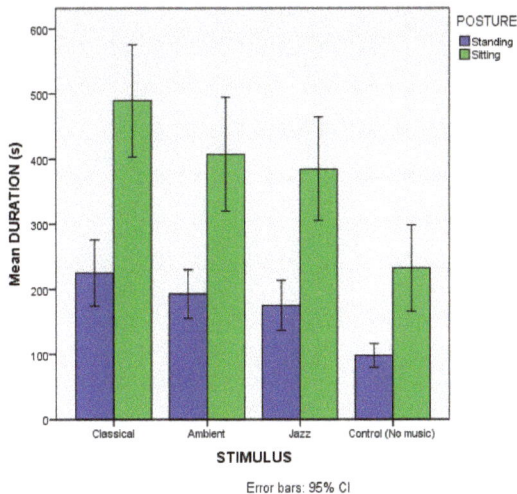

Figure 6. Mean Duration of stay (as observed) as a function of the Stimulus variable, for both the Standing and Sitting conditions.

Thus, for the investigated case, the above findings seem to suggest that music—without any kind of interaction with other additional qualitative variables—had the capacity to positively affect people's duration of stay in the observation area.

4. Discussion and Conclusions

An experiment based on covert behavioural observations was performed in a typical open public space in Sheffield, mainly used as a connection between different University buildings. Three musical excerpts (and a control condition with no music) were reproduced cyclically to test whether there is an effect of background music on the number of persons stopping in the urban space and if added sounds could affect people's duration of stay in the investigated area. Overall, the experiment reported in this paper led to two main conclusions:

- the presence of music did not affect the number of subjects stopping by the observed area; thus, the manipulation of the sound environment had no power to influence people's choice about stopping or not in the space;
- the presence of background music influenced people's mean duration of stay in the public space, with added sound (Classical and Ambient music in the investigated case) implying a longer duration of stay than the one recorded in the control (no music) condition.

The observation site considered in this research is a space with apparently no specific function other than transit; i.e., people do not "go there" as a destination. It can be considered as a place where people "stop for a moment" on their route from one point to another, which would justify the lack of an overall effect of music on people's decision to stop or go. Within the framework of this study, it was assumed that the Duration of stay variable could be used as a proxy for a measure of perceived safety and relaxation. That is, if people decide to stay longer in an apparently unattractive place, to some extent, it can be implied that they feel safe and relaxed there [6]. This is connected to the ongoing debate about outcomes and preference in soundscape studies. Brown et al. [12] suggested that people's preferred outcome with respect to the acoustic environment is context-dependent. They reported a broad spectrum of soundscape outcomes, which are likely to be related to different soundscape appreciation and preference in different contexts. For example, the desired soundscape of urban parks might be assessed against calmness or restorativeness criteria (e.g., [34]), while for downtown or commercial environments, liveliness and excitement dimensions might provide more useful insights into the soundscape assessment of such places [16]. Thus, it was considered that perceptual dimensions related to safety, sense of control, or relaxation might be more relevant for the investigated context. The outcomes of this research could be a potential complement to the existing Masterplan proposal based on traditional urban renewal practices [15]; sound as well as light or green features should be an actual tool within the broader framework of urban planning and design policies.

There are of course some limitations, which could not be controlled for. For instance, during the experimental sessions, it was not possible to precisely monitor the signal-to-noise ratio (SNR) in the observation area. Thus, in spite of the efforts to achieve a homogenous sound field during the reproduction of the stimuli, it is likely that people were exposed to slightly different sound levels, depending on where they were stopping. However, strictly controlled SNR conditions might only be achieved in laboratory experiments, the ecological validity of which has been a topic long debated in soundscape research with no clear consensus so far (e.g., [35]). Furthermore, there might have been other confounding factors affecting the duration of stay in the observation area (e.g., personal attitudes, music preference, etc.). However, given the nature of this study (i.e., covert observational research), such information was not to be sought from observed participants (e.g., through questionnaires) in order to not bias the main investigated variable.

Overall, these limitations are the price this study pays when trying to overcome a significant methodological issue for soundscape assessment in public outdoor contexts that Brown et al. [12] for soundscape research defined as the "experimenter effect" where " ... *measurement of people's preference in these situations using questionnaire methods requires first drawing their attention to something upon which they may never have consciously reflected."*

Taken together, the results of this study suggest that added music in public spaces might have the capability to increase the *liveability* and the pleasantness of places that only have practical functions (e.g., transit, waiting). Soundscape development and design can promote the attractiveness of a public space through its ability to increase the perceived quality and positively impact the psychological and physiological wellbeing of citizens, and it can help to build social cohesion amongst users and define the social use values of city spaces.

Acknowledgments: This research received funding through the People Programme (Marie Curie Actions) of the European Union's 7th Framework Programme FP7/2007-2013 under REA grant agreement n° 290110, SONORUS "Urban Sound Planner". The authors are grateful to Pierluigi Ciullo for his support in data collection, to James Uttley for his comments on the preliminary version of the manuscript and to the anonymous reviewers for their useful and constructive insights.

Author Contributions: F.A., F.L., E.K.-K., J.K. and A.A. conceived and designed the experiments; F.A., F.L. and E.K.-K. analyzed the data; F.A., F.L., E.K.-K., J.K. and A.A. wrote the paper.

Conflicts of Interest: The authors declare no conflict of interest.

References

1. Schafer, R.M. *The Tuning of the World*; Knopf: New York, NY, USA, 1977.
2. International Organization for Standardization. *ISO 12913–1:2014 Acoustics—Soundscape—Part 1: Definition and Conceptual Framework*; ISO: Geneva, Switzerland, 2014.
3. Areni, C.S.; Kim, D. The influence of background music on shopping behavior: Classical versus top-forty music in a wine store. *Adv. Consum. Res.* **1993**, *20*, 336–340.
4. Yalch, R.F.; Spangenberg, E.R. The effects of music in a retail setting on real and perceived shopping times. *J. Bus. Res.* **2000**, *49*, 139–147. [CrossRef]
5. Milliman, R.E. Using background music to affect the behavior of supermarket shoppers. *J. Mark.* **1982**, *46*, 86–91. [CrossRef]
6. Sayin, E.; Krishna, A.; Ardelet, C.; Decré, G.B.; Goudey, A. "Sound and safe": The effect of ambient sound on the perceived safety of public spaces. *Int. J. Res. Mark.* **2015**, *32*, 343–353. [CrossRef]
7. Kampfe, J.; Sedlmeier, P.; Renkewitz, F. The impact of background music on adult listeners: A meta-analysis. *Psychol. Music* **2011**, *39*, 424–448. [CrossRef]
8. Ryuma Kuribayashi, R.; Nittono, H. Speeding up the tempo of background sounds accelerates the pace of behavior. *Psychol. Music* **2015**, *43*, 808–817. [CrossRef]
9. Easteal, M.; Bannister, S.; Kang, J.; Aletta, F.; Lavia, L.; Witchel, H.J. Urban sound planning in Brighton and Hove. In Proceedings of the Forum Acusticum, Krakow, Poland, 7–12 September 2014.
10. Witchel, H.J.; Lavia, L.; Westling, C.E.I.; Healy, A.; Needham, R.; Chockalingam, N. Using body language indicators for assessing the effects of soundscape quality on Individuals. In Proceedings of the AIA-DAGA Conference on Acoustics, Merano, Italy, 18–21 March 2013.
11. Schafer, T.; Huron, D.; Shanahan, D.; Sedlmeier, P. The sounds of safety: Stress and danger in music perception. *Front. Psychol.* **2015**, *6*, 1–12. [CrossRef] [PubMed]
12. Brown, A.L.; Kang, J.; Gjestland, T. Towards standardization in soundscape preference assessment. *Appl. Acoust.* **2011**, *72*, 387–392. [CrossRef]
13. Department for Communities and Local Government. *Planning Policy Statement 3 (PPS3): Housing*; Department for Communities and Local Government: London, UK, 2006.
14. Dempsey, N. Are good-quality environments socially cohesive? Measuring quality and cohesion in urban neighbourhoods. *Town Plan. Rev.* **2009**, *80*, 315–345. [CrossRef]
15. University of Sheffield. Available online: https://www.sheffield.ac.uk/campusmasterplan (accessed on 24 July 2016).
16. Aletta, F.; Kang, J.; Axelsson, O. Soundscape descriptors and a conceptual framework for developing predictive soundscape models. *Landsc. Urban Plan.* **2016**, *149*, 65–74. [CrossRef]

17. Lòpez-Méndez, A.; Westling, C.E.I.; Emonet, R.; Eastel, M.; Lavia, L.; Witchel, H.J.; Odobez, J.-M. Automated bobbing and phase analysis to measure walking entrainment to music. In Proceedings of the International Conference on Image Processing, Paris, France, 23–30 October 2014.

18. Yang, W.; Kang, J. Acoustic comfort evaluation in urban open public spaces. *Appl. Acoust.* **2005**, *66*, 211–229. [CrossRef]

19. Stockfelt, T. Sound as an existential necessity. *J. Sound Vib.* **1991**, *151*, 367–370. [CrossRef]

20. Davies, W.J.; Adams, M.D.; Bruce, N.S.; Cain, R.; Carlyle, A.; Cusack, P.; Hall, D.A.; Hume, K.I.; Irwin, A.; Jennings, P.; et al. Perception of soundscapes: An interdisciplinary approach. *Appl. Acoust.* **2013**, *74*, 224–231. [CrossRef]

21. Yang, M.; Kang, J. Pitch features of environmental sounds. *J. Sound Vib.* **2016**, *374*, 312–328. [CrossRef]

22. Raimbault, M.; Lavandier, C.; Èrengier, M.B. Ambient sound assessment of urban environments: Field studies in two French cities. *Appl. Acoust.* **2003**, *64*, 1241–1256. [CrossRef]

23. Axelsson, Ö.; Nilsson, M.E.; Berglund, B. A principal components model of soundscape perception. *J. Acoust. Soc. Am.* **2010**, *128*, 2836–2846. [CrossRef] [PubMed]

24. Moore, B.C.J. *An Introduction to the Psychology of Hearing*; Academic Press: London, UK, 1997.

25. American Standards Association. *American Standard Acoustical Terminology (Including Mechanical Shock and Vibration*; Acoustical Society of America: New York, NY, USA, 1960.

26. Hevner, K. The affective value of pitch and tempo in music. *Am. J. Psychol.* **1937**, *49*, 621–630. [CrossRef]

27. Balkwill, L.L.; Thompson, W.F. Across-cultural investigation of the perception of emotion in music: Psychophysical and cultural cues. *Music Percept.* **1999**, *17*, 43–64. [CrossRef]

28. Krumhansl, C.L. An exploratory study of musical emotions and psychophysiology. *Can. J. Exp. Psychol.* **1997**, *51*, 336–352. [CrossRef] [PubMed]

29. Ellis, A.J.; Mendel, A. *Studies in the History of Music Pitch*; Frits Knuf: New York, NY, USA, 1968.

30. Behavioral Observation Research Interactive Software (BORIS) version 2.95 User Guide. Available online: http://www.boris.unito.it (accessed on 24 July 2016).

31. Martin, P.; Bateson, P. *Measuring Behaviour: An Introductory Guide*; Cambridge University Press: New York, NY, USA, 2007.

32. Stanton, L.A.; Sullivan, M.S.; Fazio, J.M. A standardized ethogram for the felidae: A tool for behavioural researchers. *Appl. Anim. Behav. Sci.* **2015**, *173*, 3–16. [CrossRef]

33. Jaccard, J. *Interaction Effects in Factorial Analysis of Variance*; Sage Publications: Thousand Oaks, CA, USA, 1998.

34. Payne, S.R. The production of a perceived restorativeness soundscape scale. *Appl. Acoust.* **2013**, *74*, 255–263. [CrossRef]

35. Guastavino, C.; Katz, B.F.; Polack, J.; Levitin, D.J.; Dubois, D. Ecological validity of soundscape reproduction. *Acta Acust. United Acust.* **2005**, *91*, 333–341.

Article

Global and Continuous Pleasantness Estimation of the Soundscape Perceived during Walking Trips through Urban Environments

Pierre Aumond [1,2,*], Arnaud Can [1], Bert De Coensel [3], Carlos Ribeiro [4], Dick Botteldooren [3] and Catherine Lavandier [2]

[1] AME-LAE (Environmental Acoustics Laboratory), Ifsttar (Development of Networks, French Institute of Science and Technology for Transport), 44341 Bouguenais, France; arnaud.can@ifsttar.fr

[2] ETIS, UMR 8051/ENSEA, University of Cergy-Pontoise, CNRS, 95000 Cergy, France; catherine.lavandier@u-cergy.fr

[3] Waves Research Group, Department of Infor mation Technology, Ghent University, Technologiepark-Zwijnaarde 15, 9052 Ghent , Belgium; bert.decoensel@intec.ugent.be (B.D.C.); dick.botteldooren@intec.ugent.be (D.B.)

[4] Bruitparif, 93500 Pantin, France; carlos.ribeiro@bruitparif.fr

* Correspondence: pierre.aumond@ifsttar.fr; Tel.: +33-2-4084-5619

Academic Editor: Jian Kang
Received: 14 October 2016; Accepted: 25 January 2017; Published: 5 February 2017

Abstract: This paper investigates how the overall pleasantness of the sound environment of an urban walking trip can be estimated through acoustical measurements along the path. For this purpose, two laboratory experiments were carried out, during which controlled and natural 3-min audio and audiovisual sequences were presented. Participants were asked to continuously assess the pleasantness of the sound environment along the sequence, and globally at its end. The results reveal that the global sound pleasantness is principally explained by the average of the instantaneous sound pleasantness values. Accounting for recency or trend effects improved the estimates of the global sound pleasantness over controlled sound sequences, but their contribution is not significant for the second group of stimuli, which are based on natural audio sequences and include visual information. In addition, models for global and continuous pleasantness, as a function of the instantaneous sound pressure level $L_{eq,1s}$, are proposed. The instantaneous sound pleasantness is found to be mainly impacted by the average sound level over the past 6 s. A logarithmic fading mechanism, extracted from psychological literature, is also proposed for this modelling, and slightly improves the estimations. Finally, the globally perceived sound pleasantness can be accurately estimated from the sound pressure level of the sound sequences, explaining about 60% of the variance in the global sound pleasantness ratings.

Keywords: sound pleasantness; perceptual test; urban sound environment; recency effect; urban walking trip

1. Introduction

The health benefits of practicing a physical activity on a daily basis, and walking in particular, is widely acknowledged [1]. Soft transportation modes are also known to ease traffic flows. Thus, municipalities are increasingly promoting the use of walking or cycling to their city dwellers, for commuting, and investing in facilities that encourage these practices [2–5]. However, although soft transportation modes undoubtedly have a positive global environmental effect, an increased exposure to road traffic pollutants, namely airborne pollutants, fine particles, and noise levels, amplified by the high correlation generally observed between these pollutants [6–8], is a harmful counterpart of choosing this transportation mode in urban areas. Moreover, the environmental quality at the neighborhood scale, strongly influences the choice of walking as transportation mode [9–11]. Therefore, being able to estimate the exposure associated with an urban walking trip has many potential interests, such as for informing pedestrians about the potential health benefit of their intended walk, or for optimizing the related route choice through specific algorithms [12,13].

However, estimating noise exposure is made difficult by the high spatial and temporal sound pressure level variability, typical in urban environments [14,15]. Moreover, recent works have revealed the complex relations between perceptual assessments (e.g., pleasantness of the sound environment) [16–18] and physical measurements [19,20]. The importance of the temporal and spectral dimensions of sound [19,20], the interest of explicitly introducing the contribution of different sound sources (e.g., vehicles, voices, birds, etc.) into the modeling [16–18], the influence of non-acoustical parameters [21], such as the visual scene and the openness of the space [21,22], and even non-physical factors, such as demographic, cultural, and social factors, or context factors [23–25], advocate not relying on energetic indicators when producing sound pleasantness maps or assessing the sound pleasantness of urban walking trips. Recently proposed noise mapping alternatives, which include mobile measurements, fulfil the requirements for estimating the sound pleasantness of walking trips, as they account for all of the sound sources that encompass urban sound environments, allowing one to estimate advanced indicators [26–28].

This new context makes it possible to estimate the sound pleasantness of an urban walking trip. However, this requires an understanding of how a pedestrian globally and retrospectively assesses a sound environment that varies with time. This paper investigates these relations through a modeling framework of three steps, described in Figure 1. First, models are proposed to relate perceptual assessments of continuous and overall pleasantness of the presented sound sequences (Figure 1C). Then, models of the instantaneous and overall sound pleasantness appreciation, based on sound levels (Figure 1A,B), are proposed.

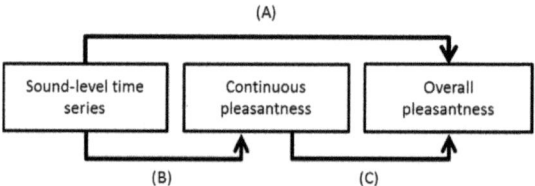

Figure 1. Modeling framework. (**A**): relations between sound-level time series and perceived overall pleasantness; (**B**) relations between sound-level time series and perceived continuous pleasantness; (**C**): relations between perceived continuous and overall pleasantness (**C**).

Previous research in the field of psychology, psychoacoustics, and soundscape, has shown that retrospective overall judgement is not a simple average of instantaneous judgment, but is significantly influenced by the following principal temporal effects (more details can be found in [29]):

- The recency effect, by which initial and final momentary judgments of a sequence are more remembered at the instant when the retrospective assessment is given, has been observed for sound sequences by Västfjäll [30,31].
- The peak-end rule, which states that the global judgement of an experiment is influenced by its most intense point and its end (negative or positive perception), has been observed in [32,33].
- The trend effect, which describes the fact that people often make predictions about the future based on trends that they have observed in the past, has been shown by Steffens & Guastavino, on a corpus of various 1-min length samples [29].

The main works that have dealt with the retrospective assessment of time-varying acoustical signals often focused on loudness perception, on very controlled stimuli (pure tones, white noise, specific sound sources, etc.), or on short sound sequences. Evaluating retrospective global judgments, such as the pleasantness of the sonic environment during urban walks, requires new experimental set-ups and stimuli, closer to the in situ experience. Recently, virtual reality and auralization tools have been proposed by some authors, in order to fulfill this requirement [34,35], and more immersive experiments could help in highlighting these temporal effects over longer sound sequences. An in-situ experiment by Aumond et al. revealed that recency or trend effects significantly influence the global judgment for very short paths (inferior to 1 min), but not for larger paths (>15 min) [36]. These results need to be compared with other experiments.

The relation between the continuous instantaneous judgement during a time-varying sound environment, and the physical properties of the stimuli, are also of particular interest. They enable one to estimate the integration, relaxation, and reaction times that link sound levels to momentary evaluations: a null reaction time and an integration time of about 2.5 s were, for example, found relevant in [37]. In addition, the links between overall pleasantness evaluations and sound levels time-series must be furthered investigated.

The present paper aims at investigating how the sound pleasantness of an urban walking trip can be estimated through measurements of the sound pressure level along walking paths in an urban environment. Two experiments are built. For both, the participants had to assess the continuous and overall sound pleasantness of sound sequences:

- A first experiment is based on different arrangements of two audio files, and aims to determine how the global temporal structure of a sound sequence affects its continuous and overall sound pleasantness appreciation. The sound sequences are built with the goal of assessing the effect of the temporal structure of the "background" sound environment. Therefore, strong markers of the soundscape or peaks in the sound levels were specifically avoided.
- A second experiment is based on the same principle, but with real sound sequences, played conjointly with video content, in order to investigate the same questions with natural sequences and a higher ecological validity.

2. Materials and Methods

2.1. Apparatus

The listening tests took place in a semi-anechoic room. Figure 2A presents the experiment set-up. Each participant performed the test individually; he/she was seated in a chair in front of a computer screen showing the test instructions. In the first experiment, a blurred image of an urban environment was projected onto a large screen located behind the computer, in order to have a realistic and comfortable luminosity in the room, without providing too much visual information, which could influence the judgments; however, the stimuli was only comprised of audio files. In the second experiment, a video sequence was added to the sound, in order to enhance the sensation of immersion.

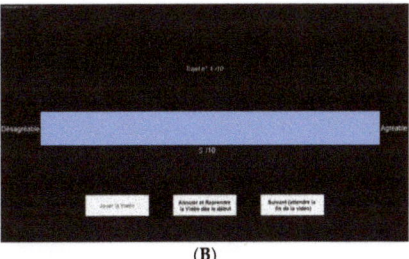

(A) (B)

Figure 2. (**A**) Experimental setup and (**B**) graphical interface for continuous assessments.

The sound sequences were transaurally reproduced; using a system composed of two loudspeakers (Tannoy) and a high quality sound card (RME Fireface 400, Audio AG, Haimhausen, Germany). The listening position was located at ±30° from the loudspeakers. The transaural listening technique has the advantage of minimizing front/back confusions, which are known to appear with headphone listening when individual HRTFs and head-tracking are not available, while preserving the perceptual characteristics of a diffused sound field [38]. The fact that participants are not using headphones improves the realism of the simulation technique.

For both experiments, the audio files were recorded using two high quality microphones (DPA 4060, Alleroed, Denmark), inserted into the operator's ears using specific ear clips. Prior to each recording, a calibration tone (1 kHz/94 dB) was recorded by the microphones, such that the sound level reproduction in the laboratory experiments could be calibrated. For experiment 2, the video sequences were simultaneously recorded with the sound recordings, with a small action camera carried by the hand of the operator at the eye's level. During both experiments, participants had to rate the pleasantness of the soundscape on the computer screen, while an urban picture (experiment 1) or a motion picture (experiment 2) was projected onto a large screen behind.

All of the statistical tests presented in this paper were realized with the Statistics and Machine Learning Toolbox™ from Matlab® (Natick, MA, USA).

2.2. Procedure

The sequences were played in a random order. Participants were first asked to continuously rate soundscape pleasantness on a semantic differential scale from unpleasant (coded 0), to pleasant (coded 10). The assessment was made, while listening, by moving a marker along a large horizontal bar with the mouse. The following instructions were orally presented to the participants: "During this experiment, you will experience 10 virtual urban trips of 3 min. You will have to point continuously with the mouse at the sound pleasantness of the presently heard sound environment: the more the sound environment is pleasant to you, the more you will move the mouse to the right; the more it is unpleasant, the more you will move the mouse to the left."

The assessed instantaneous sound pleasantness (P) ratings were collected with a time resolution of 125 ms (same sampling rate that the sound level time series). In addition, at the end of the sound sequence, the participants had to assess the global sound pleasantness (GP) of the sequence, on the same scale, from unpleasant to pleasant.

Figure 2B presents the graphical interface for continuous assessment that has been developed in the laboratory.

2.3. Participants

Two groups of 30 participants were involved in the experiments. In the first experiment, 11 women and 19 men participated, with a mean age of 33 years (SD = 14). In the second experiment, 18 women and 12 men participated, with a mean age of 33 years (SD = 14).

For the first experiment, seven participants were eliminated from the analysis. Two of them presented hearing loss, detected by preliminary audiometry (>20 dB HL) [39]. Five of them gave very incoherent responses (very incomplete, constant, or random ratings). Thus, 23 participants were included in the analysis. In the second experiment, no hearing problems were detected among the participants ("normal or subnormal hearing") [39].

In both experiments, the participants were naive with regards to the test hypotheses, and received a small monetary compensation for participation. Each participant was involved in only one of the experiments. All of the participants gave their informed written consent, prior to the experiments.

2.4. Stimuli

2.4.1. First Experiment

A total of 16 sound sequences have been constructed, based on different combinations of two initial sound sequences, α and β, each with a duration of 90 s, in order to focus on the effect of the sound sequence temporal structure on the sound pleasantness global assessment. The resulting sound sequences have a duration of 3 min, which represents the median duration of a pedestrian trip in the city of Paris [40]. The initial sound sequences α and β have been recorded with the same binaural technique in the 13th district of Paris, during April 2015; the sequence α in a small park (L_{50} = 55 dB, $L_{10} - L_{90}$ = 25 dB), and the sequence β nearby a large boulevard (approximate flow: 1000 vehicles/hour, L_{50} = 76 dB, $L_{10} - L_{90}$ = 24 dB). α and β have been carefully chosen , in orderto avoid particular events, such as too loud two wheelers, dog barks, voices with semantic understanding, or exceptionally strong sound level fluctuations. These events could become very salient markers of the sound environment, and could potentially significantly drive the global and instantaneous sound pleasantness assessment. α and β have been assessed by the participants before the beginning of the test, on a continuous pleasantness scale from unpleasant (coded 0) to pleasant (coded 10): the average perceived sound pleasantness for α and β were 8.1 (σ = 2.2) and 2.4 (σ = 2.0), respectively. Practically, the 16 sound sequences were obtained by combining α and β with different appearance times. The 16 sound sequences were formed with slow or fast alternations between α and β, evolving from calmness to noisiness, or the inverse. The transitions between each environment lasted at least 30 s ("Fast"), which was observed in situ as a minimum walking transition time. "Slow" alternation corresponds to a 3 min transition, which is the length of the sound sequence. Each sequence was presented once to the participants.

This methodology included the repetition of two 1 min initial sound sequences, assessed by the participants at the beginning of the test. Thus, some memory, demand, or transfer effects could have perturbed the experiment. Nevertheless, two points relativize this possible influence: (i) at the end of the test, the participants were orally asked to freely comment on the experiments. If some of them recognized that parts of the sequences came from the same initial sound recordings, as no strong marker of the sound environment (voice, klaxon, etc.) was present, they said something like, "I think two or three times I heard a part of the same sequence"; and (ii) all of the sequences were played in a random order to avoid the effect due to the repetition of the initial sequences, always being reported on the same sound sequences.

2.4.2. Second Experiment

The second experiment was based on 10 audio-visual urban sequences of 3 min, recorded in the 13th district of Paris, during April 2015. Similar sound environment conditions were chosen (recordings on Mondays, between 10 and 12 h, or between 14 and 16 h).

In order to obtain time-varying sound environments, the first six sequences consisted of a transition between two different sound environments, and the last four sequences were comprised of a transition between three different sound environments. The 10 sequences corresponded to five trips, run in both directions. Table 1 presents a short description of the streets travelled on during the experiment.

Table 4 and Figure 5 present the 10 sequences that alternate slowly or quickly between these described environments. Contrarily to the first experiment, the presence of the video did not allow controlling the sound sequences, thus particular events sometimes occurred in the sequences, such as loud two wheelers, or voices with semantic understanding. The sequences S9 and S10, which were 4-min long, have been artificially shortened at their center, cutting out a part of the walking trip in the "Rue des 2 avenues", in order to be coherent in length with the other sequences. Special care was taken to not alter the realism of the resulting sequences, keeping the cut as discrete as possible. Each sequence was presented once to the participants.

Table 1. Short description and labels for the travelled sound environments.

Street Name	Description	Labels
Rue de Tolbiac	Large street	T
Passage Vendrezanne	Pedestrian Street	V
Avenue Blanqui	Avenue	Bl
Jardin Brassaï	Park	Br
Avenue Italie	Large Avenue	I
Rue des 2 avenues	Pedestrian street	D
Parc de Choisy	Park	ChP
Rue du Moulinet	Street	M
Avenue Choisy	Large Street	ChA

3. Results

3.1. From Continuous to Global Perceived Pleasantness Assessment

3.1.1. First Experiment

Figure 3 depicts, for each of the 16 sequences presented in Section 2.4.1, the 1 s sound pleasantness (P) evolution (mean values and standard deviation for the 25 participants) and the 1 s sound level. The combination of the initial sequences α and β resulted in 16 sequences, with a large variety.

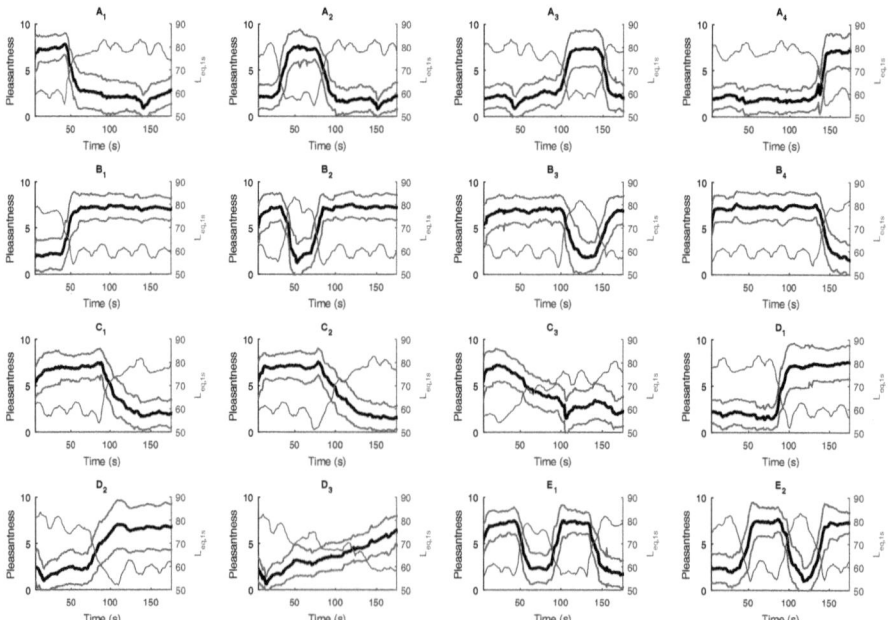

Figure 3. Continuous perceived pleasantness, mean values over participants P_{mean} (thick black line), standard deviations (light black lines), and sound level ($L_{eq,1s}$, purple) over time for the 16 sequences.

Table 2 shows the average pleasantness, of both the participants and over time (average of the 125 ms mean pleasantness ratings over the 3 min), the average global sound pleasantness (GP) of the participants, and the difference between both values ($\Delta GP\text{-}P_{mean}$), for each of the 16 sequences.

Table 2. Pleasantness averaged both over participants and over time (P_{mean}), the global sound pleasantness (GP) averaged over participants, and the difference between both ($\Delta GP\text{-}P_{mean}$), for each of the 16 sequences.

Sequences	L_{50} ($L_{10} - L_{90}$)	P_{mean}	GP	$\Delta GP\text{-}P_{mean}$	Sequences	L_{50} ($L_{10} - L_{90}$)	P_{mean}	GP	$\Delta GP\text{-}P_{mean}$
A1$_{[\alpha\beta\beta\beta\ fast]}$	76 (24)	3.7 (2.3)	2.9 (1.9)	−0.7	C1$_{[\beta\beta\alpha\alpha\ fast]}$	65 (23)	4.9 (1.9)	4.2 (1.9)	−0.7
A2$_{[\beta\alpha\beta\beta\ fast]}$	76 (25)	3.5 (2.3)	2.6 (1.2)	−0.9	C2$_{[\beta\beta\alpha\alpha\ medium]}$	63 (25)	4.8 (2.2)	4.3 (1.7)	−0.5
A3$_{[\beta\beta\alpha\beta\ fast]}$	76 (24)	3.6 (2.1)	3.4 (1.7)	−0.2	C3$_{[\beta\beta\alpha\alpha\ slow]}$	70 (21)	4.2 (2.3)	3.5 (1.8)	−0.7
A4$_{[\beta\beta\beta\alpha\ fast]}$	76 (24)	2.9 (2.0)	3.4 (1.4)	0.5	D1$_{[\alpha\alpha\beta\beta\ fast]}$	64 (26)	4.5 (2.4)	4.9 (1.6)	0.4
B1$_{[\beta\alpha\alpha\alpha\ fast]}$	60 (22)	5.9 (2.1)	6.4 (1.5)	0.6	D2$_{[\alpha\alpha\beta\beta\ medium]}$	63 (25)	4.5 (1.7)	5.5 (1.6)	1.0
B2$_{[\alpha\beta\alpha\alpha\ fast]}$	60 (22)	6.0 (2.1)	6.3 (1.4)	0.3	D3$_{[\alpha\alpha\beta\beta\ slow]}$	68 (20)	3.6 (2.2)	4.1 (1.6)	0.5
B3$_{[\alpha\alpha\beta\alpha\ fast]}$	60 (22)	5.6 (1.9)	5.7 (2.2)	0.1	E1$_{[\beta\alpha\beta\alpha\ fast]}$	62 (24)	5.0 (2.6)	4.8 (1.9)	−0.2
B4$_{[\alpha\alpha\alpha\beta\ fast]}$	60 (23)	6.3 (1.8)	5.7 (1.9)	−0.6	E2$_{[\alpha\beta\alpha\beta\ fast]}$	63 (25)	4.8 (2.2)	5.1 (2.0)	0.3

There is a statistically significant difference in $\Delta GP\text{-}P_{mean}$ between the sequences, confirmed by a one-way ANOVA ($F(15,351) = 2.84$, $p < 0.001$). Table 2 shows that, for sequences that mainly consist of a boulevard interrupted by a park sequence α (for example, compare sequences A1, A2, A3 and A4), and the more that α appears near the end of the sequence, the more the $\Delta GP\text{-}P_{mean}$ significantly increases ($F(3,88) = 4.78$, $p < 0.01$). Inversely, although less pronounced, for sequences that mainly consist of a park interrupted by the boulevard sequence (for example, compare sequences B1, B2, B3 and B4), and the more of the unpleasant environment that appears near the end of the sequence, the greater the difference in $\Delta GP\text{-}P_{mean}$ decreases. This trend is not significant ($F(3,88) = 1.75$, $p = 0.16$), but the difference in $\Delta GP\text{-}P_{mean}$ between the sequences B1 and B4 is significant ($F(1,44) = 4.52$, $p < 0.05$). Finally, the Ci sequences are significantly different to the Di sequences ($F(1,135) = 20.63$, $p < 0.01$).

In order to investigate the apparent temporal effect when assessing the global sound pleasantness of a sound sequence, a multiple linear regression is constructed over all of the sound sequences. Four presumed factors are tested (mean value, trend effect, recency effect, and primacy effect), using the variables presented in Table 3. All of the variables are calculated over the averaged temporal curve.

Table 3. Test variables for the multilinear regression.

Presumed Factors	Variables	Code
Mean value	Mean value	P_{mean}
Trend effect	Standarized coefficient of the time regression calculations as proposed in [29]	P_{trend}
Recency effect	Rate averaged over the last 30 s	P_{end}
Primacy effect	Rate averaged over the first 30 s	P_{start}

The best linear regression model is obtained through a stepwise procedure (Bidirectional elimination), maximizing the explained variance (In this paper, the explained variance corresponds to the adjusted R^2) at 95% ($R^2 = 0.95$, $F(2,14) = 136.0$, $p < 0.001$). The function selects the variables P_{mean} ($b^* = 0.81$, $t(14) = 13.6$, $p < 0.001$) and the final sound pleasantness P_{end} ($b^* = 0.45$, $t(14) = 7.6$, $p < 0.001$), which corresponds to the arithmetic average of the sound pleasantness, collected during the last 30 s of the sequence (the sequences are constructed so that the last 30 s always have a stable sound environment). This model outperforms the GP value, estimated with the unique predictor P_{mean} ($b^* = 0.87$, $t(14) = 6.5$, $p < 0.001$), which explains only 74% of the variance ($R^2 = 0.75$, $F(2,14) = 42.8$, $p < 0.001$). The significant difference between both models ($F(2,14) = 29.1$, $p < 0.001$) highlights the influence of the end of the sequence on the assessment of the global sound pleasantness, over the constituted 3-min sequences.

The variable linked to the trend effect P_{trend} can also replace the P_{end} variable as a predictor for the regression ($b^* = 0.45$, $t(14) = 7.4$, $p < 0.001$) with P_{mean} ($b^* = 0.92$, $t(14) = 15.09$, $p < 0.001$) keeping an identic-explained variance. It is worth noting that there exists a theoretical overlap between the trend and the recency effect (as reported by Steffens & Gusatavino [29]).

No influence of the speed at which the sound environment switches occur on the global sound pleasantness is observed. For example, if one compares sequences C1 and C3, which evolve from the park to the boulevard quickly or very slowly, the sound pleasantness GP is lower than P_{mean}

for both sequences, in accordance with the demonstrated recency effect, but to a similar extent (ΔGP-P_{mean} = −0.58 and −0.70 for C1 and C3). One-way ANOVA tests confirm this observation, showing that there are no significant differences between the Ci sequences ($F(2,66)$ = 0.13, p = 0.87), but also between the Di sequences ($F(2,66)$ = 0.26, p = 0.77). This would suggest that the speed at which sound environments vary from one to the other has no influence on the global sound pleasantness assessment. Finally, an one-way ANOVA test reveals that the difference between the Ei sequences, where multiple changes were present in the sound environment, is not significant ($F(1,44)$ = 1.32, p = 0.25).

The highlighted recency effect suggests the possibility to call for time series modelling, in order to account for the effect of the sound sequence temporal structure, whereas in the previous section, only the last 30 s were used. The multiscale model SIMPLE (Scale-Independent Memory, Perception and LEarning) has been proposed in psychological literature to model human memory [41]. This model estimates the probability to remember, at the end of a sequence, one specific event that occurred during the sequence. If the global sound pleasantness is considered as the sum of the 125 ms events that the participant remembers at the end of the sequence, then the global pleasantness (GP) can be expressed as the weighted average of all the instantaneous pleasantness (P) values collected during the sequence. The SIMPLE model relies on three parameters: c (temporal distinctiveness of memory representations), t (threshold), and s (slope). More details on the mathematical formulation and implementation can be found in [42].

These three parameters are optimized in the dataset (c = 40, t = 0.55, s = 11), using scale ranges for each parameter, as presented in the literature [41]. Figure 4 presents the ponderation coefficients extracted from the optimized SIMPLE model, but also for the two precedent models (average value P_{mean} with and without taking into account the P_{end} note). A threshold is observed after 150 s, resulting from the monotonous sound environment after this time instance (the last 30 s). When applying the SIMPLE model, the explained variance reaches 96% (p < 0.001), which again highlights the advantage to propose a smoother and more realistic temporal response, than an end over-weighting model. If the difference with the precedent model is not significant ($F(2,14)$ = 1.62, p = 0.18), then this approach permits one to integrate more complexity and realism into the function that models the recency effect.

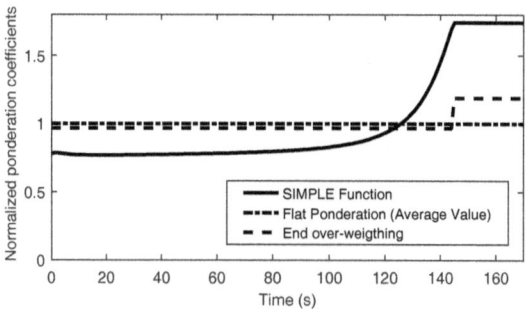

Figure 4. Normalized ponderation coefficients curves: SIMPLE (c = 40, t = 0.55, s = 11), Flat, and end overweighting.

3.1.2. Second Experiment

Figure 5 depicts, for each of the 10 sequences presented in Section 2.4.2, the 1 s sound pleasantness evolution (mean values and standard deviation of the participants) and the 1 s sound level. A large variety of sequences is observed.

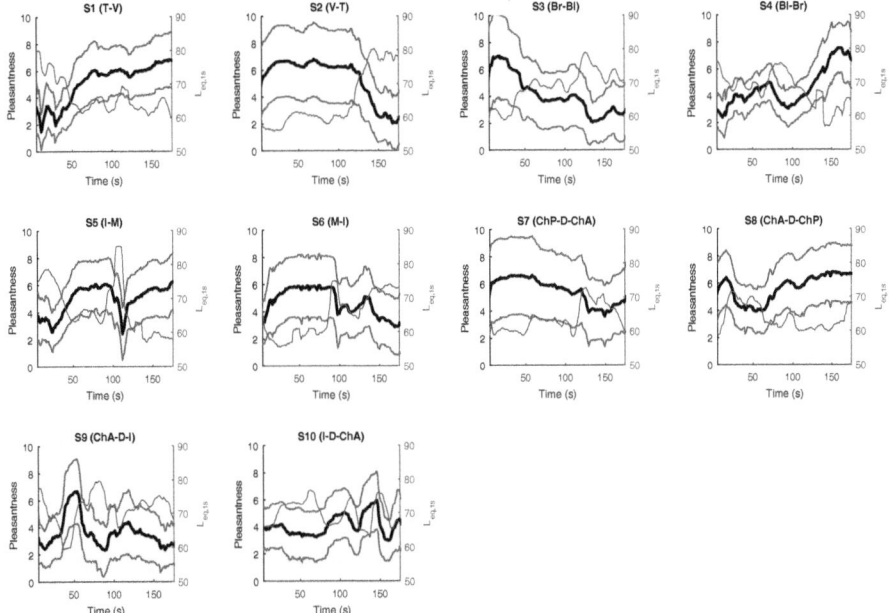

Figure 5. Continuous perceived pleasantness, mean values over participants P_{mean} (thick black line), standard deviations (light black lines), and sound level ($L_{eq,1s}$, purple) over time for the 16 sequences.

There is a statistically significant difference in the $\Delta GP\text{-}P_{mean}$ values between the sequences, as determined by the one-way ANOVA ($F(9,286) = 2.97$, $p < 0.01$), which implies that the global assessment is not only the average of the continuous ones. Table 4 shows P_{mean} and GP, along with their differences $\Delta GP\text{-}P_{mean}$, for each sequence. A more detailed analysis of the pairs of sound sequences (two of the same trips, but run in opposite directions) leads to contrasted conclusions. For S3 & S4 and S5 & S6, which are only composed of two different sound environments, the expected tendencies are observed: sequences that evolve towards improved sound environments show higher $\Delta GP\text{-}P_{mean}$ values than sequences that evolve towards deteriorated sound environments. Nevertheless, these tendencies are not statistically significant ($p > 0.05$). This tendency is also contradicted by the sequences S1 & S2, S7 & S8, and S9 & S10, which show $\Delta GP\text{-}P_{mean}$ values that are not in accordance with any recency effect.

Table 4. Pleasantness averaged both over participants and over time (P_{mean}), the global sound pleasantness (GP) averaged over participants, and the difference between both ($\Delta GP\text{-}P_{mean}$), for each of the 16 sequences.

Sequence Number	Ordered Characteristic Points	L_{50} ($L_{10} - L_{90}$)—dB	P_{mean}	GP	$\Delta GP\text{-}P_{mean}$
S1	T-V	64 (13)	5.1	6.1	1
S2	V-T	61 (22)	5.3	6.6	1.3
S3	Br-Bl	69 (16)	4.1	4.6	0.5
S4	Bl-Br	68 (17)	4.6	5.6	0.9
S5	I-M	65 (19)	5.0	5.9	0.9
S6	M-I	64 (17)	4.7	4.5	−0.1
S7	ChP-D-ChA	62 (11)	5.5	7.5	2.0
S8	ChA-D-ChP	62 (11)	5.7	6.8	1.0
S9	ChA-D-I	72 (16)	3.6	4.7	1.0
S10	I-D-ChA	69 (11)	4.1	4.0	−0.1

The best linear regression model is obtained through a stepwise procedure (Bidirectional elimination). The variance of the global pleasantness GP, explained by the unique predictor P_{mean} ($b^* = 0.87$, $t(8) = 4.9$,

$p < 0.005$), reaches 72% ($R^2 = 0.75$, $F(2,8) = 24.1$, $p < 0.005$). Interestingly, the determination coefficient and the P_{mean} standardized beta coefficient values are very similar to those observed between GP and P_{mean} in the first experiment. In accordance with the previous observations, in this experiment, taking into account that the variables P_{end} and P_{trend} do not improve the GP estimates, neither does the SIMPLE modelling.

3.2. From Measurements to Continuous and Retrospective Perceived Pleasantness

3.2.1. Continuous Sound Pleasantness Estimation Based on Noise Level Time Series

Section 3.1 demonstrated the possibility of relating the global sound pleasantness of a 3-min walking trip, to its perceived pleasantness time series. Thus, relating the perceived continuous sound pleasantness values to physical noise indicators, is a required intermediate step for proposing an estimate of the global sound pleasantness based on noise level time series. This section attempts to develop such relations, from the corpus of the 10 audiovisual sequences.

As a first step, the instantaneous sound pleasantness P, assessed at time step t, is estimated, based on a constant aggregation of the noise levels measured in the recent past. The modelling calls for two parameters, namely the response time rt, and the integration time it. The response time describes the delay between the noise event and its assessment by the participant. It corresponds to the time needed to detect the sound, then to understand and assess it in terms of pleasantness, and finally to move the cursor to the targeted point on the screen. The integration time describes the signal duration taken into account by the participant, for the instantaneous pleasantness assessment. As a result, $P(t)$ can be estimated using the following formula: $P(t) = f(t\text{-}rt\text{-}it{:}t\text{-}rt)$, where f is a time series of the noise levels between $t\text{-}rt\text{-}it$ and $t\text{-}rt$. Then, the modelling consists of finding the function f, and the rt and it values, which maximize the correlation between the estimated and the actual $P(t)$ values.

Figure 6 presents the correlations, averaged over the 10 sequences, between all the instantaneous 125 ms pleasantness rates and the calculated f function, for different rt and it values, and considering the function f and the usual noise indicators L_{50}, L_{90}, L_{10}, and L_{eq}. The presented correlation is calculated over 1000 observations (from the 3-min sequences sampled at 125 ms, but subtracting the earliest 400 values for integration purposes). The four noise indicators result in similar correlations, although correlations when using L_{90} are slightly less significant. The correlation curves simultaneously describe the influence of the two parameters, rt and it. The best couples {it; rt} range between 3 and 10 s for it, and between 0 and 2 s for rt. The maximum correlation found, 0.84, is obtained for the couple {6; 0} and the L_{eq} function. Thus, the resulting integration time, also called the "psychological or perceptual present" in [37], is about 6 s. Nevertheless, it is not possible to dissociate the couple {it; rt}, as the integration time includes *de facto* a part of the reaction time. Using the same methodology proposed by Kuwano and Namba [37], the reaction time is defined for a null integration time, which corresponds to approximatively 2 s for this experiment (couple {0; 2}). These values are slightly higher than the durations found in the literature, for the continuous assessment of sound levels. For example, the best couples {it; rt} found in [37] for perceived sound level assessment are {2.5; 0} and {0; 1}. This might be due to the higher complexity of an appreciation task.

To develop this analysis, the SIMPLE model presented in the previous section is calibrated for determining the weighting of the sound level time series. The parameter rt was added to the original ones, in order to introduce the reaction time into the SIMPLE model, adding a delay to the original weighting function. The SIMPLE parameters are optimized over the last 30 s, in order to obtain the best estimation of the instantaneous pleasantness, according to the sound level. The best optimized SIMPLE function has been obtained using the following coefficients: $c = 50$, $t = 0.55$, $s = 14$, and $rt = 0$.

The optimized SIMPLE function shows a null reaction time ($rt = 0$). The weighting function shows a flat section between $t = 0$ s to $t = -3.25$ s, which suggests that all of the events included in this time interval have the same impact on the continuous pleasantness appreciation. Then, the function decreases strongly between $t = -3.25$ to $t = -10$ s, in accordance with the integration time previously found. However, the weight does not fall totally to 0, suggesting that the sound level between $t = 30$ s and $t = 10$ s has a limited, but existing, impact on the instantaneous sound pleasantness.

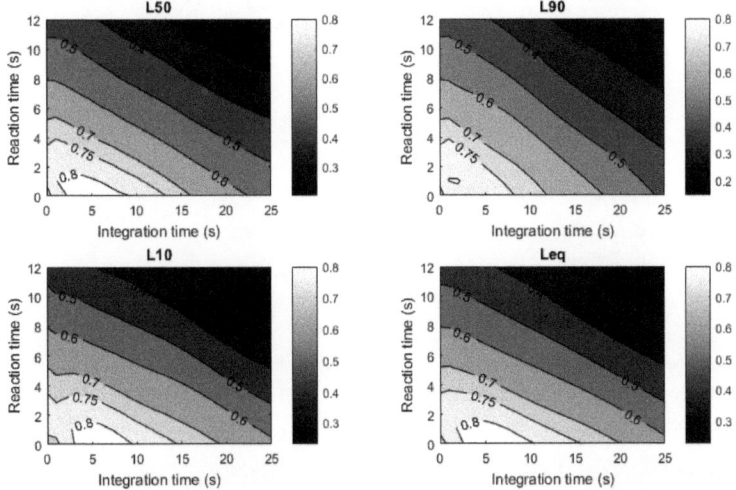

Figure 6. Pearson correlation coefficient between pleasantness and L_{50}, L_{90}, L_{10}, and L_{eq}, with varying reaction and integration times.

This more complete accounting of the noise level time series significantly increases the correlation, averaged over the 10 sequences, between the estimated instantaneous sound pleasantness using the SIMPLE model, and the observed instantaneous sound pleasantness. It reaches 0.93, compared to 0.84 in the previous analysis ($t(9) = 2.8$, $p < 0.05$). The SIMPLE model thus enables a more accurate estimation of the continuous sound pleasantness estimates.

3.2.2. Global Sound Pleasantness Estimation Based on Sound Level Time Series

In a practical case, the available data will more likely be a time series of sound levels, instead of instantaneous sound pleasantness values. Therefore, this section aims to estimate the global sound pleasantness of a walking trip, based on its sound level time series. The two proposed approaches consist of: (i) estimating GP from the instantaneous P values, which are themselves estimated in terms of noise level time series; (ii) directly estimating GP in terms of the noise level time series.

A model has been proposed in the previous section for estimating the instantaneous sound pleasantness based on the last 30 s sound level time series through SIMPLE modeling. Section 3.1.2 showed that the GP value can be estimated as the arithmetic average of these instantaneous estimated pleasantness values, $P_{estimated}$. Combining these two results enables one to estimate GP values from sound level measurements. Based on the 10 real sound sequences of the second experiment, the resulting model, built on the unique predictor $P_{mean,estimated}$ ($b^* = 0.81$, $t(8) = 3.8$, $p < 0.005$), explains 60% of the total variance ($R^2 = 0.65$, $F(2,8) = 14.9$, $p < 0.005$), with a Root Mean Square Error ($RMSE$) of 0.72. This model has the advantage of considering the short-term recency effect, but this, in return, makes the GP value dependent on the direction of the walking trip. Figure 7 presents the estimated global pleasantness obtained with this approach, versus the actual assessed global pleasantness averaged over the participants.

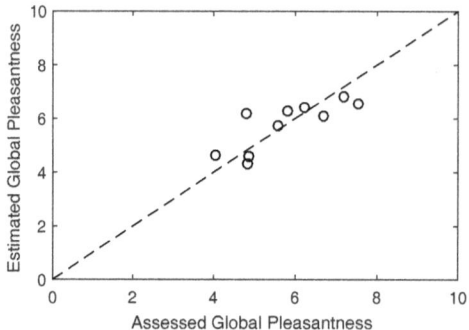

Figure 7. Estimated global pleasantness from $P_{estimated}$ versus assessed global pleasantness for the 10 sequences.

Table 5 presents the relations between the sound level time series ($L_{eq,1s}$) and the *GP*, relative to a 3-min sequence through simple indicators that neglect the recency effects. These models take advantage of simplifying the *GP* estimation by giving it the same value, whatever the direction is.

Table 5. Different models to estimate global pleasantness from physical measurements.

Equations	Explained Variance	R^2, F, p, and *RMSE* Values
$21.5 - 0.24L_{50}$	58%	$R^2 = 0.63$, $F(2,8) = 13.4$, $p < 0.01$, $RMSE = 0.58$
$27.8 - 0.33L_{mean}$	54%	$R^2 = 0.59$, $F(2,8) = 11.6$, $p < 0.01$, $RMSE = 0.77$
$18.6 - 0.18L_{eq}$	15%	$R^2 = 0.25$, $F(2,8) = 2.53$, $p = 0.15$, $RMSE = 1.06$

The tested models rely on three different indicators, namely the median and the arithmetic average of sound levels and the L_{eq}, which is often used for exposure assessment through the widely used Sound Exposure Level indicator (SEL). The two indicators L_{mean} and L_{50} enable good *GP* estimates. Inversely, there is no significant correlation between the L_{eq}, and the *GP* values calculated over the sequences. L_{eq}, contrary to L_{mean} and L_{50}, is impacted by noise peaks, explaining the poor correlation. This suggests again that there is no peak-effect on the global sound sequences assessments in the present study, in accordance with [29].

4. Discussion

The conclusions of the first experiment are in accordance with other studies [29]: (i) the mean of the continuous pleasantness assessment is the most important predictor of the global pleasantness assessment (ii) the recency effect and trend effect both influence the retrospective global assessment of the pleasantness of a sound sequence. Nevertheless, the recency effect that is observed in the first experiment tends to disappear in the second experiment. Two hypotheses are formulated:

- The sound sequences of the second experiment are less contrasted and more complex than the controlled sound sequences used in the first experiment. This attenuates the conclusions concerning a recency effect for the sound pleasantness assessment of real sound sequences. Moreover, as in the first experiment, the focus was to observe the influence of the temporal structure in an environment, so sound markers or events have been removed. Such events, as semantic content, are suspected to significantly influence the overall rating of the sound environment [43]. These events and markers, present in the second experiment, might have masked the recency and trend effects that were observed in the first experiment.
- The video content might have helped participants to analyze the sequences of the second experiment as a whole, thus attenuating the recency effect.

Finally, contrary to the first experiment, *GP* values are globally higher than the P_{mean} values. This might be the consequence of the visual factor on global pleasantness appreciation, with the help of the video. The positive effect of the video on the overall pleasantness rating has already been shown in [21,22,44]. But then, the fact that *GP* values are relatively higher than P_{mean} values, would suggest that the visual effect has no influence on the continuous assessment of the sound pleasantness, which needs to be investigated in future studies.

The estimated instantaneous pleasantness is accurately estimated by the sound level measurements in Section 3.2.1, although some discrepancies remain unexplained. Attempts to take into account the spectral content of the signal or the typology of the sound sources, did not improve the explained variance. The visual content might also explain the remaining discrepancies between the sound pleasantness estimates, as a closer look at the ending of sequence five, and the beginning of the sequence six, suggests. These sub-sequences both correspond to environments that are visually unpleasant, and precisely at these instants, the models, which do not account for the visual settings, over-estimate the sound pleasantness rating given by the participants. Another explanation for the remaining discrepancies relates to the high correlations observed between sound pleasantness and sound intensity: participants might have relied on noise intensity to assess the sound pleasantness over the continuous appreciations. Including a better description of the sound environment, for example, with specific sound source descriptors, might enhance the instantaneous estimated sound pleasantness.

Section 3.2.2 reveals that the mean or median sound level value better estimates the pleasantness of an urban path than the equivalent sound level, which is commonly used to measure sound level exposures. If this result is confirmed by further studies, this will lead to two distinct models, one for measuring the global sound exposure of an urban walk, and one for measuring its global pleasantness.

In experiment 2, it has been shown that about 60% of the variance in the global sound pleasantness can be explained by the sound level of the stimuli. Further studies should be done to determine what part of the remaining variance is due to acoustic factors other than the unique sound level, but also to non-acoustic factors such as visual information [44], personal factors such as noise sensitivity [45], and individual variability.

A 3 min length path was used in this study, since this corresponds to the average pedestrian trip durations in Paris, but it could be interesting to confront these results to other stimuli, with a larger variety of sequence time lengths. If temporal effects have been demonstrated for shorter lengths [29,36], they could disappear for sequences longer than 15 min [36]. Generalizing the test for different trip durations will help to cover wider trip characteristics.

Finally, extending the experiment to cover a wider variety of environments, including more parks, and very noisy or animated locations, is now required, in order to test the domain of the validity of the models and develop more universal models. This might also highlight further psychological effects, other than recency.

5. Conclusions

This paper aimed to estimate both the instantaneous, and the global pleasantness, of the soundscape during 3 min urban walking trips. For this purpose, two laboratory experiments were conducted, in which controlled and natural sound sequences were presented, and during which participants were asked to continuously assess the sound pleasantness along the sequence, and globally, at its end. The conclusions are:

- The modeling of the recency effect, through the state-of-the-art SIMPLE model, improves the estimation of the global sound pleasantness over the controlled sound sequences. This effect tends to decline or disappear when the sound sequences are more realistic, including, among other things, some visual information.
- The global sound pleasantness can be estimated by using the median or the arithmetic average of the instantaneous sound pleasantness values.

- The instantaneous sound pleasantness is mainly impacted by the sound level during the last few seconds. Reaction and integration times are used by participants for estimating the continuous judgment of the pleasantness of the sound environment. The sound level time series can be more accurately taken into account with the SIMPLE model, which then highlights that the last 30 s also influence, although to a lesser extent, the instantaneous sound pleasantness assessments.

- Finally, the Global sound pleasantness can be accurately estimated based on the sound level time series of the 3 min sequences, either by relying on an intermediate estimation of the instantaneous sound pleasantness values, or directly based on the sound level time series, through an arithmetic average or a median value of the $L_{eq,1s}$ values. Both approaches are relevant, explaining about 60% of the variance in the global sound pleasantness, with an error inferior to 0.75 points over an 11-points scale.

The final proposed model enables one to estimate the sound pleasantness of a walking trip along a particular path, based on the sound level time series encountered along that path. The conclusions from this work could thus be helpful for constructing models that select urban walking routes with optimal sound pleasantness.

Acknowledgments: This work has been carried out in the framework of the GRAFIC project, supported by the French Environment and Energy Management Agency (ADEME) under contract No. 1317C0028.

Author Contributions: P.A. and C.L. conceived and designed the experiments; P.A. performed the experiments; P.A., A.C. and C.L. analyzed the data; D.B., B.D.C. and C.R. contributed material/analysis tools; P.A. and A.C. wrote the paper.

Conflicts of Interest: The authors declare no conflict of interest. The founding sponsors had no role in the design of the study; in the collection, analyses, or interpretation of data; in the writing of the manuscript, and in the decision to publish the results.

References

1. *Global Recommendations on Physical Activity for Health;* World Health Organization: Geneva, Swizerland, 2010.
2. Maurer Braun, L.; Read, A. *The Benefits of Street-Scale Features for Walking and Biking;* American Planning Association: Washington, DC, USA, 2015.
3. Methorst, R.; Monterden i Bort, H.; Risser, R.; Sauter, D. Pedestrians' Quality Needs. Final Report of the COST Project 358, Cheltenham: Walk21. Tight, M., Walker, J., Eds.; Pedestrians' Quality Needs Project, Posted 2010. Available online: http://www.walkeurope.org/final_report/default.asp (accessed on 4 Febuary 2017).
4. King, E.A.; Murphy, E.; McNabola, A. Reducing pedestrian exposure to environmental pollutants: A combined noise exposure and air quality analysis approach. *Transp. Res. D Transp. Environ.* **2009**, *14*, 309–316. [CrossRef]
5. Saelens, B.E.; Sallis, J.F.; Frank, L.D. Environmental correlates of walking and cycling: Findings from the transportation, urban design, and planning literatures. *Ann. Behav. Med.* **2003**, *25*, 80–91. [CrossRef] [PubMed]
6. Ross, Z.; Kheirbek, I.; Clougherty, J.E.; Ito, K.; Matte, T.; Markowitz, S.; Eisl, H. Noise, air pollutants and traffic: Continuous measurement and correlation at a high-traffic location in New York City. *Environ. Res.* **2011**, *111*, 1054–1063. [CrossRef] [PubMed]
7. Can, A.; Rademaker, M.; Van Renterghem, T.; Mishra, V.; Van Poppel, M.; Touhafi, A.; Theunis, J.; De Baets, B.; Botteldooren, D. Correlation analysis of noise and ultrafine particle counts in a street canyon. *Sci. Total Environ.* **2011**, *409*, 564–572. [CrossRef] [PubMed]
8. Dekoninck, L.; Botteldooren, D.; Panis, L.I. An instantaneous spatiotemporal model to predict a bicyclist's Black Carbon exposure based on mobile noise measurements. *Atmos. Environ.* **2013**, *79*, 623–631. [CrossRef]
9. Guo, Z. Does the pedestrian environment affect the utility of walking? A case of path choice in downtown Boston. *Transp. Res. D Transp. Environ.* **2009**, *14*, 343–352. [CrossRef]
10. Botteldooren, D.; Dekoninck, L.; Gillis, D. The influence of traffic noise on appreciation of the living quality of a neighborhood. *Int. J. Environ. Res. Public Health* **2011**, *8*, 777–798. [CrossRef] [PubMed]
11. Davies, G.; Whyatt, J.D. A network-based approach for estimating pedestrian journey-time exposure to air pollution. *Sci. Total Environ.* **2014**, *485*, 62–70. [CrossRef] [PubMed]
12. Lwin, K.K.; Murayama, Y. Modelling of urban green space walkability: Eco-friendly walk score calculator. *Comput. Environ. Urban Syst.* **2011**, *35*, 408–420. [CrossRef]

13. Can, A.; Van Renterghem, T.; Botteldooren, D. Exploring the use of mobile sensors for noise and black carbon measurements in an urban environment. *Acoustics* **2012**, *2012*.

14. Brocolini, L.; Lavandier, C.; Quoy, M.; Ribeiro, C. Measurements of acoustic environments for urban soundscapes: Choice of homogeneous periods, optimization of durations, and selection of indicators. *J. Acoust. Soc. Am.* **2013**, *134*, 813–821. [CrossRef] [PubMed]

15. Liu, J.; Kang, J.; Luo, T.; Behm, H.; Coppack, T. Spatiotemporal variability of soundscapes in a multiple functional urban area. *Landsc. Urban Plan.* **2013**, *115*, 1–9. [CrossRef]

16. Coensel, B.D.; Vanwetswinkel, S.; Botteldooren, D. Effects of natural sounds on the perception of road traffic noise. *J. Acoust. Soc. Am.* **2011**, *129*, EL148. [CrossRef] [PubMed]

17. Lavandier, C.; Defréville, B. The contribution of sound source characteristics in the assessment of urban soundscapes. *Acta Acust. United Acust.* **2006**, *92*, 912–921.

18. Ricciardi, P.; Delaitre, P.; Lavandier, C.; Torchia, F.; Aumond, P. Sound quality indicators for urban places in Paris cross-validated by Milan data. *J. Acoust. Soc. Am.* **2015**, *138*, 2337–2348. [CrossRef] [PubMed]

19. Ishiyama, T.; Hashimoto, T. The impact of sound quality on annoyance caused by road traffic noise—An influence of frequency spectra on annoyance. *JSAE Rev.* **2000**, *21*, 225–230. [CrossRef]

20. Berglund, B.; Hassmén, P.; Preis, A. Annoyance and Spectral Contrast Are Cues for Similarity and Preference of Sounds. *J. Sound Vib.* **2002**, *250*, 53–64. [CrossRef]

21. Jeon, J.Y.; Lee, P.J.; Hong, J.Y.; Cabrera, D. Non-auditory factors affecting urban soundscape evaluation. *J. Acoust. Soc. Am.* **2011**, *130*, 3761–3770. [CrossRef] [PubMed]

22. Jeon, J.Y.; Hong, J.Y.; Lee, P.J. Soundwalk approach to identify urban soundscapes individually. *J. Acoust. Soc. Am.* **2013**, *134*, 803–812. [CrossRef] [PubMed]

23. Yu, L.; Kang, J. Factors influencing the sound preference in urban open spaces. *Appl. Acoust.* **2010**, *71*, 622–633. [CrossRef]

24. Steele, D.; Guastavino, C. The role of activity in urban soundscape evaluation. In Proceedings of the Euronoise 2015, Maastricht, The Netherlands, 31 May–3 June 2015; pp.1507–1512.

25. Tarlao, C.; Steele, D.; Fernandez, P.; Guastavino, C. Comparing soundscape evaluations in French and English across three studies in Montreal. In Proceedings of the Inter-Noise 2016, Hamburg, Germany, 21–24 August 2016; pp. 21–24.

26. Can, A.; Guillaume, G.; Gauvreau, B. Noise Indicators to Diagnose Urban Sound Environments at Multiple Spatial Scales. *Acta Acust. United Acust.* **2015**, *101*, 964–974. [CrossRef]

27. Bennett, G.; King, E.; Curn, J.; Cahill, V.; Bustamante, F.; Rice, H. Environmental noise mapping using measurements in transit. In Proceedings of the ISMA 2010, Leuven, Belgium, 20–22 September 2010; pp. 1795–1809.

28. De Coensel, B.; Sun, K.; Wei, W.; Van Renterghem, T.; Sineau, M.; Ribeiro, C.; Can, A.; Aumond, P.; Lavandier, C.; Botteldooren, D. Dynamic Noise Mapping based on Fixed and Mobile Sound Measurements. In Proceedings of Euronoise 2015, the 10th European Congress and Exposition on Noise Control Engineering, Maastricht, The Netherlands, 31 May–3 June 2015.

29. Steffens, J.; Guastavino, C. Trend Effects in Momentary and Retrospective Soundscape Judgments. *Acta Acust. United Acust.* **2015**, *101*, 713–722. [CrossRef]

30. Västfjäll, D. The "end effect" in retrospective sound quality evaluation. *Acoust. Sci. Technol.* **2004**, *25*, 170–172. [CrossRef]

31. Susini, P.; McAdams, S.; Smith, B.K. Global and Continuous Loudness Estimation of Time-Varying Levels. *Acta Acust. United Acust.* **2002**, *88*, 536–548.

32. Ponsot, E.; Verneil, A.-L.; Susini, P. Effect of sound duration on loudness estimates of increasing and decreasing intensity sounds. *J. Acoust. Soc. Am.* **2013**, *134*, 4063. [CrossRef]

33. Fiebig, A.; Sottek, R. Contribution of Peak Events to Overall Loudness. *Acta Acust. United Acust.* **2015**, *101*, 1116–1129. [CrossRef]

34. Luigi, M.; Massimiliano, M.; Aniello, P.; Gennaro, R.; Virginia, P.R. On the Validity of Immersive Virtual Reality as tool for multisensory evaluation of urban spaces. *Energy Procedia* **2015**, *78*, 471–476. [CrossRef]

35. Maillard, J.; Kacem, A. Evaluation de la Qualité Acoustique des Parcours Piétonniers Urbains par Auralisation. In Proceedings of the CFA 2016, Le Mans, France, 11–15 April 2016.

36. Aumond, P.; Can, A.; De Coensel, B.; Botteldooren, D.; Ribeiro, C.; Lavandier, C. Sound pleasantness evaluation of pedestrian walks in urban sound environments. In Proceedings of the ICA 2016, Buenos Aires, Argentina, 5–9 September 2016; p. 11.

37. Kuwano, S.; Namba, S. Continuous judgment of level-fluctuating sounds and the relationship between overall loudness and instantaneous loudness. *Psychol. Res.* **1985**, *47*, 27–37. [CrossRef] [PubMed]

38. Takeuchi, T.; Nelson, P.A. Optimal Source Distribution for Binaural Synthesis over Loudspeakers. *J. Acoust. Soc. Am.* **2002**, *112*, 2786. [CrossRef] [PubMed]

39. Audiometric Classification of Hearing Impairements—BIAP Recommendation 02/1 Bis. Available online: http://www.biap.org/index.php?option=com_content&view=article&id=5%3Arecommandation-biap-021-bis&catid=65%3Act-2-classification-des-surdites&Itemid=19&lang=en (accessed on 19 December 2016).

40. *Le Bilan des Déplacements en 2014 à Paris*; L'observatoire des Déplacements à Paris: Paris, France, 2014.

41. Brown, G.D.A.; Neath, I.; Chater, N. A temporal ratio model of memory. *Psychol. Rev.* **2007**, *114*, 539–576. [CrossRef] [PubMed]

42. Brown, G.D.A. HomePage: Brown, Gordon D.A. Available online: http://homepages.warwick.ac.uk/staff/G.D.A.Brown/simple/ (accessed on 19 Junuary 2016).

43. Fan, J.; Thorogood, M.; Pasquier, P. Automatic Soundscape Affect Recognition Using A Dimensional Approach. *J. Audio Eng. Soc.* **2016**, *64*, 646–653. [CrossRef]

44. Viollon, S.; Lavandier, C.; Drake, C. Influence of visual setting on sound ratings in an urban environment. *Appl. Acoust.* **2002**, *63*, 493–511. [CrossRef]

45. Gille, L.-A.; Marquis-Favre, C.; Weber, R. Noise sensitivity and loudness derivative index for urban road traffic noise annoyance computation. *J. Acoust. Soc. Am.* **2016**, *140*, 4307. [CrossRef] [PubMed]

Article

The Personal Viewpoint on the Meaning of Tranquility Affects the Appraisal of the Urban Park Soundscape [†]

Karlo Filipan [1,*,‡], Michiel Boes [1], Bert De Coensel [1], Catherine Lavandier [2], Pauline Delaitre [2], Hrvoje Domitrović [3] and Dick Botteldooren [1]

[1]   Department of Information Technology, Ghent University, Research group WAVES, 9052 Ghent, Belgium; michiel.boes@ugent.be (M.B.); bert.decoensel@ugent.be (B.D.C.); dick.botteldooren@ugent.be (D.B.)
[2]   Equipes Traitement de l'Information et Systèmes, Université de Cergy Pontoise, 95302 Cergy-Pontoise, France; catherine.lavandier@u-cergy.fr (C.L.); pauline.delaitre@u-cergy.fr (P.D.)
[3]   Department of Electroacoustics, Faculty of Electrical Engineering and Computing, University of Zagreb, 10000 Zagreb, Croatia; hrvoje.domitrovic@fer.hr
*   Correspondence: karlo.filipan@ugent.be; Tel.: +32-9-264-3325
†   This paper is an extended version of our paper published in Botteldooren, D.; Filipan, K.; Boes, M.; De Coensel, B. How the meaning a person gives to tranquility could affect the appraisal of the urban park soundscape. In Proceedings of the 43rd International Congress on Noise Control Engineering (Inter-Noise 2014), Melbourne, Australia, 16–19 November 2014; pp. 1–6.
‡   Current address: iGent Technologiepark-Zwijnaarde 15, 9052 Gent, Belgium.

Academic Editor: Jian Kang
Received: 30 September 2016 ; Accepted: 11 January 2017 ; Published: 17 January 2017

Abstract: Previous research has shown that tranquil areas in the city, such as urban parks, are usually perceived as positive and have a restorative effect on visitors. However, visitors could experience these spaces differently depending on the meaning they assign to the concept of tranquility. To investigate how individuals' personal views on tranquility affect their perception of the sonic environment, a soundscape study was conducted in several city parks in Antwerp, Belgium. Mobile sound measurements were combined with a questionnaire survey amongst 660 park visitors. Within the survey, the participants' viewpoint on tranquility was evaluated using their agreement with a set of previously established prototypical statements, categorizing them into one out of three main tranquility viewpoint groups: people that associate tranquility with silence, those that associate it with hearing natural sounds, or those that associate it with social relationships. Next to this, the sounds that participants had heard during their visit were noted, and their perception of the overall quality of the soundscape and the degree to which it matched their expectation were assessed. Results show that the park visitors who associate tranquility with natural sounds or to silence are more often found amongst those that report hearing mechanical sounds a lot. The same groups of visitors rate the overall quality of the sonic environment of the park more often bad to very bad. These findings suggest that park visitors pay attention more to the sounds they do not expect to hear, and that the higher their expectations about the soundscape, the more critical they become in their appraisal of the soundscape.

Keywords: soundscape; tranquil areas; urban parks; personal viewpoint

PACS: 43.66.Lj; 43.50.Qp; 43.50.Rq; 43.28.Hr

Appl. Sci. **2017**, *7*, 91

1. Introduction

People widely acknowledge urban parks as places for appreciating tranquility and a restorative soundscape. The term soundscape has previously been defined by different practitioners such as composers, acousticians, architects and psychologists [1–3]. Within the ISO 12913-1 international standard, the term soundscape is defined as "the acoustic environment as perceived or experienced and/or understood by a person or people, in context" [4]. The soundscape is generally considered as not equal to the sound environment, and therefore not measurable using only standard sound measurement equipment. Fundamentally, soundscape is shaped within a context of a person–environment interaction. This context is induced by all sensory stimulations, most importantly by auditory and visual observations. However, other senses, such as smell and touch variably contribute to overall perception. Additionally, context is also shaped by the knowledge that people have accumulated about the space, its use, purpose and cultural meaning, people's motivations and purposes, associated activities and other factors [5].

The soundscape of urban environments has been thoroughly investigated during recent years [6–8]. Even though the soundscape of urban parks only represents a small subset of all existing soundscape types, its context has been reasonably well described [9–11]. In this description, urban parks are frequently regarded as calm and tranquil areas within the liveliness of the city. Moreover, the concept of tranquility has been studied in various research areas closely related to soundscape. For instance, a direct brain response with relation to perceived tranquility was measured with neural imaging [12]. Additionally, the tranquility of natural places has been investigated and evaluated with established soundscape indicators [13]. Finally, tranquility is considered to be an important characteristic of the soundscape of religious spaces [14].

A study on linguistic representations of tranquility has been conducted among the French population [15,16]. In this research, three major groups of people were identified: those who associate tranquility to social relationships, those that mention sounds, in particular natural sounds with relation to tranquility, and those that focus on silence. Although these categories were quantitatively assessed for "*zones calmes*" (quiet areas), there has been no attempt to relate these findings to the perception of the sonic environment. Therefore, linking these findings with widely used soundscape evaluation methods could provide new insights into the assessment of urban parks.

In a broader context, this paper focuses on the influence of the viewpoints or beliefs related to tranquility and the way they affect the perception of the sonic environment. The present study combines a tranquility viewpoints extraction methodology with the soundscape perception data from questionnaires administered in urban parks, and aims to quantitatively and directly link this personal factor to the perception of the sonic environment in urban parks. Based on the theoretical consideration on the perception of soundscape given in [17], two hypotheses are formulated.

A first hypothesis relates directly to attention mechanisms, the component of sensory processing that prioritizes on the basis of motivational relevance [18]. Known sounds trigger attention more than unknown sounds and a keen interest in these sounds may sustain voluntary attention to them. Thus, people associating tranquility to hearing specific sounds, in particular natural ones, may have a better knowledge and sensitivity for them and hence a higher probability for noticing these sounds. Moreover, it could also be expected that these people report hearing natural sounds more often when asked about their experience while visiting a park. Similarly, people that associate tranquility to social sounds could be expected to notice human voices more often. Recently, it was observed that environment-related attitudes influence perceptions of green space, in particular that nature-oriented attitude leads to valuing natural sounds more highly [19]. This result could support our first hypothesis, yet the questions about natural sounds used in this study were more oriented towards valuation than towards observation. At the higher level of auditory object formation, incongruent sound may, however, also attract attention more often. Nevertheless, incongruence depends primarily on the presence of other sounds and is not expected to be strongly influenced by beliefs on tranquility [20]. In summary, based on the first hypothesis, one could expect that people who associate tranquility with hearing natural sounds would report hearing more natural sounds than their peers. Additionally, people who associate tranquility with social relationships could be expected to report hearing more sounds of people.

A second hypothesis links tranquility viewpoints to expectations, the component of sensory processing that interprets a stimulus with respect to its prior likelihood. Therefore, expected sounds do not add information about a place and thus would most likely not be noticed and remembered when a person is asked to describe what he or she had heard during a park visit. The role of consistency with schema expectation in remembering elements from a scene has been established in earlier studies [21]. Therefore, in our study, people that associate tranquility to hearing natural sounds would notice non-natural sounds more often and people associating tranquility to silence would hear all sounds more often than others. In addition, although a mild violation of expectation that does not offend the listener may be appraised as pleasing [22], expectation violation is assumed to trigger mainly negative appraisals. Because of the overall sonic environment, parks in urban settings are less likely to match expectations of the listeners who associate tranquility with natural sounds or silence. Hence, these people would not only notice unexpected sounds more often, they would also appraise the soundscape as less pleasing.

Section 2 of this paper introduces the methodology for extracting the viewpoints on tranquility. Section 3 describes the case study in Antwerp, on which data from the hypotheses are tested, and Section 4 discusses the results. Note that part of the results presented in this paper were published in a previous conference paper [23].

2. Main Viewpoints on Tranquility

In order to provide an overview of the different meanings given to tranquility, an online survey has been conducted in France using Q-methodology with 302 participants [15,16]. This study revealed the main beliefs shared by different groups of the population. A brief description of the methodology is given in this section, but, for the complete study, we refer to [16].

2.1. Methodology of Extraction

The participants were asked to rank 47 sentences (called Q-statements) depending on their agreement with the specific statement. The statements were chosen based on the earlier lexicographic studies [24]. In a survey, participants placed the statements into a pyramid with an 11-point scale from "mostly disagree" (−5) to "mostly agree" (+5). A matrix ($n \times p$), where n stands for the number of statements (47) and p for the number of participants (302), was created from the obtained data. The x_{ij}-th element of the matrix corresponds to the agreement score on the scale for statement i, as given by person j. To identify similar participants, a principal component analysis (PCA) [25] was conducted, where the objects represent the statements, and the participants the variables. A Varimax rotation [26] was implemented in order to maximize the correlations r_{jk} between the variables (persons) and the components.

Each component was then interpreted as a typical viewpoint shared by all of the statistically significant correlated members. Afterwards, only exclusive contributors, i.e., correlated to one component alone, were kept for the interpretation of each component. The weights of each exclusive contributor w_{jk} were defined (Equation (1)) from the correlation coefficients r_{jk} between the corresponding contributor (person) j and component k:

$$w_{jk} = \frac{r_{jk}}{1 - r_{jk}^2}. \tag{1}$$

Finally, the weighted mean scores in the pyramid were ranked again by giving the lowest score −5 to the two lowest values, −4 for the three following values, and so forth until reaching +5 for the two highest values. This final pyramid corresponded to "factor array" [27] and provided understanding of beliefs shared by the members contributing exclusively to each component.

2.2. Viewpoint Groups

Within the French survey, nine components were interpreted as nine different meanings of tranquil areas, although only three included more than 10 exclusive contributors.

2.2.1. The "Social Relationships" Group

This group consisted of people who agreed with the idea that tranquility could be experienced with other people. For them, a quiet area is symbolized as a shared space which facilitates social relationships and enables spending time with others. In this group, the percentage of people who live in city centers (53%) is found to be larger than in the initial corpus.

2.2.2. The "Natural Sound Sources" Group

Exclusive contributors to this group agreed with the sentences "in a quiet area, there is nature" (+5); "the presence of birds reinforces the tranquility" (+4); and "the presence of water contributes to the tranquility" (+4). In turn, this experienced natural atmosphere provided them with escape from the urban context. No special profile of the members of this group has been found. Therefore, this viewpoint was shared by various demographic groups.

2.2.3. The "Silence" Group

People belonging to this group mostly agreed with the sentence "a quiet area must be silent" (+5). Accordingly, they stated that they did not desire any sound such as sounds from people's activities or facilities. This group mainly consisted of men (71%), compared to the initial corpus (45%). The members of this group were also older than the others (36% were over 50 years old, compared to 17% in the initial corpus), and 29% of exclusive contributors stated that they held management work positions.

3. Antwerp Parks Survey Campaign

3.1. Study Area

This study was conducted during 22 days in August and September 2013. The data were gathered in eight different urban parks located in the city of Antwerp (Figure 1). Antwerp has a population of about 500,000 people and an economy centered around an important European harbor. Therefore, the traffic going to and from the city has a big impact on the urban sound environment.

The investigated parks, chosen in cooperation with the city council environmental authority, were expected to thoroughly represent the Antwerp park environment. They were located in different urban areas: city center (Stadspark), near the big highway junction (Rivierenhof) and in various living districts (six other parks). Moreover, their sizes also varied considerably from the smallest park (Bischoppenhof, around 0.03 km^2 in size) to the largest park (Rivierenhof, around 1.3 km^2 in size).

3.2. People

During the survey campaign, 660 participants were interviewed inside the investigated parks. The average age of the participants was 49.2 years while the standard deviation was 19.3 years (minimum and maximum age was 18 and 93 years, respectively). In total, 301 male participants (46% of the total sample) and 359 female participants (54% of the total sample) were interviewed. Most of the participants reported that they had a normal hearing (579 participants); however, 81 participants reported having one or more problems related to hearing: 32 participants reported being sensitive to noise, 16 reported using a hearing aid, 19 reported suffering from tinnitus and 27 participants reported they had other hearing problems. Participants voluntarily took part in the questionnaire. Nevertheless, an additional incentive was given by the possibility of winning a lottery prize of 100 euros.

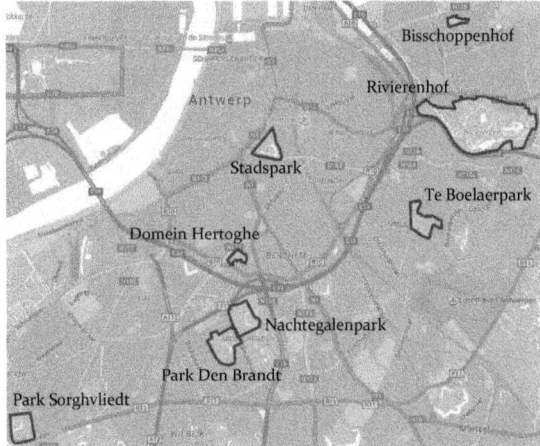

Figure 1. Locations of the eight parks in the city of Antwerp studied in the survey campaign.

3.3. Mobile Measurements

Measurements were performed using mobile recording devices carried in backpacks by two to three people per park. Researchers carrying the backpacks were specifically instructed to mind their walking manner in order not to disturb the recorded sonic environment. Paths were chosen to cover the whole area of the park while no specific walking directions were given. Additionally, approximately every half hour, the researcher would stop to make stationary recordings by placing the backpack on the closest bench for 10 min. Moreover, in order to capture the sound environment outside the park, the researchers also walked on the roads surrounding the park.

The devices used in measurements were custom-made, Linux-based sensor network mobile nodes [28] adapted to incorporate both sound and location recording. Therefore, the collected data comprised sound recordings, 1/3-octave band levels saved eight times per second, as well as GPS positions recorded one time per second. To facilitate data processing and presentation, spectral levels and GPS values were later transferred to a spatial database.

A set of indicators characterizing the sonic environment was extracted from the stored measurement data. These indicators were calculated from recorded 1/3-octave band values selected with a moving window of one minute duration and 10 s time step. Thus, every 10 s, one value was calculated, integrated over the last minute. Consequently, there was a 50 s overlap of data with the previous indicator value. Finally, location data (GPS positions) were included and related to the acoustic indicators by interpolating the dataset to the same 10-second period division.

3.4. Soundscape Questionnaire

A questionnaire (in Dutch) was created based on previous research [6,29] and a survey was conducted amongst park visitors. The interviewers aimed to collect at least 80 completed questionnaires in the central area of each park. The questionnaire included questions about the visitors' general profile, their use of the park, their evaluation of the soundscape along a number of perceptual dimensions [6], their perception of the environmental quality of the park and other factors.

In particular, the questionnaire inquired about the noticing of sound sources during the park visit. The three groups of sounds were listed as "human sounds (talking people, playing children, ...)", "natural sounds (wind in the leafs, birds, water, ...)" and "mechanical sounds (traffic, airplanes, machines, small electronic accessories, ...)". Participants were asked to rank hearing sounds in these categories on a 5-point ordinal category scale with categories: "not at all", "a little", "moderately", "much" and "very much".

Another question examined the participants' agreement with the statement "the sounds in this park are the sounds that one expects to hear in a park". The answers were listed on a 5-point ordinal category scale with values: "completely agree", "agree", "neither agree/nor disagree", "disagree" and "completely disagree". Additionally, participants were asked on the overall quality of the sonic environment during their visit. Their opinion was marked on the 5-point ordinal category scale with labels: "very bad", "bad", "neither good/nor bad", "good" and "very good".

Finally, participants were asked, in a direct question, on their opinion about the purpose of a park in general. Corresponding to the tranquility viewpoint groups: "Natural sound sources", "Silence" and "Social relationships" (Section 2.2), three mutually exclusive options were provided for park as a: "place for appreciating nature", "place for appreciating silence" and "place for meeting other people", and the participants were asked to select only one option.

3.5. Tranquility Statements

The questionnaire also included the 13 statements on tranquility presented in Table 1. They were selected from the 47 statements used in the French population quiet areas study [16] to be the most differentiating between tranquility viewpoints (Section 2). In accordance with the methodology, participants ranked their preference on an ordinal scale with 11 numbers ranging from −5 to +5 with the labels only on both ends: "do not agree at all" (−5) and "completely agree" (+5).

The degree of similarity between the prototypical tranquility viewpoint and the participants' responses was extracted by connecting the prototypical group markings from the French study (Table 1) with the participants' answers (ranging from −5 to +5) on the same 13 tranquility statements.

For this, the value m_{ji} (i.e., the response of participant j to statement i) was first selected. At the same time, the prototypical group marking g_{ki} (all values shown in Table 1) for each tranquility viewpoint group k and statement i was obtained. Secondly, using the data for all 13 tranquility statements, the degree of similarity $G_j(k)$ between the response of participant j and the group k was calculated using the overlap-integral method (Equation (2)). Therefore, three values representing degree of similarity to three tranquility groups (Section 2.2) were assigned to each of the 660 participants. Finally, $G_j(k)$ can be interpreted as the partial membership of person j to tranquility viewpoint group k in a probabilistic way:

$$G_j(k) = \frac{\sum\limits_i m_{ji} g_{ki}}{\sqrt{\sum\limits_i m_{ji}^2}\sqrt{\sum\limits_i g_{ki}^2}}. \tag{2}$$

3.6. Relative Membership to Tranquility Groups

Relative membership to each tranquility viewpoint group was introduced to compare people's responses to other questions, taking into account their specific tranquility viewpoint group. Firstly, the degree of similarity (partial membership) $G_j(k)$ (Equation (2)) for each participant j and tranquility viewpoint group k was normalized to the average membership of group k between all 660 responses (Equation (3)). $G_j'(k)$ can be interpreted as how much more participant j belongs to the tranquility viewpoint group k than the average over all participants:

$$G_j'(k) = \frac{G_j(k)}{\frac{1}{N}\sum\limits_j G_j(k)}, N = 660. \tag{3}$$

Table 1. Tranquility statements used in the Antwerp parks survey campaign with their corresponding reference number to the French quiet areas study [16]. Prototypical group markings (g_{ki}) are provided for each statement i and three tranquility groups k: (1)—"Social relationships" group, (2)—"Natural sound sources" group, (3)—"Silence" group.

i	No. in [16]	Survey Statement	Translated Statement	(1)	(2)	(3)
1	11	Een rustgevende plek is een toevluchtsoord	A quiet area is a refuge	3	1	5
2	29	Achtergrondgeluid stoort mij niet	Background sound does not bother me	1	-4	-4
3	22	Een plek is rustgevend als er geen kinderen zijn	A quiet area is an area without children	-5	-3	0
4	33	Een rustgevende plek moet stil zijn	A quiet area must be silent	-2	0	5
5	20	Een rustgevende plek nodigt uit om een tijdje te blijven hangen	In a quiet area, I can linger	4	3	3
6	13	Een rustgevende plek wordt nog rustgevender door het contrast met de omgeving	A quiet area is even quieter when it contrasts with its surroundings	2	-1	3
7	34	Het is rustgevend als specifieke geluiden hoorbaar zijn	Tranquility, it is being able to hear specific sounds	3	2	1
8	44	Op een rustgevende plek kunnen er winkeltjes en horeca zijn	In a quiet area, there may be shops	1	-2	-3
9	46	Op een rustige plek ben ik bang om alleen te zijn	In a quiet area, I am afraid of being alone	-4	-5	-5
10	42	Rust is er om te delen met anderen	Tranquility can be experienced with others	5	0	2
11	32	Vogels dragen bij tot het rustgevende karakter van een plek	The presence of birds reinforces the tranquility	0	4	1
12	36	Water draagt bij tot het rustgevende karakter van een plek	The presence of water contributes to the tranquility	4	4	2
13	47	Een plek kan rustgevend zijn, zelfs met voorbijgangers	We can be tranquil, even if there is movement around	4	-3	-4

Secondly, the set of persons j that answered value l to question Q (e.g., "not at all" for question "hearing human sounds") was selected. Finally, the relative membership $H_{Q,l}$ (Equation (4)) was calculated as an average of the normalized degree of similarity $G'_j(k)$ over the persons that selected the l-th answer to question Q (the sum in denominator in Equation (4) effectively represents this number of participants). Additionally, for the complete representation of the selected dataset, standard deviations were also calculated:

$$H_{Q,l}(k) = \frac{\sum\limits_{j|Q_{j=l}} G'_j(k)}{\sum\limits_{j|Q_{j=l}} 1}. \tag{4}$$

With a similar procedure, relative membership to each tranquility viewpoint group was also extracted for the participants from each park separately. To this purpose, in Equation (4), question Q was evaluated as the park location and answer l as the specific park.

4. Results and Discussion

4.1. Tranquility Groups in Antwerp Parks

Visitors of the surveyed parks were classified according to their tranquility viewpoints extracted with the procedure described in Section 3.5. Each participant was then assigned to only one of the three tranquility groups by selecting the group with the largest value $G_j(k)$. In turn, it was found that 74% of the 660 interviewed participants adhere to the viewpoint that a tranquil park is a place for social relationships, whereas only 18% associate a tranquil park to silence. The remaining group (8%) identifies their tranquility viewpoint with natural sound sources. This differs from the results previously reported by Lavandier and Delaitre [16], where 62%, 57% and 14% of participants associated tranquility to social relationships, natural sound sources and silence, respectively.

This difference could be explained by various factors. Firstly, in the French population study, it was observed that the participants could have multiple tranquility viewpoints, not limited to the three major groups (Section 2.2). Nevertheless, for the prototypical response values (Table 1), only the three strongest principle components for tranquility viewpoints from the French study were retained. Additionally, for this analysis, each participant was assigned to only one tranquility viewpoint group. Finally, it should be noted that this study's context is urban parks, in contrast to the French study, in which tranquil areas in a general sense were considered. Tranquility in urban parks may be less associated to hearing natural sounds, than tranquility in general. Therefore, this difference might explain the relative lack of tranquility viewpoints related to natural sound sources in this study, as compared to the earlier one [16].

4.2. Noticing Sounds

Relative membership to tranquility viewpoint (Equation (4)) was evaluated to observe how tranquility viewpoint affects people's perception of soundscape. Since previous work [30–32] has found a strong relationship between the sounds that people report to have heard while in a public place and the pleasantness of the soundscape, the relationship between the sounds that people have heard and their membership to a tranquility viewpoint group was assessed first. For brevity, the fact that people reported that sounds belonging to a specific category (mechanical, natural, human) have been frequently heard is labeled as noticing these sounds.

Survey participants answered the question about hearing different categories of sound on a 5-point ordinal category scale. The calculated membership to tranquility viewpoint groups is furthermore assessed as a continuous variable as it aggregates the answers from an 11-point scale and 13 questions with an overlap integral method (Equation (2)). In Figure 2, the results are therefore shown as the relative membership to tranquility viewpoint groups, i.e., the average of the normalized degree of similarity calculated by Equations (3) and (4), for different answer categories on the questions about hearing particular sounds. This may look slightly unconventional, as it is more popular to show expected effects as a function of expected cause.

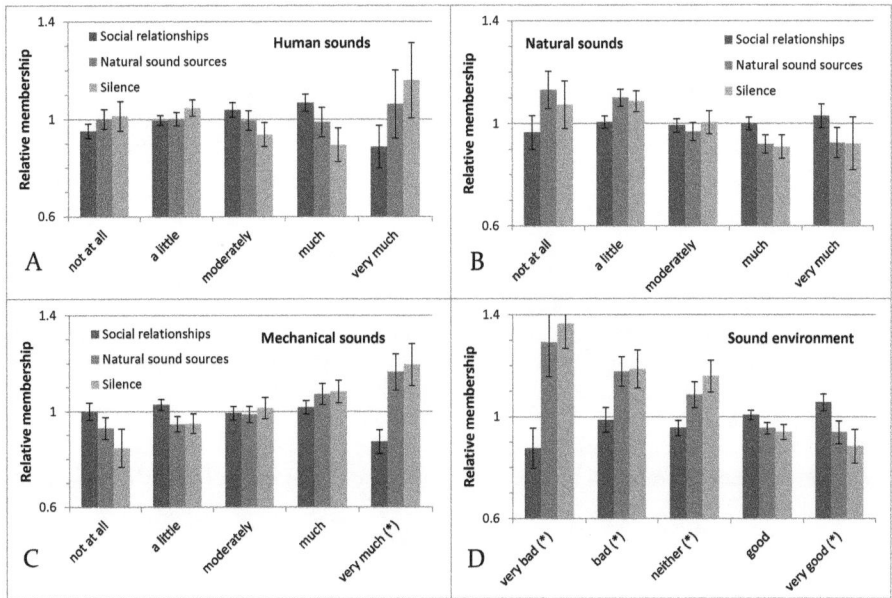

Figure 2. Relative membership to tranquility viewpoint groups shown in relation to hearing sound sources: (**A**) human, (**B**) natural and (**C**) mechanical. In (**D**): relative membership in relation to evaluation of the quality of the sonic environment is presented. Whiskers indicate one standard error of the dataset. A star indicates statistically significant difference confirmed by the analysis of variance between tranquility groups within one answer category.

Given that the descriptive analysis shows some possible trends, the statistical significance was assessed using the Kendall rank correlation coefficient (τ_b) (statistical analyses were performed using the Python programming language with *Scipy* [33] (analysis of variance (ANOVA) and correlation) and *Statsmodels* [34] (Tukey test) modules). Table 2 shows this correlation coefficient between noticing sounds belonging to one of the three categories (human sounds, natural sounds, mechanical sounds) and the relative adherence to the tranquility viewpoint groups ("Social relationships", "Natural sound sources", "Silence"). Belonging to the tranquility viewpoint group "Social relationships" (first row in Table 2) does not correlate statistically significant with noticing sounds from any of the categories, yet there is a weak trend for noticing more human sounds. However, the trends between belonging to the tranquility viewpoint group "Natural sound sources" and noticing natural sound (negative) and noticing mechanical sounds (positive) are highly statistically significant. Likewise, the positive trend between belonging to the tranquility viewpoint "Silence" and noticing mechanical sounds is statistically significant, while the negative trend between belonging to the tranquility viewpoint "Silence" and noticing natural sounds is statistically significant but also weaker. Finally, there is no statistically significant or pronounced trend between belonging to either of these last two tranquility viewpoint groups and noticing human sounds.

Table 2. Rank correlation coefficients with significance values between participants' responses to questions on hearing sounds (human, natural and mechanical) and belonging to a specific tranquility group. In the last column, the same is shown for the question on the quality of the sonic environment.

Question:	Human Sounds	Natural Sounds	Mechanical Sounds	Sound Environment
Tranquility Group				
Social relationships	$\tau_b = 0.066$ $p = 0.011$	$\tau_b = 0.008$ $p = 0.747$	$\tau_b = -0.048$ $p = 0.066$	$\tau_b = 0.072$ $p = 0.006$
Natural sound sources	$\tau_b = 0.000$ $p = 0.998$	$\tau_b = -0.118$ $p < 0.001$	$\tau_b = 0.114$ $p < 0.001$	$\tau_b = -0.130$ $p < 0.001$
Silence	$\tau_b = -0.060$ $p = 0.022$	$\tau_b = -0.073$ $p = 0.005$	$\tau_b = 0.106$ $p < 0.001$	$\tau_b = -0.142$ $p < 0.001$

Rank correlation only allows detecting monotonous trends. Although these already illustrate the main effect, visual inspection of Figure 2 seems to reveal that less people associating tranquility to social relationships report hearing human and mechanical sounds "very much". Only the latter is confirmed by a one-way ANOVA test: there is a statistically significant difference between the participants belonging to different tranquility groups who reported hearing mechanical sounds "very much" $(F(2,168) = 5.969, p = 0.003)$.

A Tukey post hoc test revealed that the relative membership of people belonging to tranquility groups "Silence" $(H = 1.195, SD = 0.088, p = 0.006)$ and "Natural sound sources" $(H = 1.164, SD = 0.076, p = 0.014)$ was statistically significantly different from the relative membership of "Social relationships" group $(H = 0.872, SD = 0.050)$. In brackets, H represents the relative membership to the stated tranquility viewpoint group (Equation (4)), whereas SD represents the standard deviation of the dataset used to calculate this relative membership (Section 3.6). Additionally, no statistically significant difference could be found between the relative memberships to tranquility groups "Silence" and "Natural sound sources" using the Tukey test.

These statistically significant trends reject the hypothesis that persons associating tranquility to social relationships would report hearing human sounds more often as well as the hypothesis that persons associating tranquility to natural sound sources would report hearing natural sounds more often as they would pay more attention to noticing these sounds.

4.3. Quality of the Sonic Environment

As could be expected on the basis of the known relationship between hearing particular sounds and overall quality judgment of the sonic environment and the results discussed in Section 4.2, statistically significant trends are found between relative adherence to tranquility viewpoints and judgment of the quality of the sonic environment. Indeed, the last column of Table 2 shows a statistically significant negative correlation coefficient between relative membership to the tranquility viewpoint groups "Natural sound sources" and "Silence" and the judgment of the overall quality of the sound environment. Thus, persons adhering to these tranquility viewpoints judge the quality of the sonic environment worse.

Although these statistically significant trends as a function of the appraisal of the sonic environment highlight the effect of relative membership to the tranquility viewpoints "Natural sound sources" and "Silence" on this appraisal, it is also useful to study the difference between membership of tranquility viewpoints within each of the five sonic environment quality judgment groups.

A statistically significant difference determined by one-way ANOVA between tranquility groups was observed within several categories of the overall quality appraisal of the sonic environment. The difference was found for the responses: "very bad" $(F(2,30) = 6.147, p = 0.006)$, "bad" $(F(2,162) = 3.373, p = 0.037)$, "neither good, nor bad" $(F(2,366) = 4.353, p = 0.014)$ and "very good" $(F(2,273) = 3.107, p = 0.046)$. For the responses "neither good, nor bad" and "very good", results from Tukey post hoc tests revealed that the difference is statistically significant only between the tranquility groups "Silence" and "Social relationships" (with Tukey test significance levels of $p = 0.011$ for the response "neither good, nor bad", and $p = 0.041$ for the response "very good"). Furthermore, Tukey tests showed that the response "very bad" had a statistically significant difference between the groups "Natural sound sources" and "Social relationships" ($p = 0.025$) as well as between the groups "Silence" and "Social relationships" ($p = 0.007$). For the response "bad", no statistically significant result was found with the post hoc test.

The questionnaire also asked about the degree to which the sounds that people heard while visiting a park matched their expectations (Section 3.4). The Kendal correlation coefficient shows no statistically significant correlation between reported matching expectations and the relative membership to the "Social relationships" tranquility group. There is, however, a statistically significant negative correlation between the degree of matching of the sounds that people heard with their expectations and the relative membership to tranquility group "Natural sounds sources" ($\tau_b = -0.121$, $p < 0.001$) and "Silence" ($\tau_b = -0.109$, $p < 0.001$).

Both statistically significant trends discussed in this section may be indicative of the fact that persons associating tranquility to hearing natural sounds, or to silence, do not find their expectations matched in the city parks of Antwerp, and, therefore, also tend to rate the quality of the sonic environment worse than other people visiting the park. It should nevertheless be noted that the causality chain has not been proven. It might be that the persons belonging to these tranquility viewpoint groups are more demanding on the sonic environment when assessing its quality and, at the same time, have higher expectations than those associating tranquility to social relationships.

4.4. Differences between Parks

In previous sections, a relationship was established between some tranquility viewpoints and sounds that persons visiting a park notice. Similarly, a relationship between some tranquility viewpoints and the overall assessment of the quality of the sonic environment was established. In this section, the influence of the park where the persons were encountered is studied in relation to the tranquility viewpoint and whether visitors' expectations were matched. Therefore, relative membership was also calculated for people interviewed in each park (Equation (4)).

The results show that, although the viewpoint on tranquility may have an influence on the park that is visited, this influence seems not to be statistically significant. Indeed, one could imagine plenty of other factors such as proximity, visual environment, infrastructure, etc., that affect which park people select.

In addition, Table 3 presents the percentage of the persons that stated that the sounds heard in the park matched their expectations. In particular, participants who stated "agree" or "completely agree" on the questionnaire statement "the sounds in this park are the sounds that one expects to hear in a park" (Section 3.4) were considered to have the expectations of the sonic environment of the park matched.

Whether or not the sound environment matches the expectations of the park visitor could depend on many different factors. For example, the intrinsic quality of the sound environment in the park could match expectations of park visitors in general. However, a possible deviation in the sonic environment, as compared to the usual situation that the visitor might know from earlier visits, could also lead to an expectation mismatch. Finally, the expectations regarding the sounds a visitor would like to encounter in a park could be related to the tranquility viewpoint to which that person adheres. However, no statistically significant trends were found with Pearson correlation analysis. Therefore, at the park level, a multitude of other factors influencing whether the sonic environment matches expectations obscures the trend observed for some viewpoints seen at the level of the individual (Sections 4.2 and 4.3).

Table 3. Membership of the tranquility viewpoint groups normalized to indicate in which parks persons adhering to these viewpoints are found more often than average (arrows point to difference of more than 5% to overall average). Matching expectations are shown with the percentage of the visitors that stated "agree" or "completely agree" on the questionnaire statement "the sounds in this park are the sounds that one expects to hear in a park" (Section 3.4). The last column presents the average and standard deviation of the 50-percentile A-weighted sound pressure level from data aggregated over the whole park (Section 3.3).

Park	Tranquility Viewpoint			Matching Expectations (%)	L_{A50}, (dBA)
	Social Relationships	Natural Sound Sources	Silence		
Bisschoppenhof	0.929↓	0.905↓	0.969	88	49.7 ± 3.6
Domein Hertoghe	0.991	1.004	1.079↑	86	52.9 ± 5.2
Nachtegalenpark	1.001	1.055↑	0.921↓	69	53.6 ± 5.1
Park Den Brandt	1.002	1.094↑	1.093↑	79	47.9 ± 4.0
Park Sorghvliedt	1.006	0.933↓	0.948↓	93	51.9 ± 4.8
Rivierenhof	1.002	0.993	1.048	71	55.9 ± 5.4
Stadspark	0.996	0.984	0.946↓	73	56.2 ± 4.1
Te Boelaerpark	1.070↑	1.030	0.997	66	53.9 ± 4.4

4.5. Sound Levels in the Parks

Although this publication and the underlying study do not aim at identifying physical indicators for the quality of the sonic environment of parks, the reader may be interested in sound levels in the parks. Therefore, Table 3 also presents the 50-percentile A-weighted sound pressure level (L_{A50}), an indicator which is often reported to relate well to people's overall tranquility experience of a sonic environment [35]. The values in this table represent an average over the whole park, calculated from one-minute indicator values obtained using the procedure described in Section 3.3.

When comparing the levels between the parks, the range in level spans 8.3 dB, with Park Den Brandt having the highest L_{A50} and Stadspark having the lowest L_{A50}. Accordingly, visitors who associate tranquility to silence (and natural sound sources) were found more often than average in Park Den Brandt. In the same manner, visitors who were found in Stadspark adhere less often to the tranquility viewpoint associated with silence. However, no statistically significant trend can be found from Kendall rank correlation between the tranquility group memberships in the investigated parks and the L_{A50}. This is further illustrated by Domein Hertoghe. For this park, the relative membership of the visitors to tranquility groups "Silence" and "Natural sound sources" is higher than the average of both groups, and, moreover, the sounds heard in this park match expectations, yet the L_{A50} is slightly higher than the average over parks. This could potentially be explained by the observation that this park is almost completely covered by forest and green paths and the knowledge that visual elements contribute to the perception of tranquility [13].

4.6. Reported Park Purpose in Relation to Derived Tranquility Viewpoints

Rather than identifying tranquility viewpoints from the 13 questions, as explained in Section 3.5, one could attempt to deduct this viewpoint from a more direct question about the belief on the purpose of a park. Figure 3 compares the tranquility viewpoint between groups of people reporting different purposes of a park. On the direct question on park purpose, most respondents answer that a park is a place for appreciation of nature.

Membership of tranquility viewpoint groups was compared with a one-way ANOVA within park purpose groups. Results for the answer for park as a place for appreciating nature were not statistically significant ($F(2,1320) = 1.089$, $p = 0.337$). However, for park as a place for appreciating silence, the analysis shows statistically significant difference between groups ($F(2,396) = 21.541$, $p < 0.001$). A Tukey post hoc test unveiled that the difference was statistically significant for all comparisons. In particular, statistical significance of p less than 0.001 was identified between "Natural sound sources" ($H = 1.049$, $SD = 0.040$) and "Silence" ($H = 1.269$, $SD = 0.048$) tranquility viewpoint groups as well as "Social relationships" ($H = 0.893$, $SD = 0.034$) and "Silence". In brackets, H represents the relative membership to the stated tranquility viewpoint group (Equation (4)) and SD represents the standard deviation of the dataset used to calculate this relative membership (Section 3.6). Additionally, relative membership to "Natural sound sources" ($H = 1.049$, $SD = 0.040$, $p = 0.019$) was found to be statistically significantly higher than to "Social relationships" ($H = 0.893$, $SD = 0.034$).

For persons that identify a park as a place for meeting other people, statistically significant difference between the groups of people belonging to different tranquility groups was found ($F(2,255) = 8.611$, $p < 0.001$). However, results from a Tukey test suggest that the statistical significance is only between people associating tranquility to silence ($H = 0.691$, $SD = 0.073$, $p < 0.001$) and those associating it to social relationships ($H = 1.033$, $SD = 0.034$). For comparison of people belonging to "Natural sound sources" tranquility group ($H = 0.870$, $SD = 0.061$) and to two other groups, no statistically significant difference was found.

The difference between the results for the direct question on the purpose of a park and the results from the indirect viewpoint extraction method is most obvious for people stating that they are considering parks as places where they can appreciate nature. Within this group, each tranquility viewpoint is equally present. However, people that explicitly stated that they were considering a park as a place for appreciating silence also belong more frequently to the group that associates tranquility to silence. Similarly, the last group that perceives a park as a place for meeting people also puts an emphasis on social relationships different to the two other tranquility groups. Thus, for these latter categories, the direct question could be used as a proxy for deriving the tranquility viewpoint.

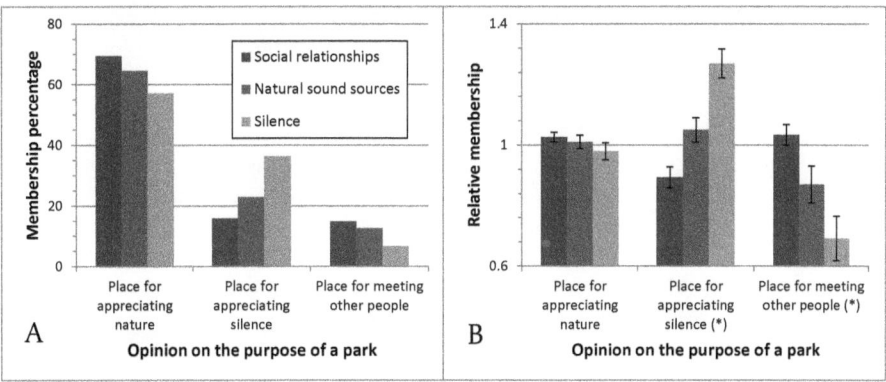

Figure 3. Membership of tranquility viewpoint groups, as a function of the response to the direct question on park purpose: (**A**) percentages of people responding to an opinion statement in each tranquility group; (**B**) relative membership to tranquility group per opinion on the park purpose. In (**B**): whiskers correspond to one standard error, and stars indicate statistically significant difference confirmed by analysis of variance between tranquility groups.

5. Conclusions

In this study, the influence of a particular contextual factor—the viewpoint of a park visitor on tranquility—on the perception of the sonic environment was investigated. To extract the viewpoint on tranquility, the results from an earlier study about the meaning of *"zones calmes"* (quiet areas) [16] were translated to a set of 13 most differentiating statements. A survey with 660 participants in eight urban parks in Antwerp was used to relate these viewpoints to different aspects of the soundscape.

The results obtained in this work show a tendency to falsify the first hypothesis stated in the introduction. Persons associating tranquility to hearing natural sounds do not tend to notice natural sounds more during their visit to a park. Moreover, the trend between belonging to this viewpoint group and hearing natural sounds is slightly but statistically significantly negative. Therefore, persons adhering to the "Natural sound sources" viewpoint notice less natural sounds than their peers, and, thus, it is expected that they do not pay more attention to the natural sounds. However, no statistically significant trend was found between noticing human sounds and belonging to the tranquility viewpoint "Social relationships". In turn, this result neither confirms nor falsifies the first hypothesis.

Turning to the second hypothesis: non-expected sounds are likely to be noticed more often than the expected ones. The results demonstrate that indeed people more frequently notice and report hearing sounds other than the ones associated with their tranquility viewpoint. In particular, it was found that the participants who belong to groups that associate tranquility to natural sound sources or to silence were more often found amongst those that reported hearing mechanical sounds a lot, and that there was a statistically significant positive trend for belonging to these tranquility viewpoint groups and noticing mechanical sounds. On the other hand, persons belonging to the tranquility viewpoint group "Social relationships" do not hear mechanical sounds more often.

In addition, we hypothesized that the people who notice these unexpected sounds would also assess soundscapes as less pleasing. In turn, statistically significant trends were found for people who associate tranquility to natural sound sources or to silence and their rating of the overall quality of the sonic environment. Therefore, people seem to pay more attention to the sounds that they do not expect to hear and rate the quality of the sound environment in Antwerp parks as less pleasing. The role of expectation is confirmed by the statistically significant negative trend between the answer to a direct question on whether the sounds that were heard matched the person's expectation and their membership to tranquility viewpoint groups "Natural sound sources" and "Silence". All of these aforementioned results confirm the statements in the second hypothesis.

Our study also showed that there is no one-to-one relationship between the viewpoint on tranquility as assessed using the proposed 13 statements and the response to a direct question on the purpose of an urban park in general. Specifically, most of the people reported a park as a place for appreciating nature. However, no statistically significant difference between the membership to tranquility groups was found. On the other hand, people that see a park as a place for appreciating silence belong to the "Silence" tranquility viewpoint group statistically significantly more often.

Finally, it was observed that, although there were slight differences in the membership of different tranquility viewpoint groups depending on the park where participants were encountered, no statistically significant differences were found. The same holds for the degree to which the park matched the expectations of the visitor as well as the overall sound level (L_{A50}) in the park. This confirms that the tranquility viewpoint assessed using the 13 statements about tranquility is orthogonal to the quality of the specific park where the person was interviewed. Consequently, it indicates that the tranquility viewpoint is a personal factor.

To summarize, this study shows that there is a diversity in opinions on the meaning of tranquility, with a vast majority stressing its social component. In addition, it was shown that this tranquility viewpoint is a personal factor that influences the sounds that are noticed during a park visit, the degree to which these sounds match expectations and the overall perceived quality of the soundscape. This conclusion, however, only holds for specific viewpoints that might be associated with more critical listening.

Acknowledgments: The research leading to these results has received funding from the People Programme (Marie Curie Actions) of the European Union's Seventh Framework Programme *FP7/2007–2013/* under REA Grant agreement 290110, SONORUS "Urban Sound Planner", and from the Research Foundation Flanders (FWO-Vlaanderen) under Grant G0D5215N, ERC Runner-up project MAESTRO. Furthermore, Michiel Boes is a doctoral fellow of the Research Foundation Flanders; the support of this organization is gratefully acknowledged.

Author Contributions: Dick Botteldooren, Bert De Coensel, Catherine Lavandier and Pauline Delaitre designed the experiments; Karlo Filipan, Michiel Boes, Dick Botteldooren and Bert De Coensel performed the experiments; Karlo Filipan, Dick Botteldooren and Hrvoje Domitrović analyzed the data; Karlo Filipan, Dick Botteldooren, Catherine Lavandier and Bert De Coensel wrote the paper.

Conflicts of Interest: The authors declare no conflict of interest.

References

1. Brown, A.L. A review of progress in soundscapes and an approach to soundscape planning. *Int. J. Acoust. Vib.* **2012**, *17*, 73–81.
2. Kang, J. *Urban Sound Environment*; Taylor & Francis: London, UK, 2007.
3. Schafer, R.M. *The Soundscape: Our Sonic Environment and the Tuning of the World*; Destiny Books: Rochester, VT, USA, 1994.
4. International Organization for Standardization. *ISO 12913-1:2014 Acoustics—Soundscape—Part 1: Definition and Conceptual Framework*; International standard; International Organization for Standardization: Geneva, Switzerland, 2014.
5. Botteldooren, D.; Lavandier, C.; Preis, A.; Dubois, D.; Aspuru, I.; Guastavino, C.; Brown, A.L.; Nilsson, M.E.; Andringa, T.C. Understanding urban and natural soundscapes. In Proceedings of the Forum Acusticum, Aalborg, Denmark, 27 June–1 July 2011.
6. Axelsson, Ö.; Nilsson, M.E.; Berglund, B. A principal components model of soundscape perception. *J. Acoust. Soc. Am.* **2010**, *128*, 2836–2846.
7. Oldoni, D.; De Coensel, B.; Boes, M.; Rademaker, M.; De Baets, B.; Van Renterghem, T.; Botteldooren, D. A computational model of auditory attention for use in soundscape research. *J. Acoust. Soc. Am.* **2013**, *134*, 852–861.
8. Kang, J.; Chourmouziadou, K.; Sakantamis, K.; Wang, B.; Hao, Y. (Eds.) *COST TUD Action TD0804: Soundscape of European Cities and Landscapes*; Soundscape-COST: Oxford, UK, 2013.
9. Brambilla, G.; Gallo, V.; Zambon, G. The soundscape quality in some urban parks in Milan, Italy. *Int. J. Environ. Res. Public Health* **2013**, *10*, 2348–2369.
10. Jabben, J.; Weber, M.; Verheijen, E. A framework for rating environmental value of urban parks. *Sci. Total Environ.* **2015**, *508*, 395–401.
11. Liu, J.; Kang, J.; Behm, H.; Luo, T. Effects of landscape on soundscape perception: Soundwalks in city parks. *Landsc. Urban Plan.* **2014**, *123*, 30–40.
12. Hunter, M.D.; Eickhoff, S.B.; Pheasant, R.J.; Douglas, M.J.; Watts, G.R.; Farrow, T.F.D.; Hyland, D.; Kang, J.; Wilkinson, I.D.; Horoshenkov, K.V.; et al. The state of tranquility: Subjective perception is shaped by contextual modulation of auditory connectivity. *NeuroImage* **2010**, *53*, 611–618.
13. Watts, G.R.; Pheasant, R.J. Tranquillity in the Scottish Highlands and Dartmoor National Park—The importance of soundscapes and emotional factors. *Appl. Acoust.* **2015**, *89*, 297–305.
14. Jeon, J.Y.; Hwang, I.H.; Hong, J.Y. Soundscape evaluation in a Catholic cathedral and Buddhist temple precincts through social surveys and soundwalks. *J. Acoust. Soc. Am.* **2014**, *135*, 1863–1874.
15. Delaitre, P.; Lavandier, C.; Dedieu, R.; Gey, N. Meaning of quiet areas in urban context through people viewpoints. In Proceedings of the Acoustics 2012 Nantes Conference, Nantes, France, 23–27 April 2012.
16. Lavandier, C.; Delaitre, P. Individual and shared representations on *"zones calmes"* ("quiet areas") among the French population in urban context. *Appl. Acoust.* **2015**, *99*, 135–144.
17. Botteldooren, D.; Andringa, T.; Aspuru, I.; Brown, A.L.; Dubois, D.; Guastavino, C.; Kang, J.; Lavandier, C.; Nilsson, M.; Preis, A. From Sonic Environment to Soundscape. In *Soundscape and the Built Environment*; Kang, J., Schulte-Fortkamp, B., Eds.; CRC Press: Boca Raton, FL, USA, 2015; pp. 17–43.
18. Summerfield, C.; Egner, T. Expectation (and attention) in visual cognition. *Trends Cogn. Sci.* **2009**, *13*, 403–409.
19. Gunnarsson, B.; Knez, I.; Hedblom, M.; Sang, Å.O. Effects of biodiversity and environment-related attitude on perception of urban green space. *Urban Ecosyst.* **2016**, pp. 1–13.
20. Gygi, B.; Shafiro, V. The incongruency advantage for environmental sounds presented in natural auditory scenes. *J. Exp. Psychol. Hum. Percept. Perform.* **2011**, *37*, 551–565.
21. Pezdek, K.; Whetstone, T.; Reynolds, K.; Askari, N.; Dougherty, T. Memory for real-world scenes: The role of consistency with schema expectation. *J. Exp. Psychol. Learn. Mem. Cogn.* **1989**, *15*, 587–595.
22. Huron, D.B. *Sweet Anticipation: Music and the Psychology of Expectation*; MIT Press: Cambridge, MA, USA, 2006.
23. Botteldooren, D.; Filipan, K.; Boes, M.; De Coensel, B. How the meaning a person gives to tranquility could affect the appraisal of the urban park soundscape. In Proceedings of the 43rd International Congress on Noise Control Engineering (InterNoise), Melbourne, Australia, 16–19 November 2014.

24. Delaitre, P.; Lavandier, C.; Cance, C.; Pruvost, J. What is the definition for the French word calme in the European Directive related to "Quiet Areas"? A lexicographic study from the 16th century until today. *Acta Acust. United Acust.* **2012**, *98*, 734–740.

25. Jolliffe, I.T. *Principal Component Analysis*, 2nd ed.; Springer Series in Statistics; Springer: New York, NY, USA, 2002.

26. Abdi, H. Factor rotations in factor analyses. In *The SAGE Encyclopedia of Social Science Research Methods*; Lewis-Beck, M.S., Bryman, A., Futing Liao, T., Eds.; SAGE Publications: Thousand Oaks, CA, USA, 2003.

27. Brown, S.R. A primer on Q methodology. *Operant Subj.* **1993**, *16*, 91–138.

28. De Coensel, B.; Sun, K.; Wei, W.; Van Renterghem, T.; Sineau, M.; Ribeiro, C.; Can, A.; Aumond, P.; Lavandier, C.; Botteldooren, D. Dynamic noise mapping based on fixed and mobile sound measurements. In Proceedings of the 10th European Congress and Exposition on Noise Control Engineering (Euronoise), Maastricht, The Netherlands, 31 May–3 June 2015; pp. 2339–2344.

29. Yu, L.; Kang, J. Factors influencing the sound preference in urban open spaces. *Appl. Acoust.* **2010**, *71*, 622–633.

30. Axelsson, Ö.; Nilsson, M.E.; Hellström, B.; Lundén, P. A field experiment on the impact of sounds from a jet-and-basin fountain on soundscape quality in an urban park. *Landsc. Urban Plan.* **2014**, *123*, 49–60.

31. Davies, W.J.; Adams, M.D.; Bruce, N.S.; Cain, R.; Carlyle, A.; Cusack, P.; Hall, D.A.; Hume, K.I.; Irwin, A.; Jennings, P.; et al. Perception of soundscapes: An interdisciplinary approach. *Appl. Acoust.* **2013**, *74*, 224–231.

32. Hall, D.A.; Irwin, A.; Edmondson-Jones, M.; Phillips, S.; Poxon, J.E. An exploratory evaluation of perceptual, psychoacoustic and acoustical properties of urban soundscapes. *Appl. Acoust.* **2013**, *74*, 248–254.

33. Jones, E.; Oliphant, T.; Peterson, P. SciPy: Open source scientific tools for Python. Available online: http://www.scipy.org/ (accessed on 11 November 2016).

34. Seabold, S.; Perktold, J. Statsmodels: Econometric and Statistical Modeling with Python. In Proceedings of the 9th Python in Science Conference, Austin, TX, USA, 28–30 June 2010.

35. De Coensel, B.; Botteldooren, D. The quiet rural soundscape and how to characterize it. *Acta Acust. United Acust.* **2006**, *92*, 887–897.

Article

Personality Traits Bias the Perceived Quality of Sonic Environments

PerMagnus Lindborg [1,*] and Anders Friberg [2]

[1]   Area of Interactive Media, School of Art, Design, and Media, Nanyang Technological University, 637458 Singapore, Singapore

[2]   Department of Speech, Music, and Hearing, School of Computer Science and Communication, KTH Royal Institute of Technology, 100 44 Stockholm, Sweden; afriberg@kth.se

*   Correspondence: permagnus@ntu.edu.sg; Tel.: +65-6316-8727

Academic Editor: Jian Kang

Received: 30 September 2016; Accepted: 23 November 2016; Published: 3 December 2016

Abstract: There have been few empirical investigations of how individual differences influence the perception of the sonic environment. The present study included the Big Five traits and *noise sensitivity* as personality factors in two listening experiments ($n = 43$, $n = 45$). Recordings of urban and restaurant soundscapes that had been selected based on their type were rated for *Pleasantness* and *Eventfulness* using the Swedish Soundscape Quality Protocol. Multivariate multiple regression analysis showed that ratings depended on the *type* and *loudness* of both kinds of sonic environments and that the personality factors made a small yet significant contribution. Univariate models explained 48% (cross-validated adjusted R^2) of the variation in *Pleasantness* ratings of urban soundscapes, and 35% of *Eventfulness*. For restaurant soundscapes the percentages explained were 22% and 21%, respectively. *Emotional stability* and *noise sensitivity* were notable predictors whose contribution to explaining the variation in quality ratings was between one-tenth and nearly half of the soundscape indicators, as measured by squared semipartial correlation. Further analysis revealed that 36% of *noise sensitivity* could be predicted by broad personality dimensions, replicating previous research. Our study lends empirical support to the hypothesis that personality traits have a significant though comparatively small influence on the perceived quality of sonic environments.

Keywords: soundscape; environment; perception; personality; psychoacoustics; *noise sensitivity*; Big Five

---

1. Introduction

People respond in different ways to the soundscape, the "acoustic environment as perceived or experienced and/or understood by a person or people, in context" [1,2]. Thus, 'acoustic environment' refers to a physical phenomenon and 'soundscape' to a perceptual construct. Differences at societal and cultural levels influence the perception of sonic environments [3–5]. A large survey [6] found that some socio-economic factors, notably occupation and education, were more strongly associated with the perceived sound level than factors such as age, gender, or residential status. At the level of the individual, psychological differences can be charted in terms of broadly defined personality dimensions [7–10] or narrowly defined traits, such as *noise sensitivity* [11–14]. A trait of the latter kind can be described as a "lower order personality construct" ([15], p. 166). A question of interest is the extent to which personality traits, both narrow and broad, influence the soundscape.

The negative impact of environmental noise on health is considerable [16–19]. As an external stress factor, sound has been shown to cause neurophysiological changes in the brain, in particular in regions of the prefrontal cortex, amygdala, and hippocampus, which are involved in cognitive and emotional processing [20]. To some extent, individuals might be able to consciously modulate their cognitive appraisal of an environment ([21], p. 19), but the common belief that people will adapt to sustained high noise exposure levels is not supported by evidence from studies of annoyance among people living close to airports [12,22,23]. However, increased familiarity with an environment that allows for some level of control leads to more positive evaluations [24,25]. A sense of agency might give relevance and meaning to everyday environments [26–28]. The ways people actively regulate their affective relationship with the environment can be understood as coping strategies [29].

Sound activates the autonomous nervous system, causing emotional responses such as relaxation or stress. Changes in heart rate and peripheral skin temperature are correlated with soundscape loudness or evaluative qualities such as calm or chaos [30]. Sudden foreground sounds engage the listener's directed attention reorientation reflex, and chaotic soundscapes do not offer sufficient time in between sonic events for psychological mechanisms, inhibiting arousal to return towards a normal, relaxed state ([31], p. 7). If the soundscape is generally unpleasant, an individual might avoid annoyance by leaving, or avoid fatigue by suppressing the stressor; for example, by putting on headphones while commuting ([24], p. 228) and adjusting sound level and equalisation in order to optimise the listening experience [32]. If on the other hand the soundscape is pleasant, it may allow visitors to regain their default capacity for direct attention restoration. A restorative environment is one that invites undirected mental activities, e.g., sleep and daydreaming, or facilitates aesthetic experiences. Payne [33] showed that an urban park was perceived to have a lower restorative potential than a rural park, yet a higher restorative potential than a grey urban environment. Differences were significant both in a laboratory reproduction setting and in an on-site survey.

McCrae and Costa [8] described personality as a system of basic tendencies, adaptations, and self-concepts, with biological bases (revealed as traits) that are formed by the external environment (revealed as moods, states, or feelings) [9]. Mental processing associated with specific traits is associated with neurological variation in the brain, supporting a biological basis for personality theory [10]. The dimensions in the Five Factor Model, a.k.a. the Big Five, are called *extraversion, agreeableness, conscientiousness, emotional stability* and *openness* (or *openness to new experiences*). The fourth factor sometimes appears in reverse and is then labelled Neuroticism. These constructs originate in the Lexical Hypothesis, which posits that attributes of socially relevant personality characteristics are encoded in natural language, since it is necessary for individuals to communicate traits and states for bonding and, ultimately, for survival (for a historic overview, see [7]).

Noise sensitivity is one of the key constructs in psychoacoustics [34]. It is an aspect of personality that describes the "internal states (be they physiological, psychological (including attitudinal), or related to life style or activities conducted) of any individual which increase their degree of reactivity to noise in general" ([16], p. 59; see also [18]). It is a complex trait that, while being relatively stable over an individual's lifetime, manifests itself differently depending on situation, meaning, attitudes, and motivation [23]. Job [16] suggested that *noise sensitivity* is produced by two latent factors, which make an individual more vulnerable to noise in general: sensitivity to distant, louder noises (e.g., a traffic drone), and sensitivity to close, quieter noises (e.g., a distracting voice). It is a predictor of annoyance [12] but it is independent of noise exposure [16], hearing acuity [13], or a "predisposition to perceive sound events more intensely" ([35], pp. 1471–1472). Because *noise sensitivity* is a self-report measure, it captures an evaluative predisposition towards sounds rather than aspects of auditory processing per se.

Despite a surge in soundscape studies over the past decade, much is still unknown about how individual differences influence the perception of sonic environments. We are not aware of published research investigating the extent to which personality traits can explain ratings of soundscape quality in listening tests, specifically in relation to stimuli variables such as environmental type or loudness. Therefore, the aim of the present work was to address this lacuna of knowledge. We conducted two consecutive experiments: The first involved recordings of urban environments, and the second focussed on restaurants.

2. Methods

2.1. Sound Recordings and Psychoacoustic Descriptors

Soundscape recordings were made using Ambisonic techniques (CoreSound TetraMic, Teaneck, NJ, USA, and SoundDevices 788t, Reedsburg, WI, USA) and transformed to binaural versions suitable for headphone listening (see [36]). Simultaneous on-site sound pressure level (SPL; unweighted $L_{eq,90s}$) was captured with a calibrated Type 1 meter (Extech 407790, Nashua, NH, USA).

From recordings and SPL measurements various audio features were extracted computationally. Psychoacoustic descriptors of time-varying and spectrally complex sounds developed since the 1950s [37,38] have more recently found their way into soundscape research [39–45]. *Loudness* expresses the experience of a sound's intensity and is measured in sone. It is related to acoustic intensity, the distribution of energy in the frequency domain, and time-domain masking phenomena (for details, see [38]; [37], pp. 179–189). *Loudness* was extracted from the B-format omni (W) channel, each file calibrated with the original SPL, using the Dynamic Loudness Model [46] in Psysound3 [47], with values sampled every 0.002 s. See also Section 5.1 Soundscape Indicators, below.

2.2. Quality Ratings

Ratings of soundscape quality were made using the Swedish Soundscape Quality Protocol (SSQP; 41). This protocol asks "To what extent do you agree with the 8 statements below on how you experience the present surrounding sound environment?"; the statements are the adjectives pleasant, exciting, eventful, chaotic, annoying, monotonous, uneventful, and calm. The authors of the SSQP chose these adjectives as the best scale labels to span a circumplex model that they had previously developed. In relation to urban soundscapes, they are assumed to be equally strong semantic concepts. In our implementation of the protocol, listeners rated on continuous scales, anchored by "Agree completely" and "Disagree completely", which were displayed as horizontal sliders with an actual computer screen width of 100 mm. The order of scales on the screen was randomised for each participant and soundscape. Following the theoretic approach behind the circumplex, composite quality scores were calculated from the adjective scales, as follows:

$$Pleasantness = \sum R_{Adj}\cos(2\pi S_{Adj}/8),$$
$$Eventfulness = \sum R_{Adj}\sin(2\pi S_{Adj}/8), \tag{1}$$

where R_{Adj} is a vector of ratings and S_{Adj} is a whole number {0 ... 7} corresponding to the scale's index in the list of adjectives above.

2.3. Personality Traits

Broad personality traits were measured using the Ten-Item Personality Inventory (TIPI; [48]). Despite its brevity, the authors of the TIPI reported good test-retest reliability and convergence to larger instruments. The inventory is headed by the statement "I see myself as ... " which is followed by ten pairs of adjectives, such as "anxious, easily upset" and "extraverted, enthusiastic". Responses are marked on five-point Likert scales anchored by "Disagree strongly" and "Agree strongly". The participants filled out a computer-based implementation with adjectives in randomised order for each person.

Noise sensitivity was measured using Weinstein's Noise Sensitivity Scale (NSS [11] in an adapted version by [14]). It is headed by: "Attitudes to noise. To what extent do you agree with the statements?" and 21 statements including: "I wouldn't mind living on a noisy street if the apartment I had was nice", "When I want to be alone, it disturbs me to hear outside noises", and "I get used to most noises without much difficulty". Certain scales are reverse coded. In our computer implementation, responses are marked on continuous scales anchored by "I totally agree" and "I totally disagree". As before, participants were presented horizontal scales in randomised order. A single-value estimate for *noise sensitivity* is calculated by summing across all scales.

3. Material

The first experiment focussed on urban soundscapes. We selected twelve representative recordings in four *types* of environment, namely Rural parks, Urban parks, Eateries, and Shops. Excerpts of 90 s with a high degree of internal consistency according to informal listening were used. The same stimuli had been employed previously in a different setting [30]. Table 1 gives an overview of their general characteristics.

Table 1. Characteristics of urban soundscapes in Experiment 1. Sound level ($LA_{eq,90s}$) in dB *re* 20 µPa; Loudness (N_{10}) in sone. *Pleasantness* and *Eventfulness* = mean scores from Swedish Soundscape Quality Protocol (SSQP) ratings.

Type	Description	Sound Level	Loudness	Pleasantness	Eventfulness
Rural park	Tropical garden, with faint noises from farm machinery and a distant airplane.	44.5	6.3	1.11	−0.90
	Early morning recording from a nature reserve, with two singing-birds clearly audible.	43.9	7.6	1.05	−0.76
	Mangrove reserve, close to the water, faint city hum in the background.	55.7	14.6	1.20	−0.83
Urban park	Mid-day at a small concrete-and-grass park, with some people resting and a child playing; continuous noise from nearby diesel generator.	74.9	31.7	−1.16	−0.71
	Early evening, with some people sitting on park benches and others passing by; bar music in distance.	54.4	11.3	0.65	−0.70
	Evening at the rooftop garden of a large mall, with groups of young people laughing and chatting.	79.6	44.2	−0.21	0.71
Eatery	Crowded, large and worn-down foodcourt, with noisy fans and plates being scraped.	71.8	29.5	−0.24	0.02
	Well-visited café, with chairs scratching the floor; from outside, church bells and some traffic can be heard.	59.8	14.1	0.33	−0.00
	Crowded street-side restaurants by night, with noise from slow-moving traffic.	68.9	28.3	−0.34	0.44
Shop	Large, old-style market, mid-morning, with sounds of butchers chopping meat.	74.3	38.2	−0.34	0.18
	Large mall between a row of shops and moving escalators. The sound of a child bouncing a ball is audible, and dense traffic in the background.	69.4	25.5	−0.36	0.81
	Very crowded, huge mall in the midst of shop fronts, a cinema entrance, and moving escalators.	81.7	42.5	−0.78	0.79

Experiment 2: Restaurant Soundscapes

The second experiment focussed on restaurant soundscapes, following on from the previous experiment by making finer distinctions within the Eatery type. Restaurants, being a type of servicescape, are characterised by multimodal complexity and more or less elaborate acoustic design [45]. We selected fifteen representative recordings from restaurants in four predetermined environmental *types* according to their design style, a concept that had emanated from a previous study [45]. The *types* were: Café (4 places), Bar (3), MixFusion (4), and Dining (4). Excerpts of 120 s with a high degree of internal consistency according to informal listening were chosen. This set of stimuli was more homogenous in character than the previous one. Table 2 gives an overview.

Table 2. Characteristics of restaurant soundscapes in Experiment 2. Units as in Table 1.

Type	Description	Sound Level	Loudness	*Pleasantness*	*Eventfulness*
Bar	Large mix-fusion bar outdoors near the sea; floor tiles, parasols, beach; medium music; sparse with people.	66.4	21.8	0.99	0.21
	Medium-size mix-fusion bar outdoors near golf court greens; stone tiles, wood tables, open/roofed area; low music; sparse with people.	60.9	21.8	0.06	−1.07
	Very small Western-style bar outdoors near pedestrian walkway and a river; tiles, wood furniture, parasols; low music; practically no people.	61.8	15.9	0.72	−0.85
Café	Medium-size Western-style café; concrete, glass panes, small, entrance from large hospital lobby; medium-level music; medium level of crowding.	74.6	34.8	−0.41	0.46
	Small Western-style café; sofas and chairs, open towards mall; prominent music; extremely crowded	71.0	26.6	−0.58	0.17
	Small Western-style table-served café; wooden floor and furniture, table cloths, glass partition walls, inside open luxory mall; low music; very crowded.	72.0	27.7	−0.02	0.23
	Small international-style café; wood floor, glass panels, medium size, entrance from large mall lobby; medium-level music; medium level of crowding.	72.7	30.5	−0.21	0.10
Mix Fusion	Very large mix-fusion restaurant, outdoor near the sea; canvas roof, stone and wood floor, artificial waterfall in distance; low music; not so crowded.	63.4	17.3	−0.81	0.72
	Large mix-fusion-style restaurant, long wall open to large shopping mall; hard floor, absorbant false ceiling, painted brick walls; low music; sparse with people.	67.7	22.7	−0.05	−0.02
	Small mix-fusion style lunch restaurant; laminate floor, false ceiling, glass panels, medium size; loud music; medium level of crowding.	75.7	33.2	0.03	0.49
	Medium-size mix-fusion style buffet in luxory hotel; hard floor, ceiling treatments, large elongated open area with floor levels, no inner wall separations; low-level music; medium level of crowding.	71.0	26.1	−0.08	−0.46
Dining	Small Taiwanese-style small restaurant; hard surfaces, wooden tables, wall open to large shopping mall; medium-level music; not so crowded	67.3	21.8	0.15	−0.34
	Large Western-style diner entrance inside activity complex; thin carpet, some wood panels on concrete walls, medium size; prominent music; not so crowded.	71.0	27.6	0.03	0.53
	Large Chinese-style fine dining restaurant with entrance from very large mall; hard surfaces, plastic and concrete; low music; medium level of crowding.	62.5	17.2	−0.04	−0.01
	Medium-size Chinese style fine dining restaurant in quiet area country club; carpets, table cloths, curtains; low-level music; medium level of crowding.	66.5	22.3	0.32	0.01

4. Participants and Procedure

Participants in Experiment 1 ($n = 43$) were university students enrolled in music or sound-related courses. Ages were between 19 and 26; mean 22.0 years; 33 were women. Participants in Experiment 2

($n = 45$) were university staff and students enrolled in various programs, aged between 19 and 46; mean 26.1 years; 26 were women. There was no overlap of participants between the two experiments. They consented to participation after receiving full information about procedure and purpose, and received a cinema voucher as a token of appreciation.

The two experiments took place in a laboratory generally suited for sound work. Participants used studio quality circumaural headphones (type AKG K270) with sound playback via a digital audio interface from an individual computer. There was no intermittent disturbance at any time (e.g., heavy rain or construction noise). The participants could listen to stimuli in any order by clicking on graphical objects representing soundscapes. Double-clicking opened a sub-window where ratings were made. They could go back and adjust earlier ratings at any point.

The soundscape recordings had been made at a certain fixed input level and therefore their relative sound levels were correct. However, we did not have access to equipment with which to measure the SPL produced by the headphones at the entrance of the participant's ear canal. Therefore, in Experiment 1, the overall headphone playback level was set at an identical and fixed volume that the experimenter had subjectively found was to be close to the original level at the recording sites. The participants could not change this level. In Experiment 2, headphone playback was calibrated in two steps. First, the sound output of high-quality studio loudspeakers (Genelec 8030) was adjusted to be within ± 1 dB of the original soundscape level, as measured with a calibrated SPL meter (Extech 407790) on A- and C-weighted scales. Second, the experimenter adjusted the headphone level and equalisation to match the SPL of the loudspeakers.

All procedures for data collection were carried out in compliance with approval #2013-05-011 from the Institutional Review Board of Nanyang Technological University, Singapore.

5. Results

5.1. Soundscape Indicators

Several acoustic measures were calculated, referring to the overall level, the level variability over time, and the spectral content of the soundscape stimuli. The analysis reported below follows the approach taken by Axelsson, Nilsson, and Berglund [41]. We included the A-weighted equivalent continuous sound-pressure level in dB L_{Aeq} (excerpts were 90 s in Experiment 1 and 120 s in Experiment 2) and the Zwicker loudness in sone exceeded 10% of the time, N_{10}, as indicators of the overall loudness of the soundscape excerpts. We used the difference between levels exceeded 10% and 90% of the time as indicators of the soundscape variability, either expressed in A-weighted sound pressure-level in dB L_{A10}–L_{A90} or Zwicker loudness in sone N_{10}–N_{90}. We used the difference between A- and C-weighted sound-pressure level in dB $L_{Ceq,x}$–$L_{Aeq,x}$, where x is the duration of excerpts, hereafter L_{C-A}, as a measure of the relative proportion of low-frequency sound. Tables 3 and 4 show cross-correlations between the five soundscape indicators and the two soundscape descriptors that were extracted from SSQP, namely *Pleasantness* and *Eventfulness*, as described below, averaged across participants. It can be noted that the values are very close to those in Table II in Axelsson et al. [41], which we believe strengthens the validity of our present results.

Table 3. Pearson's coefficient of correlation amount soundscape indicators and descriptors for the 12 urban soundscapes in Experiment 1. For explanations, see text. * $p \leq 0.05$, ** $p \leq 0.01$, *** $p \leq 0.001$.

Indicator	Pleasantness	Eventfulness	L_{Aeq}	N_{10}	L_{A10}–L_{A90}	N_{10}–N_{90}
L_{Aeq}	−0.90 ***	0.76 **	-	-	-	-
N_{10}	−0.83 ***	0.75 **	0.97 ***	-	-	-
L_{A10}–L_{A90}	0.51	−0.12	−0.34	−0.18	-	-
N_{10}–N_{90}	−0.35	0.63 *	0.63 *	0.75 **	0.34	-
L_{C-A}	0.68 *	−0.73 **	−0.85 ***	−0.79 **	0.12	−0.60 *

Table 4. Pearson's coefficient of correlation amount soundscape indicators and descriptors for the 15 restaurant soundscapes in Experiment 2. For explanations, see text. * $p \leq 0.05$, ** $p \leq 0.01$, *** $p \leq 0.001$.

Indicator	Pleasantness	Eventfulness	L_{Aeq}	N_{10}	$L_{A10}–L_{A90}$	$N_{10}–N_{90}$
L_{Aeq}	−0.55 *	0.77 ***	-	-	-	-
N_{10}	−0.55 *	0.76 **	0.99 ***	-	-	-
$L_{A10}–L_{A90}$	−0.02	0.67 **	0.26	0.31	-	-
$N_{10}–N_{90}$	−0.31	0.89 ***	0.79 ***	0.82 ***	0.77 ***	-
L_{C-A}	0.61 *	−0.38	−0.25	−0.22	−0.097	−0.20

5.2. Personality Traits

The scores on Big Five personality traits of the participants in the two experiments were compared with results from a large sample ($n = 1813$) provided by Gosling and collaborators [48]. Descriptive statistics are provided in Table 5.

For each trait, we tested whether the sample mean diverged from the norm's mean with Mann-Whitney's test. Normality of distributions was tested with Shapiro-Wilk's test; however it should be noted that Gosling does not provide information on distribution shapes and it is therefore not clear if personality traits, as measured by TIPI, are expected to be normally distributed in the population.

Among Experiment 1 participants, no significant difference with the norm was found for any trait (Mann-Whitney U = {370 ... 550}, $p > 0.15$). The distributions were not normal (Shapiro-Wilk W = {0.91 ... 0.95}, p = {0.003 ... 0.042}). Among Experiment 2 participants, *conscientiousness* was slightly different from Gosling's norm (U = 335, p = 0.04) while the other traits passed the test (U = {345 ... 542}, $p > 0.05$). Distributions of *conscientiousness* and *openness* were slightly non-normal (both W = 0.95, p = 0.04) and other traits were normal (W = {0.96 ... 0.96}, p = {0.08 ... 0.54}).

We believe that the overall differences with Gosling's normative sample are small and that the two participant samples are acceptable within the context of an explorative study. Nevertheless, interpretation of results, particularly involving *conscientiousness*, should be made cautiously.

Table 5. Personality characteristics of participants in Experiment 1 and 2, compared with normative data published by Gosling et al. [48].

	Experiment 1 ($n = 43$)			Experiment 2 ($n = 45$)			(48; $n = 1813$)	
Trait	Mean	SD	Range	Mean	SD	Range	Mean	SD
Extraversion	4.5	1.4	1 ... 6.5	3.8	1.6	1 ... 7	4.4	1.5
Agreeableness	4.9	1.0	2 ... 6.5	5.1	1.1	2.5 ... 7	5.2	1.1
Conscientiousness	5	1.2	2 ... 7	4.8	1.3	2.5 ... 7	5.4	1.3
Emotional stability	5.1	1.1	2.5 ... 7	4.9	1.3	1.5 ... 7	4.8	1.4
Openness	5.4	1.1	3 ... 7	5.3	1.1	2.5 ... 7	5.4	1.1
Noise sensitivity	-	-	-	−4.7	12.5	−29 ... 26	-	-

Composite scores for *Pleasantness* and *Eventfulness* were calculated as described in the Methods section. Unsurprisingly, the perceived quality differences were more pronounced among the urban soundscapes in Experiment 1 than what they were among the restaurant soundscapes in Experiment 2.

5.3. Quality Ratings

The average perceived quality of the sonic environment by predetermined *type* is illustrated in Figure 1. There are parallels between the respective *types* in the two experiments. Rural parks and Bars were rated as most *calm*, while Shops and Cafés were most *chaotic*. The other *types* were rated in between; that is, within their respective contexts, Eateries and Urban Parks, and MixFusion and Dining, were perceived as neutral. The plots reveal that the environmental *types* line up quite close to the *calm–chaotic* axis. This suggests that a single perceptual dimension might be sufficient for these types of soundscapes. See [5] for a discussion of soundscape descriptors, and [44] for an interesting approach that involves functional context of environments. More work is needed to rule out an effect of the sampling method, or that the method of calculating composite scores for *Pleasantness* and *Eventfulness* is sub-optimal.

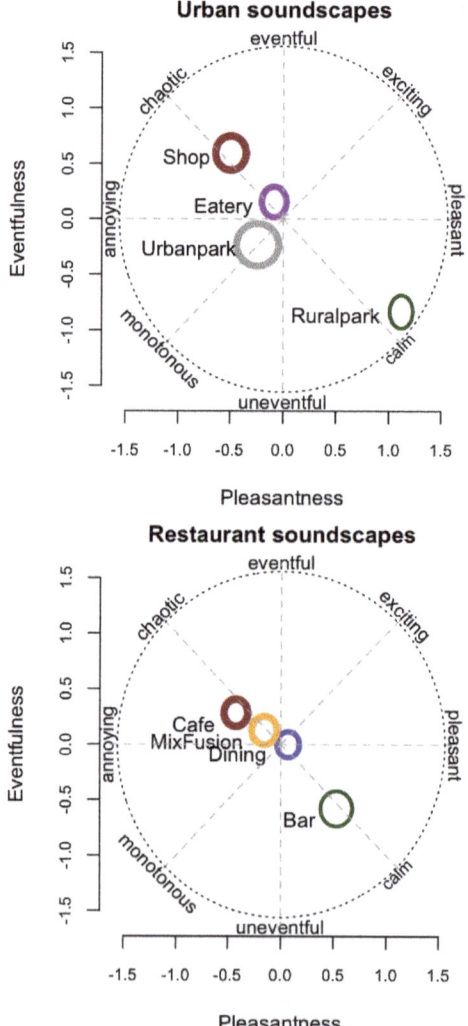

Figure 1. Perceived quality of urban and restaurant soundscape *types* plotted in the *Pleasantness–Eventfulness* circumplex. For details, see Methods section. 95% confidence ellipses are plotted, i.e., the ellipses have radii corresponding to 97.5% confidence intervals around means on *x* and *y* axes. The thickness of the ellipse circumference is proportional to the mean *loudness* within the *type*.

5.4. Regression Analysis

The analysis was carried out in three phases: (1) multivariate multiple regression analysis aiming to find the best set of predictor variables among the soundscape indicators included in the cross-correlation analysis above; (2) extending the multivariate model to include personality trait variables as predictors; (3) exploring the relationship between personality traits and soundscape indicator variables in separate univariate multiple regression models.

Please note that in the context of a prediction, no distribution assumptions are required for statistics such as ß, sr^2 (squared semipartial correlation), or R^2 (total amount of variation explained); see Howell ([49], p. 504) for a discussion. However, the probability values attached to these statistics do depend on distribution assumptions such as homoscedasticity, normality, and linearity. This point is important, and since our present data did not fulfil all required assumptions, the interpretation of significance levels and effect sizes of regression models will be tentative. An effect size statistic for sequential multiple regression is given by Cohen [50,51].

In the first analysis phase, we conducted a process of forward stepwise multivariate linear regression analysis aiming to find the best set of independent variables for simultaneous prediction of *Pleasantness* and *Eventfulness* averaged across participants. We considered the five soundscape indicators that Axelsson et al. [41] had reported (N_{10}, L_{Aeq}, $N_{10}-N_{90}$, $L_{10}-L_{90}$, and L_{A-C}) and the predetermined soundscape *type* categorical variable. Not unexpectedly, *type* explained the largest amount of variation. In Experiment 1, which had 12 cases, *type* on its own explained 68.2% (multiple R^2) of the variation in mean ratings of *Pleasantness* and *Eventfulness*. In Experiment 2, which had 15 cases, soundscape *type* explained 51.8% of the variation in the two dependent variables.

We then analysed if the predictive model could be improved by the addition of one or more of the acoustic variables. The difference between basic and extended models was tested using ANOVA. In Experiment 1, an extended model with *type* and *loudness* (N_{10}) as predictors explained 79.1% of the variation in the dependent variables. The increase over the basic model was significant (Pillai = 0.62, $p = 0.05$). In Experiment 2, the amount of variation explained by the extended model was raised to 64.0%, but in this case the increase was not significant (Pillai = 0.37, $p = 0.12$). Adding a third variable did not make any significant improvements and the process was stopped at this point.

In the second phase, we investigated the influence of individual differences on soundscape evaluations and moved from using averaged responses to using all the available data. The personality trait variables have been described previously. Note that since the models in the previous phase predicted average responses, the amounts explained are quite high. Because a certain amount of error is attached to the measurement of individual participant traits, as well as error attached to their individual quality ratings, we expected the multiple R^2 to be lower when all the data were included.

In this situation, the model with soundscape *type* and N_{10} as predictors explained 42.3% of the variation in *Pleasantness-Eventfulness* in Experiment 1, and 20.4% in Experiment 2. However, the point of interest in this analysis phase was to determine the increase in explanatory strength provided by the personality trait variables. In Experiment 1, an extended model where the Big Five variables were added explained 44.7% of the variation in *Pleasantness-Eventfulness*. The increase over the smaller model was significant (Pillai = 0.076, $p < 0.001$), with a small effect size (Cohen's $f^2 = 0.044$). In Experiment 2, an extended model including Big Five and *noise sensitivity* variables explained 23.6%; this represented a significant increase (Pillai = 0.080, $p < 0.001$), likewise with a small effect size (Cohen's $f^2 = 0.041$).

While these results are encouraging it must be recalled that the probability values calculated above are tentative, since we could not show that homoscedasticity and other required assumptions were met. Future research might want to focus on selecting larger participant samples, representative of a population, and assure that distribution assumptions are fulfilled.

In the third and final phase, we carried out four univariate multiple regressions with the extended set of predictor variables. The results are given in Table 6.

In Experiment 1, the model explained 48.5% of *Pleasantness* and 35.2% of *Eventfulness* variance. Note that these amounts are the cross-validated adjusted R^2, and that the relatively small difference compared to overall R^2 indicates that the model is fairly robust [52]. Table 6 also gives 95% confidence intervals around the means for these statistics. In Experiment 2, the amount of variance explained was lower; 22.2% for *Pleasantness* and 20.7% for *Eventfulness*. The lower levels might in part be due to the smaller range of acoustic variation among the restaurant soundscape stimuli.

The *type* of environment was a strong predictor for both *Pleasantness* and *Eventfulness* in the two experiments. Note that since *type* was a dummy encoded categorical variable, standardized beta indicates the amount of difference in the dependent variable associated with a shift from one *type* to another. The values in Table 6 refer to the largest differences, i.e., between Shop and Ruralpark, and Café and Bar, respectively.

Loudness was a significant predictor of *Eventfulness* over and above *type*. Within environments of all the kinds defined in the two experiments, louder soundscapes were perceived as more eventful. As discussed above, note that the probability values and significance levels in the present results must be taken as tentative, since homoscedasticity and other required assumptions were not met. We will continue the interpretation of results with caution, but please keep this limitation in mind.

In Experiment 1 and within its *types*, louder soundscapes were rated as less pleasant. However, *loudness* was not a significant predictor of *Pleasantness* in Experiment 2 when the effect of *type* was partialled out. This needs to be discussed, in particular since the corresponding relation in the study by Axelsson et al. [41] was clearly significant. In our data from Experiment 2, separate analysis of each *type* revealed that the expected negative effect was significant only in Cafés. In Bars, there was a significant effect in the opposite direction: louder Bars were rated as more pleasant. The same tendency was observed in MixFusion, but did not reach significance. Looking at the Eateries in Experiment 1, the negative effect of *loudness* on *Pleasantness* was strong. See also Table 2. The weak or even contradictory results within certain restaurant *types* might be due to the influence of other soundscape factors, such as the kinds of sound sources that are prevalent in an environment rather than their *loudness* [53]. Certain sounds might cue expectations in listeners that cause them to adapt their internalised affective responses. For example, if we hear sounds that let us understand that we are in a bar, then 'loud is good'; but on the other hand, if we hear the sounds of a café or a park, then 'loud is bad'. These effects might be investigated in future work.

The influence of *emotional stability* on *Pleasantness* was significant in both experiments. *Emotional stability* was associated with rating the sonic environment as less pleasant, over and above the effects of *type* and *loudness*. Alternatively, we can say that neuroticism was associated with rating environments as more pleasant. The influence of this trait on the soundscape is illustrated in Figure 2, and discussed more thoroughly below.

Noise sensitivity was significantly and negatively related with *Pleasantness*. In other words, the more noise-tolerant participants were, the higher they rated the restaurant environments in terms of pleasantness, controlling for the effects of *type* and *loudness*. This was an expected finding given well-established theory, thus supported by new empirical evidence in restaurants.

The negative influence of *emotional stability* on *Eventfulness* was strong in the first experiment with urban soundscapes, so that neuroticism was associated with rating these environments as more eventful. It did not reach significance for the restaurant soundscapes in Experiment 2.

The squared semipartial correlation of a predictor indicates the amount of variation it explains in response variable, controlling for other predictors. As Table 6 shows, *emotional stability* and *noise sensitivity* were significant predictors in several univariate cases. The explanatory strength of *emotional stability* was approximately one-tenth of the stimuli variables, *type* and *loudness*, for both *Pleasantness* and *Eventfulness* ratings. *Noise sensitivity* was on its own almost half as strong as environmental *type* in Experiment 2.

Table 6. Regression analysis results for Experiment 1 and 2. R^2 = amount explained. Adj. R^2 = R^2 adjusted for the number of predictor variables. Cross-val. adj. R^2 = mean 10-fold cross-validated adjusted R^2 across 3000 iterations [52], with 95% confidence interval around the mean in parenthesis. β = standardized beta coefficient. p = probability value. sr^2 = squared semipartial correlation. Note that since *type* is a dummy encoded categorical variable, the numerical values given are for the pair of levels that was associated with the largest shift in the dependent variable. * $p \le 0.05$, ** $p \le 0.01$, *** $p \le 0.001$.

	Experiment 1—Urban Soundscapes (12 × 43 = 516 Cases)						Experiment 2—Restaurant Soundscapes (15 × 45 = 675 Cases)					
	Pleasantness			Eventfulness			Pleasantness			Eventfulness		
Statistic												
R^2	0.508	-	-	0.379	-	-	0.247	-	-	0.225	-	-
Adj. R^2	0.498	-	-	0.366	-	-	0.234	-	-	0.212	-	-
Cross-val. adj. R^2	0.485 (0.31 … 0.65)			0.352 (0.17 … 0.55)			0.222 (0.09 … 0.41)			0.207 (0.08 … 0.39)		
Variable	β	p	sr^2	β	p	sr^2	β	p	sr^2	β	p	sr^2
Type	0.893	0.000 ***	0.118	0.842	0.000 ***	0.092	1.296	0.000 ***	0.105	0.396	0.003 **	0.052
N_{10}	−0.393	0.000 ***	0.066	0.325	0.000 ***	0.043	0.025	0.615	-	0.395	0.000 ***	0.074
Extraversion	0.005	0.891	-	0.112	0.003 **	0.006	−0.059	0.141	-	−0.081	0.048 *	0.005
Agreeableness	−0.046	0.156	-	−0.065	0.075	-	0.126	0.000 ***	0.013	−0.021	0.549	-
Conscientiousness	0.037	0.250	-	0.044	0.224	-	0.110	0.007 **	0.007	0.023	0.582	-
Emotional stability	−0.111	0.000 ***	0.009	−0.112	0.002 **	0.008	−0.102	0.004 **	0.008	−0.026	0.479	-
Openness	−0.053	0.096.	-	−0.005	0.889	-	−0.018	0.612	-	0.012	0.735	-
Noise sensitivity	-	-	-	-	-	-	−0.262	0.000 ***	0.046	−0.047	0.251	-

Finally, *agreeableness* and *conscientiousness* both had significant influence on *Pleasantness* in Experiment 2 but not in Experiment 1. We cannot at this point advance an explanation, and might return to this question in future research. Overall, the regression results indicate that both broad and narrow personality factors might have a predictable influence on quality ratings. We suggest that individual variation such as personality traits be considered in future research that aims to create robust predictive models of perceived quality of various sonic environments.

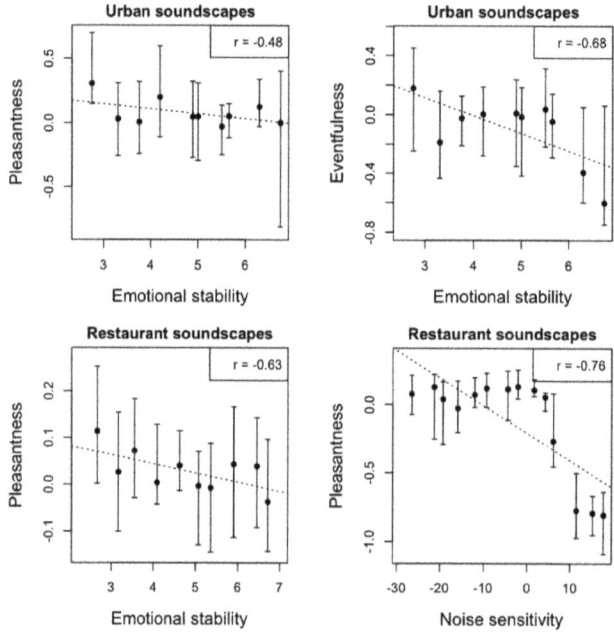

Figure 2. The influence of certain personality factors on ratings of soundscape quality in the two experiments. In the plots, participant trait variables are grouped in equal-sized subdivisions along the *x*-axis, and the median of the response variable within each group plotted with 95% confidence intervals formed by a bootstrap method [52]. For purposes of illustration, linear regression between medians and the middle value of the groups are drawn (dotted lines and Pearson's *r*).

5.5. Relation between Higher and Lower Personality Constructs

Finally, we report results from our data following the investigation by Shepherd and collaborators [15], who hypothesised that *noise sensitivity* might be an expression of underlying and broader personality dimensions. They reported that a linear regression model with the Big Five dimensions as predictors explained 33% of the variance in *noise sensitivity* among their participants. This approach produced very similar results for our data, with 36% (overall R^2) explained. Moreover, the relative strengths of the predictor variables, as indicated by standardised beta, were also similar. As shown in Table 7, each of the broad personality dimensions contributed to *noise sensitivity* in the same directions as in the previous study. Lastly, by taking the beta values they reported, we set up a prediction equation. The correlation between predicted and actual scores in our data was strongly significant ($r = 0.55$, $p = 0.0001$ ***), indicating a robust relationship between broad personality domains and *noise sensitivity*.

Table 7. Prediction of *noise sensitivity* from Big Five traits for participants in Experiment 2. Note that Shephard used the neuroticism construct, which is considered the inverse of *emotional stability*.

Trait	Experiment 2 ($n = 45$)	[15] ($n = 185$)
Extraversion	−0.43	−0.38
Agreeableness	0.05 n.s.	0.25
Conscientiousness	0.46	0.34
Emotional Stability	−0.10 n.s.	−0.19 n.s.
Openness	−0.17	−0.07 n.s.

6. Discussion

In Experiment 1 (urban soundscapes) the stimuli were overall quite similar in character to the ones that Axelsson, Nilsson, and Berglund investigated [41]. This resulted in cross-correlations between perceptual ratings and acoustic variables showing similar patterns in the two studies, as can be seen by comparing Axelsson's Table II with our Tables 4 and 5. The predictive models in the two studies also resemble each other in terms of the variables included and the overall amount of variation explained, as can be seen by comparing Axelsson's Tables III and IV with our results from the first phase of the multivariate regression analysis, reported above. We believe that these parallels strengthen the modelling approach where soundscape indicators of different kinds are included, i.e., both acoustic and psychoacoustic measures, such as *loudness*, and categorical variables that describe more general characteristics. The latter might be a variable emanating from Technological/Human/Natural ratings or a categorical *type* variable such as the one we determined in our initial selection of stimuli.

In both Experiment 1 and Experiment 2, trait *emotional stability* emerged as a significant predictor of *Pleasantness*. Low *emotional stability* (i.e., more neurotic) was associated with high *Pleasantness* ratings over and above soundscape *type* and *loudness*. The predictive strength of this personality trait was similar in both soundscape contexts. Theory holds that neurotic individuals are sensitive to reward and punishment cues and that they are more prone to emotional contagion, i.e., their emotional state is more easily influenced by their appraisal of the environment [5]. Hedonic tone is a concept linked to a neurological mechanism that underpins reward and aversion behaviour, in such a way as to safeguard the individual against unpleasantness when arousal levels soar [54]. Consider also that participants in perceptual experiments may exhibit a tendency for response bias, i.e., to subconsciously adapt their rating in the direction they imagine is preferred by the experimenter. In the present study, those generally more sensitive to reward cues might have exhibited a demand bias, producing higher *Pleasantness* ratings (discussed in e.g. [11,12,55]). Conversely, theory says that individuals who are more emotionally stable tend to use a wider range of emotion words expressing pleasure, thus emphasising the hedonic content of experiences [9].

Noise sensitivity correlated negatively with ratings of *Pleasantness*, which replicates previous findings [15] and is in line with the definition of the construct. Noise-tolerant participants were biased to rate the restaurant soundscapes as more pleasant. Inspection of the third plot in Figure 2 suggests that the relationship might not be linear. The optimum stimulation level theory [56] links evaluative perception of a stimulus to its information rate via a ∩-shaped relationship. Whether a similar mechanism is relevant to *noise sensitivity* might be investigated in the future.

The relationship between lower order *noise sensitivity* and higher order broad personality characteristics is complex. Weinstein [11] found *noise sensitivity* to be associated with intelligence, self-confidence in social interactions, and "desire for privacy", but Iwata [55] reported that highly noise sensitive individuals tended to be less well-adjusted (that is, more neurotic) and less healthy. Stansfeld [13] also found that *noise sensitivity* was associated with mental health problems, in particular depression, and Weinstein [12] (p. 465) reported that it correlated negatively with *extraversion*. However, the relationship might not be straightforward. While Dornic and Ekehmmar corroborated Weinstein's finding for "low and middle extraverts", they reported that the "neurotic extraverts" in their study were highly sensitive to noise [54] (p. 991). On the other hand, stable (i.e., non-neurotic) extraverts might have a higher tolerance for external stressors, and it has been suggested that this is associated with chronically lower levels of cortical arousal in such individuals (see [11] (p. 462); also [23]).

Our present results corroborate the findings by Shepherd et al. [15], producing robust evidence that *noise sensitivity* can be predicted from *extraversion* and *conscientiousness*. Note that *emotional stability* was not a significant predictor in both of these studies. This might indicate that this specific personality trait is relatively independent of *noise sensitivity*; however, an interaction effect of the kind suggested by [54] cannot be ruled out. We believe that future studies might illuminate this question by working with alternative and complementary constructs of *noise sensitivity* that are based on other data than self-report, such as behavioural and psychophysiological measurements.

Because of the modest sample sizes in the listening tests we have conducted, both in terms of the number of stimuli and the number of participants, the present results have limited generalizability. We have shown that the explanatory strength of personality traits in the multivariate regressions was small, yet significant. Thus the influence of some traits might have been drowned in experiment noise. This limitation can be overcome by having larger participant groups, or by targeting specific traits, foremost *emotional stability* and *noise sensitivity*. Moreover, the mechanisms behind how personality traits cause a bias in affective responses to soundscapes are not well understood. This question calls for work in theory as well as empirical approaches, such as comparing cognitive appraisal with individual physiological responses (e.g., [30,57]).

In a recent publication, Aletta, Kang, and Axelsson [5] laid out a roadmap for soundscape research, especially predictive modelling, which forms the basis for planning and design. The authors highlight the distinction between soundscape descriptors (predictants, which enter as dependent variables in a predictive model) and soundscape indicators (predictors, which enter as independent variables that describe stimuli). This perspective is important in the investigation and selection of variables for modelling. In our present work we adopted the SSQP [41] to generate soundscape descriptors (*Pleasantness* and *Eventfulness*), and we selected stimuli variables (*type* and N_{10}, i.e., soundscape indicators) that were either predetermined or significant in the initial multivariate analysis. We have attempted to explain more of the variation in dependent variables (soundscape descriptors) by considering ratings from individual participants. Our results indicate that *Pleasantness* and *Eventfulness* might to a small yet probably significant extent be predicted by personality traits, over and above soundscape indicators.

Trait variables could be seen as moderating variables in a predictive model. Our present results are tentative due to the limitations discussed above; this concerns the effect sizes and probability values associated with regression model statistics (in particular R^2 and sr^2; but note that these statistics themselves are legitimate regardless of variable distributions). These limitations might be addressed in future work, which would also consider a formal analysis of the influence of moderating variables. A predictive model might include semantic descriptors of sound sources that are relevant and powerful cues for knowing (or imagining) what type of soundscape one is hearing. Because environments are multimodal, non-auditive cues might also be included, notably visual.

People are indeed different, and yet some of the ways in which sound affects us are systematic. Acoustic designers need to be knowledgeable about predictable variation and take it into account when planning for urban spaces and restaurants. Rather than "non-places" [26], people deserve access to healthy places full of meaningfulness, where they can work creatively, communicate, relax, and play.

Author Contributions: PerMagnus Lindborg conceived, designed, and performed the experiments; PerMagnus Lindborg and Anders Friberg analyzed the data and wrote the paper.

Conflicts of Interest: The authors declare no conflict of interest.

References

1. Schafer, R.M. *The Soundscape: Our Sonic Environment and the Tuning of the World*, 2nd ed.; Inner Traditions & Bear: Rochester, VT, USA, 1993; pp. 1–320.

2. BS/ISO 12913-1. Acoustics. In *Soundscape*; Part 1: Definition and conceptual framework; ICS Classification; International Organization for Standardization: Geneva, Switzerland, 2014.
3. Guski, R. Personal and social variables as co-determinants of noise annoyance. *Noise Health* **1999**, *1*, 45. [PubMed]
4. Brown, A.L.; Kang, J.; Gjestland, T. Towards standardization in soundscape preference assessment. *Appl. Acoust.* **2011**, *72*, 387–392. [CrossRef]
5. Aletta, F.; Kang, J.; Axelsson, Ö. Soundscape descriptors and a conceptual framework for developing predictive soundscape models. *Landsc. Urban Plan.* **2016**, *149*, 65–74. [CrossRef]
6. Yu, L.; Kang, J. Effects of social, demographical and behavioral factors on the sound level evaluation in urban open spaces. *J. Acoust. Soc. Am.* **2008**, *123*, 772–783. [CrossRef] [PubMed]
7. Digman, J.M. Personality Structure: Emergence of the Five-Factor Model. *Annu. Rev. Psychol.* **1990**, *41*, 417–440. [CrossRef]
8. McCrae, R.R.; Costa, P.T. A Five-Factor Theory of Personality. In *Handbook of Personality*, 2nd ed.; Theory and Research; Guilford Press: New York, NY, USA, 1999; pp. 139–153.
9. John, O.P.; Srivastava, S. The Big Five Trait Taxonomy: History, Measurement, and Theoretical Perspectives. In *Handbook of Personality*, 2nd ed.; Theory and Research; Guilford Press: New York, NY, USA, 1999; pp. 102–138.
10. DeYoung, C.G.; Hirsh, J.B.; Shane, M.S.; Papademetris, X.; Rajeevan, N.; Gray, J.R. Testing Predictions from Personality Neuroscience: Brain Structure and the Big Five. *Psychol. Sci.* **2010**, *21*, 820–828. [CrossRef] [PubMed]
11. Weinstein, N.D. Individual Differences in Reactions to Noise: A longitudinal study in a College Dormitory. *J. Appl. Psychol.* **1978**, *63*, 458–466. [CrossRef] [PubMed]
12. Weinstein, N.D. Individual differences in critical tendencies and noise annoyance. *J. Sound Vib.* **1980**, *68*, 241–248. [CrossRef]
13. Stansfeld, S.A. *Noise, Noise Sensitivity and Psychiatric Disorder: Epidemiological and Pychophysical Studies*; Monograph Supplement 22; Psychological Medicine: Cambridge, UK, 1992.
14. Heinonen-Guzejev, M. Noise Sensitivity—Medical, Psychological and Genetic Aspects. Ph.D. Thesis, University of Helsinki, Helsinki, Finland, 2009; pp. 1–87.
15. Shepherd, D.; Heinonen-Guzejev, M.; Hautus, M.J.; Heikkilä, K. Elucidating the relationship between noise sensitivity and personality. *Noise Health* **2015**, *17*, 168–171. [CrossRef] [PubMed]
16. Job, R.F.S. Noise sensitivity as a factor influencing human reaction to noise. *Noise Health* **1999**, *1*, 57–68. [PubMed]
17. Van Kempen, E.E.; Kruize, H.; Boshuizen, H.C.; Ameling, C.B.; Staatsen, B.A.; de Hollander, A.E. The association between noise exposure and blood pressure and ischemic heart disease: A meta-analysis. *Environ. Health Perspect.* **2002**, *110*, 307. [CrossRef] [PubMed]
18. Stansfeld, S.A.; Haines, M.M.; Burr, M.; Berry, B.; Lercher, P. A review of environmental noise and mental health. *Noise Health* **2000**, *2*, 1–8.
19. Berglund, B.; Nilsson, M.E. Summary of the studies in soundscape perception. In *Spång, K.: Soundscape Support to Health*; Swedish Foundation for Strategic Environmental Research (Mistra): Stockholm, Sweden, 2007; pp. 14–23.
20. Hill, E.M. Noise Sensitivity and Diminished Health: The Role of Stress-Related Factors. Ph.D. Thesis, Auckland University of Technology, Auckland, New Zealand, 2012; pp. 1–329.
21. Truax, B. *Acoustic Communication*; Greenwood Publishing Group: Westport, CT, USA, 2001; pp. 1–284.
22. Weinstein, N.D. Community noise problems: Evidence against adaptation. *J. Environ. Psychol.* **1982**, *2*, 87–97. [CrossRef]
23. Belojevic, G.; Jakovljevic, B.; Slepcevic, V. Noise and mental performance: Personality attributes and noise sensitivity. *Noise Health* **2003**, *6*, 77–89. [PubMed]
24. Davies, W.J.; Adams, M.D.; Bruce, N.S.; Cain, R.; Carlyle, A.; Cusack, P.; Hall, D.A.; Hume, K.I.; Irwin, A.; Jennings, P.; et al. Perception of soundscapes: An interdisciplinary approach. *Appl. Acoust.* **2013**, *74*, 224–231. [CrossRef]
25. Hatfield, J.; Job, R.F.S.; Hede, A.J.; Carter, N.L.; Peploe, P.; Taylor, R.; Morrell, S. Human response to environmental noise: The role of perceived control. *Int. J. Behav. Med.* **2002**, *9*, 341–359. [CrossRef] [PubMed]

26. Augé, M. Non-Places. Available online: http://www.acsu.buffalo.edu/~jread2/Auge%20Non%20places.pdf (accessed on 30 September 2016).

27. Hall, T.; Lashua, B.; Coffey, A. Sound and the Everyday in Qualitative Research. *Qual. Inq.* **2008**, *14*, 1019–1040. [CrossRef]

28. Cohen, A.J.; Campanella, A.; Marshall, L.; Grant, C. Perspectives on acoustics in environmental design. *J. Architect. Plan. Res.* **1987**, *4*, 162–179.

29. Lazarus, R.S.; Folkman, S. Coping and adaptation. In *Handbook of Behavioral Medicine*; Guilford Press: New York, NY, USA, 1984; pp. 282–325.

30. Lindborg, P.M. Physiological measures regress onto acoustic and perceptual features of soundscapes. In Proceedings of the 3rd International Conference on Music Emotion (ICME3), Jyväskylä, Finland, 11–15 June 2013.

31. Andringa, T.C. Soundscape and core affect regulation. Available online: https://www.researchgate.net/profile/TC_Andringa/publication/228411828_Soundscape_and_core_affect_regulation/links/0046351568dca9302f000000.pdf (accessed on 30 September 2016).

32. Lindborg, P.M.; Lim, M.J.Y. Design of an Interactive Earphone Simulator and Results from a Perceptual Experiment. In Proceedings of the Sound and Music Computing Conference 2013 (SMC 2013), Stockholm, Sweden, 30 July–3 August 2013.

33. Payne, S. The production of a Perceived Restorativeness Soundscape Scale. *Appl. Acoust.* **2013**, *74*, 255–263. [CrossRef]

34. Dzhambov, A.M. Noise sensitivity: A neurophenomenological perspective. *Med. Hypotheses* **2015**, *85*, 650–655. [CrossRef] [PubMed]

35. Ellermeier, W.; Eigenstetter, M.; Zimmer, K. Psychoacoustic correlates of individual noise sensitivity. *J. Acoust. Soc. Am.* **2001**, *109*, 1464–1473. [CrossRef] [PubMed]

36. Pulkki, V.; Karjalainen, M. *Communication Acoustics*; Wiley: Hoboken, NJ, USA, 2015.

37. Fastl, H.; Zwicker, E. *Psychoacoustics: Facts and Models*, 3rd ed.; Springer: Heidelberg, Germany, 2007; pp. 1–463.

38. Moore, B.C.J. *An Introduction to the Psychology of Hearing*, 6th ed.; Emerald Group Publishing: Bingley, UK, 2012.

39. Hall, D.; Irwin, A.; Edmonson-Jones, M.; Philips, S.; Poxon, J. An exploratory evaluation of perceptual, psychoacoustic and acoustical properties of urban soundscapes. *Appl. Acoust.* **2013**, *74*, 248–254. [CrossRef]

40. Rychtáriková, M.; Vermeir, G. Soundscape categorization on the basis of objective acoustical parameters. *Appl. Acoust.* **2013**, *74*, 240–247. [CrossRef]

41. Axelsson, Ö.; Nilsson, M.E.; Berglund, B. A principal components model of soundscape perception. *J. Acoust. Soc. Am.* **2010**, *128*, 2836–2846. [CrossRef] [PubMed]

42. Cain, R.; Jennings, P.; Poxon, J.; Scott, A. Emotional dimensions of a soundscape. In Proceedings of the 38th International Congress and Exposition on Noise Control Engineering 2009 (INTER-NOISE 2009), Ottawa, ON, Canada, 23–26 August 2009; Institute of Noise Control Engineering: Washington, DC, USA; pp. 4660–4667.

43. Cain, R.; Jennings, P.; Poxon, J. The development and application of the emotional dimensions of a soundscape. *Appl. Acoust.* **2013**, *74*, 232–239. [CrossRef]

44. Joo, Y.H.; Jin, Y.J. Influence of urban contexts on soundscape perceptions: A structural equation modeling approach. *Landsc. Urban. Plan.* **2015**, *141*, 78–87.

45. Lindborg, P.M. Psychoacoustic, Physical, and Perceptual Features of Restaurants: A Field Survey in Singapore. *Appl. Acoust.* **2015**, *92*, 47–60. [CrossRef]

46. Chalupper, J.; Fastl, H. Dynamic Loudness Model (DLM) for Normal and Hearing-Impaired Listeners. *Acta Acust. United Acust.* **2002**, *88*, 378–386.

47. Cabrera, D.; Ferguson, S.; Schubert, E. Psysound3: Software for acoustical and psychoacoustical analysis of sound recordings. In Proceedings of the 13th International Conference on Auditory Displays, Montréal, QC, Canada, 26–29 June 2007; pp. 356–363.

48. Gosling, S.D.; Rentfrow, P.J.; Swann, W.B. A very brief measure of the Big-Five personality domains. *J. Res. Personal.* **2003**, *37*, 504–528. [CrossRef]

49. Howell, D. *Statistical Methods for Psychology*; Cengage Wadsworth: Belmont, CA, USA, 2010.

50. Cohen, J. *Statistical Power Analysis for the Behavioral Sciences*; Routledge: Abingdon, UK, 1988.

51. Fritz, C.O.; Morris, P.E.; Richler, J.J. Effect size estimates: Current use, calculations, and interpretation. *J. Exp. Psychol. Gen.* **2012**, *141*, 2. [CrossRef] [PubMed]

52. Kohavi, R. A Study of Cross-Validation and Bootstrap for Accuracy Estimation and Model Selection. In Proceedings of the International Joint Conference on Artificial Intelligence, Montreal, QC, Canada, 20–25 August 1995; Volume 14, pp. 1137–1145.

53. Lindborg, P.M. A taxonomy of sound sources in restaurants. *Appl. Acoust.* **2016**. [CrossRef]

54. Dornic, S.; Ekehammar, B. Extraversion, Neuroticism, and Noise Sensitivity. *Pers. Indiv. Differ.* **1990**, *11*, 989–992. [CrossRef]

55. Iwata, O. The relationship of noise sensitivity to health and personality. *Jpn. Psychol. Res.* **1984**, *26*, 75–81.

56. Berlyne, D.E. *Studies in the New Experimental Aesthetics: Steps toward an Objective Psychology of Aesthetic Appreciation*; Hemisphere: Greensboro, NC, USA, 1974.

57. Hume, K.; Ahtamad, M. Physiological responses to and subjective estimates of soundscape elements. *Appl. Acoust.* **2013**, *74*, 275–281. [CrossRef]

Article

Analysis of Psychoacoustic and Vibration-Related Parameters to Track the Reasons for Health Complaints after the Introduction of New Tramways

Michael Cik [1,*], Manuel Lienhart [1] and Peter Lercher [2]

[1] Institute of Highway Engineering and Transport Planning, Faculty of Civil Engineering,
    Graz University of Technology, Rechbauerstraße 12/II, Graz 8010, Austria; manuel.lienhart@tugraz.at
[2] Division of Social Medicine, Department of Hygiene, Microbiology and Social Medicine,
    Medical University Innsbruck, Peter-Mayr-Straße 4b, Innsbruck 6020, Austria; peter.lercher@i-med.ac.at
*   Correspondence: michael.cik@tugraz.at; Tel.: +43-316-873-6224

Academic Editor: Jian Kang
Received: 9 October 2016; Accepted: 22 November 2016; Published: 30 November 2016

Abstract: Background: A change to new tramways in Graz (Austria) led to severe complaints in residential areas. To understand the underlying reasons for these complaints, a systematic measurement campaign was designed. Methods: Six locations in Graz and two locations in a comparably sized city were selected. Parallel indoor recordings of sound and vibrations were conducted from 8:00 p.m. to 8:00 a.m. (due to sleep problems) at all locations. Results: Vibration levels remained below the limits of the Austrian standard (Wm-weighting) although variability was observed among sites, tram types and pass-bys. A complex characteristic of the acoustic feature space was found with A-weighting (differences between A- and C-weighting of more than 15 dB were observed). C-weighted background to peak noise ratios clearly distinguished "old" from "new" trams. Psychoacoustic indices indicated a high variability between locations and tram types. Roughness and loudness was higher in "new" versus "old" trams at most locations. "New" trams exhibited high sharpness values and variability, especially at higher speeds—when compared with trams from a control city. Conclusions: Standard indicators of sound and vibration were not sensitive enough to uncover the reasons for the complaints. Only the integrated analysis of the ambient soundscape (high signal-to-noise-ratio), the more noticeable sound (in psychoacoustic terms) and the observed high variance of the immissions provided guidance to implement appropriate technical solutions.

Keywords: tramway; vibration; noise; psychoacoustics; annoyance; sleep; health risk assessment

1. Introduction

The demand for public transport is increasing continuously, not only for large, but also for medium and smaller sized cities in order to mitigate congestion and provide flexible mobility. There is still an ongoing cross-disciplinary discussion about costs, flexibility and environmental impacts of tram (Light Rail Transport) versus Bus (Bus Rapid Transport) solutions [1–3]. Interestingly, potential adverse health effects of noise and especially vibrations are rarely discussed, while effects of air pollution and related climate issues are the central themes [4].

There are a decent number of (older) studies related to tram sound emissions [5,6], determining factors [6,7] and about special issues such as squeal noise [8–10]. However, the current scientific data base regarding tramway immissions is small, most (except [11–13]) reported sound levels only in dBA, neglecting potential low frequency components and other specific characteristics of tramway sounds, which are produced by the various noise sources of this complex vehicle [7].

Only few studied annoyance responses at the community level [14,15] and no exposure response data from field studies are available. The majority of publications report results from experimental studies [12,13,16]. Often, articles concentrate only on vibration generation and propagation [17,18], simulation/model validation [19] or strategies for abatement of emissions [20,21]. Often, the knowledge base stems from railway vehicles or metros [22,23].

Publications covering both tram noise and vibration measurements in homes are rare [17]. The consideration of potential effects of trams in combination with other sound sources or effects of combined sound and vibration exposure was studied only in the laboratory [12,24] and is not yet considered in national standards.

In contrast, the body of evidence for railway induced vibration [25,26] and associated health impacts [27–33] increased substantially during the last decade and changes in policy are addressed [34]. The research on potential adverse health effects of tram noise, vibrations and structure born sounds has never received that level of attention—although the tram pass-by happens closer to residential buildings and national approval procedures for trams apply the same sound criteria as for mainline railways.

This is particularly surprising, because the tramway systems and its public use have undergone a profound change in the past two decades in European countries [7]. The typical weight of modern trams in use is now around 40 tons compared with 25 to 30 tons of older trams, as illustrated by the example of Graz, visualized in Figure 1 [35–37]. However, the track systems were often not properly adapted to the new demands. Moreover, the night and morning hours of operation of the tram services were extended (from 11:00 p.m. to 12:00 p.m. and 5:30 a.m. to 04:30 a.m.). These hours are acoustically highly sensitive in terms of the potential for sleep interference, as the background to peak noise ratio increases. Typically, the overall traffic noise decreases and silence is interrupted by passing trams, especially in quieter suburban areas. In addition, sleep research has found these so-called shoulder hours (10:00 p.m. to 12:00 p.m. and 5:00 a.m. to 7:00 a.m.) to be sensitive times for noise exposure and subsequent interference with the sleep and restoration process [38–40]. Eventually, noise and vibrations show potential for mutual interactive effects on annoyance and sleep disturbance [24,41–46].

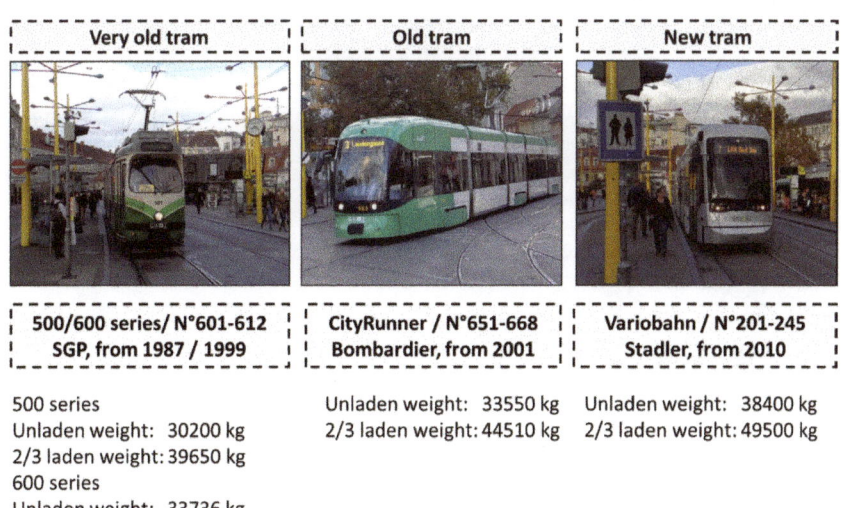

Very old tram	Old tram	New tram
500/600 series/ N°601-612 SGP, from 1987 / 1999	CityRunner / N°651-668 Bombardier, from 2001	Variobahn / N°201-245 Stadler, from 2010

500 series
Unladen weight: 30200 kg
2/3 laden weight: 39650 kg
600 series
Unladen weight: 33736 kg
2/3 laden weight: 46515 kg

Unladen weight: 33550 kg
2/3 laden weight: 44510 kg

Unladen weight: 38400 kg
2/3 laden weight: 49500 kg

Figure 1. Tramway fleet in Graz with technical information.

After the introduction of a new tram system in the city of Graz (2011) several citizen initiatives issued complaints about the new trams regarding both higher noise and vibrations exposure.

The operator commissioned acoustic and vibration measurements. A few measures resulted in improvements at vibration hotspots after two years. However, complaints remained at a high level.

Acoustic and health experts from two Universities were commissioned in 2014 to conduct a new independent measurement series covering both noise and vibration in a more integrated fashion including psychoacoustic methods to gain insight into the key disturbing moments of the new trams in the context of the soundscape of Graz [47].

In order to respond appropriately to the citizen's concern, the main aims of the current study were: Firstly, the application of psychoacoustic analyses to uncover the main triggers responsible for the expressed annoyance and sleep interference. Secondly, to examine whether the current regulations and standards for vibration and noise sufficiently protect against potential health effects from trams (health risk assessment). Thirdly, whether the existing approval procedure for trams is appropriate to support the prevention of adverse health effects in the general population.

2. Materials and Methods

2.1. Areas of Investigation, Tramway Types and Sound (Psychoacoustic) Recordings

In this study six different sampling points in single homes and flats (Figures 2–4) in the city of Graz were analyzed. The areas were selected primarily on the perception and complaints of local residents and balanced against an expert judgment related to critical and representative sections of the tram network. Three tram types were in use: very old (500/600 series), old (City Runner) and new (Variobahn) (Figure 1). The pass-by noise of the tramway types (old and new trams, Figure 1) was binaurally recorded with a dummy head measurement system HSU III.2 in combination with a SQuadriga II mobile recording system (HEAD acoustics GmbH, Herzogenrath, Germany).

We asked inhabitants not to be at home during recording time or to sleep in another part of the house or flat to get a true representation of the existing background noise. All recordings were done from 8:00 p.m. in the evening until 8:00 a.m. the next morning to analyze especially the time periods corresponding to "going to bed", "sleep" and "getting up at morning". During about 1:00 a.m. to 4:00 a.m., there is no tramway traffic in Graz. In addition, speed was measured and the vehicle number of each tramway was logged for assignment to the noise and vibration measurements, in order to get information about differences of vehicles at the same location and between other measuring points. The amount of vehicles varied at each measuring point due to the operational plan; especially the very old tram (Series 500/600) was recorded only a few times. However, the main issue in that regard is the more frequent constellation Variobahn/CityRunner.

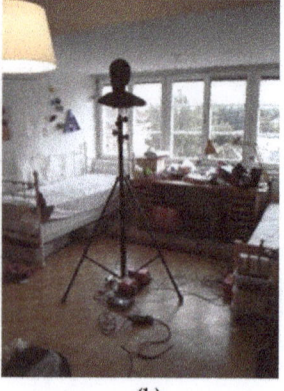

(a)   (b)

Figure 2. Measuring Point 3, single house, 2nd floor: (a) outside view facing tramway rails; and (b) measurement setup in the children's room.

(a)   (b)

Figure 3. Measuring Point 5, flat, 2nd floor: (**a**) outside view facing tramway rails; and (**b**) measurement setup in the living room.

(a)   (b)   (c)

Figure 4. Measuring Point 6, flat, 2nd floor: (**a**) outside view facing tramway rails; (**b**) measurement setup in the bedroom; and (**c**) vibration measuring system with triaxial acceleration sensor based in the center of the room below dummy head measurement system.

Although structure born sound was sometimes noticeable at a few of the measuring points, it was not a constant perceptual phenomenon, therefore we did not include it in the overall analysis.

2.2. Vibration Recordings

Vibration measurements were done with a triaxial acceleration sensor (Model Isotron65H, from Endevco, Irvine, CA, USA). Recordings of vibrations were also done with the SQuadriga II mobile recording system (HEAD acoustics GmbH, Herzogenrath, Germany) to operate in synchrony with sound recordings (Figure 4c).

2.3. Calculation and Analysis of Objective Parameters

Based on all recordings at the six points of investigation, 422 single tramway pass-bys were extracted from the recorded database. Every recorded pass-by has been carefully (1–5 times) listened to and was afterwards rated for the observed audio quality. This step ensured the exclusion of pass-bys during which other unrelated sounds were also recorded and thus providing a database of recorded pass-bys without the influence of third party noise sources. Basic sound pressure parameters

(Maximum, A-weighted and C-weighted energy-equivalent sound level) were calculated for every single tramway pass-by. In addition to standard sound parameters (SPL), psychoacoustic parameters (loudness, roughness, sharpness, tonality and fluctuation strength) were analyzed for all single passing tramways by means of the Psychoacoustics Module of the ArtemiS Analysis System (HEAD acoustics, Herzogenrath, Germany).

Finally, measured vibrations were analyzed based on Wm-weighted acceleration with time weighting slow (according to [48]), but also with fast time weighting to compare with the German standard.

3. Results

Figure 5 shows the boxplots of Wm-weighted acceleration measurements at the six measuring points. The observed differences are mainly due to different housing conditions/characteristics and differences in velocity levels of trams per each measuring point. However, all peak values (except measuring Point 2) are slightly above the noticing level outlined by the Austrian standard ([48]). The variability at each point is also noticeable in terms of human perception.

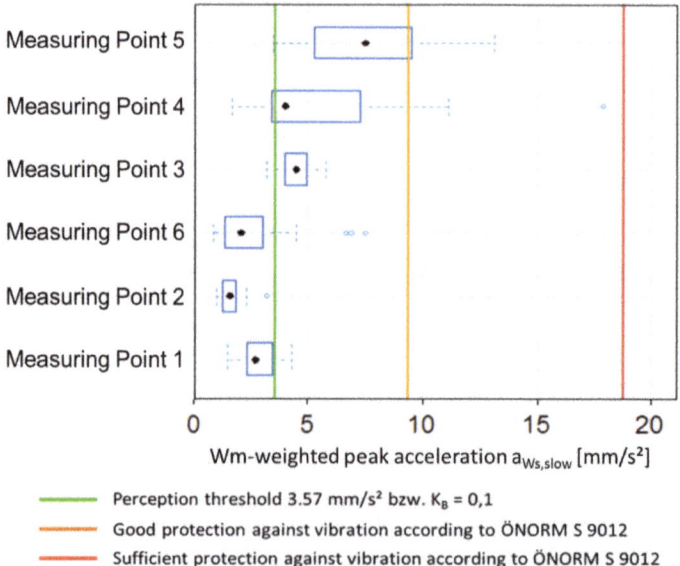

Figure 5. Vibration measurement results for each measurement point—compared with the Austrian Standard.

Overall, mean peak acceleration levels of "New Trams" are a bit higher than those from "Old Trams" at most measuring points (see Table A1 in the Appendix A). The "fast" time weighting (as used in the German standard) indicates that a slight underestimation of (potentially noticeable) peak exposure can occur with the time weighting "slow" (see Table A1 in the Appendix A).

As the sound analysis revealed strong low frequency components and the classical A-weighting curve is known to underestimate this acoustic feature and may lead to incorrect assessment of the true disturbance of the exposed people [49], we analyzed the difference between the A-weighting and the C-weighting as recommended by DIN 45680 in such cases [50].

The observed large difference between A- and C-weighted levels (Table 1) indicates that a dBA-assessment may indeed not be an appropriate estimation of the actual perceived exposure.

Table 1. Noise exposure (Maximum-SPL A- and C-weighted) of analyzed tramways.

Measuring Points	Number of Measurements	$L_{AF,max}$ (dB) Mean	$L_{CF,max}$ (dB) Mean	$L_{CF,max}$ (dB) – $L_{AF,max}$ (dB) Mean
MP 1	54	48.4	63.8	15.4
MP 2	51	31.5	53.8	22.3
MP 3	67	42.3	54.1	11.8
MP 4	47	32.6	58.2	25.6
MP 5	119	37.1	56.9	19.8
MP 6	85	41.6	57.9	16.3

This hypothesis is supported by a further analysis, which includes the background to peak noise ratio to compare "old" with "new" trams: while a difference between the trams is not significant with the A-weighting, a highly significant and clearly noticeable difference (~6 dBC) shows up with the C-weighted levels (Figures 6 and 7).

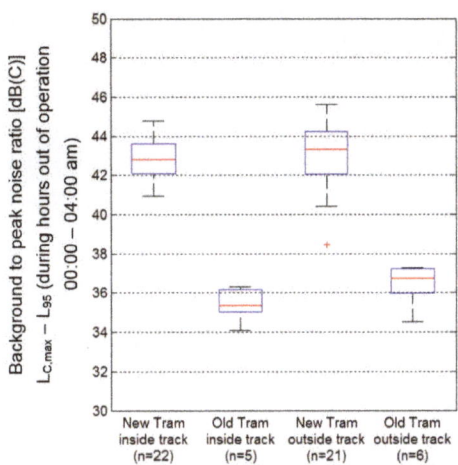

Figure 6. Background to peak noise ratio C-weighted: tram comparison at measuring point 1.

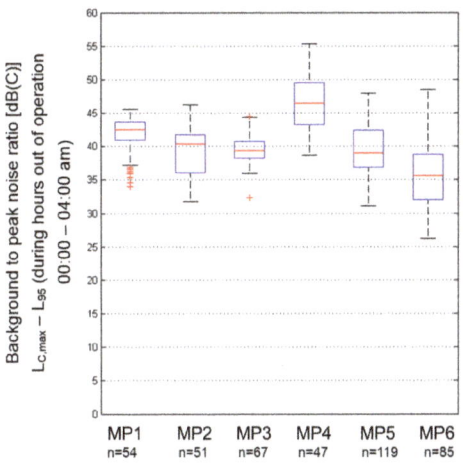

Figure 7. Background to peak noise ratio C-weighted: site comparison.

Figure 8 shows a comparison of a passing A- and C-weighted sound pressure level of the same "new tram (type Variobahn)" calculated by Fast Fourier transform algorithm over a time of 1 min. Especially at lower frequencies, a significant difference in the sound pressure levels is noticeable and points to the importance of these frequency spectra for assessing the annoyance and sleep interference potential of the studied tramways.

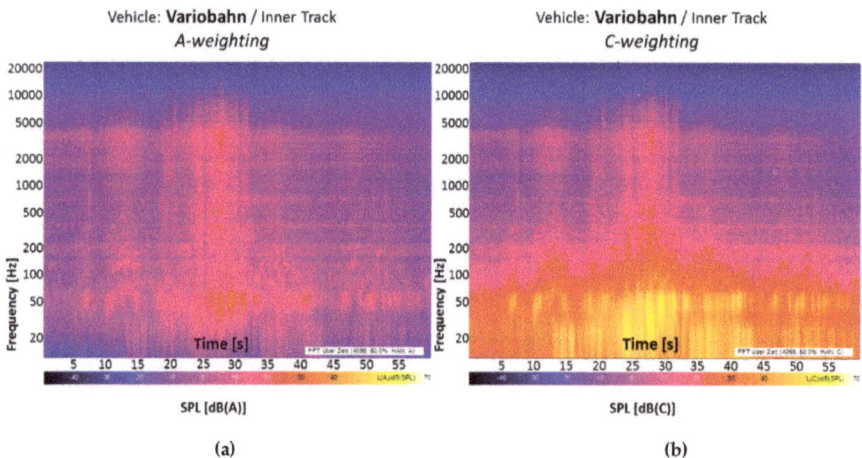

Figure 8. Pass-by sound pressure level of the same "new tram (type Variobahn)" calculated by Fast Fourier transform algorithm: (**a**) A-weighted signal; and (**b**) C-weighted signal.

Additionally to the classical acoustic analysis, psychoacoustic parameters were used for detailed investigation. Results revealed a high variability in loudness and roughness at different locations and tram types. No systematic difference was observed with parameters like tonality and fluctuation.

Figure 9 shows the N5 percentile loudness level for all passing tramways at each measuring point and Figure 10 for the three tram types in use. Both Figures 9 and 10 indicate a perceptually relevant variability for the psychoacoustic parameter loudness across the locations and tram types.

The data of Figure 10 show a significant difference in loudness values between the "new tram (Variobahn)" and the "old tram (CityRunner)" (Mann–Whitney U test—*p*-value: 2.574×10^{-15}). Loudness values were calculated based on ISO 532 B for a diffuse sound field. The latter shows also a smaller variability of the loudness distribution. Note: An increase in median sone from one to two means doubling of perceived loudness. As the spread goes from below one to five a substantial variation in the loudness of the Variobahn pass-by is therefore a perceptually relevant change.

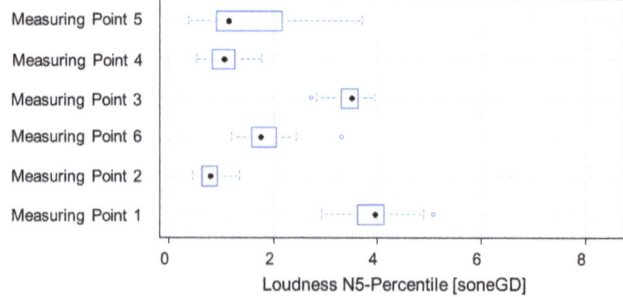

Figure 9. Loudness N5-Percentile in (soneGD) at each measuring point for all passing tramways.

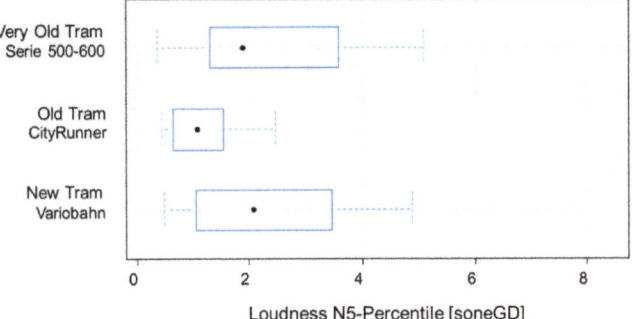

Figure 10. Loudness N5-Percentile in [soneGD] over all measuring points subdivided into "New Tram (Variobahn)", "Old Tram (CityRunner)" and "Very Old Tram (Series 500/600)".

Figures 11 and 12 show an even higher variability for the psychoacoustic parameter roughness for several locations—with very high values at Point 3. Figure 12 points to the substantially larger variability in roughness of the "new tram (Variobahn)", as well as significant higher values compared to the "old tram (CityRunner)" (Mann–Whitney U test—p-value: 1.239×10^{-11}). Loudness values were calculated based on Hearing Model after Sottek for a diffuse sound field [51]. Note: The perceptual threshold for roughness is slightly below 0.1 asper. Therefore, the large variability is not only well perceptible but in addition impairs the adaption of the exposed citizen.

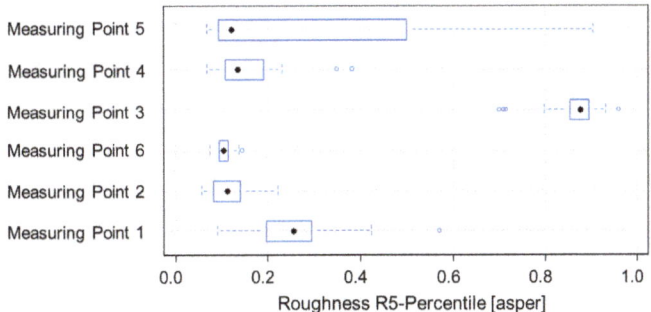

Figure 11. Roughness R5-Percentile in (asper) at each measuring point for all passing tramways.

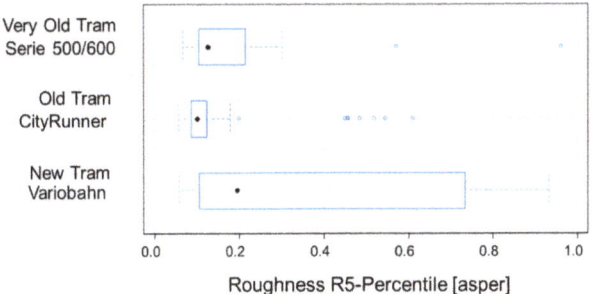

Figure 12. Roughness R5-Percentile in (asper) over all measuring points subdivided into "New Tram (Variobahn)", "Old Tram (CityRunner)" and "Very Old Tram (Series 500/600)".

Figure 13 shows the maximum of sharpness levels for each passing tramway at each measuring point. Sharpness values were calculated based on Aures' method in combination with ISO 532 B for a diffuse sound field. The very high values and the high variability provide a strong support for a perceptually critical acoustic situation.

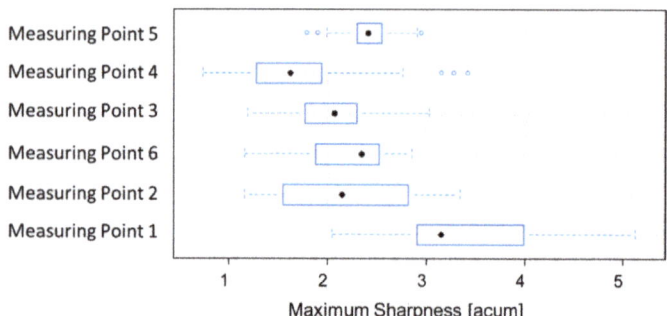

Figure 13. Maximum Sharpness in (acum) at each measuring point for all passing tramways.

Furthermore, higher values and variability were found in the sharpness analysis for the "new" trams—but only at higher speed levels (Figure 14)—compared to no increase in sharpness with speed in case of the previous tram version (the older "CityRunner"). Note: The trams in a comparably sized city also show a slight increase with speed—but the peak values do not exceed three acum at higher speed and the variability of the observed value range is much smaller.

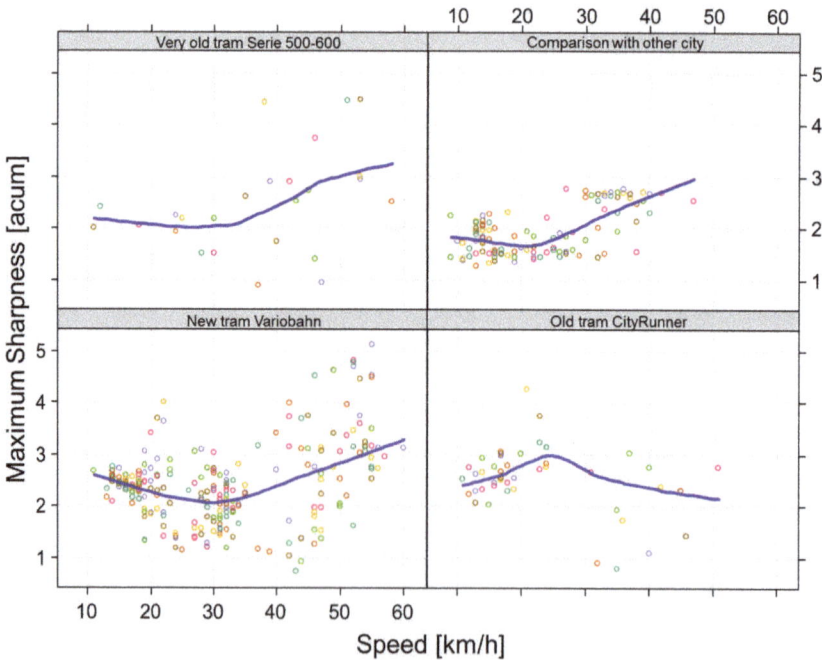

Figure 14. Maximum of Sharpness in (acum) by speed over all measuring points subdivided by tram type with a comparison of trams in a different city (upper right corner).

4. Discussion

In a field study of homes, parallel indoor recordings of ground-borne vibrations and sounds were carried out for three tramway types in current use. To sufficiently account for the variety of the involved sound characteristics, an integrated psychoacoustic approach was applied. We found compelling support for the accuracy of the issued complaints (especially sleep interference) of the citizens and a poorer acoustical performance of the "new" introduced tram (Variobahn) when compared with the "old" tram (CityRunner) mainly in use before 2011. In addition, the "very old" trams showed lower median values of roughness. However, their number of pass-bys was small compared to the "new" trams and did not dominate the soundscape.

To assess the potential risk of sleep disturbance the measured maximum indoor sound levels were used to estimate awakening probabilities. Based on the 42 dBA threshold value of the WHO-night noise guidelines [52], we computed the percentage of exceedances (see Table A2 in the Appendix A). The "new" trams showed significantly higher threshold exceedances (47%) compared with the "old" (20%) and even with the "very old" tramways (32%). The exceedances varied from location to location. At one location the threshold was even exceeded in 100 percent of the recorded events during nighttime. As with a large number of exceedances the awakening probability increases, these data support both the issued complaints about sleep disturbance and the citizen's perception of a deterioration after the introduction of the "new" trams.

Furthermore, dBC-dBA-analysis (Table 1) revealed strong low frequency components: all sites showed differences larger than 15 dB, which is the recommended criterion when the prediction of annoyance is the main aim [53]. Three sites even met the stricter DIN 45680 criteria of 20 dB, which would clearly indicate the inappropriateness of the use of the dBA-weighting in such a case [54]. Leventhall judged the use of the A-weighting in situations with strong low frequency components as inadequate and leading to incorrect decisions by regulatory authorities [49]. Schomer has proposed a 10 dB penalty in the case of relevant low frequency components—depending on the level of the ambient soundscape [55]. Due to the very low background sound levels at most locations we conducted an additional C-weighted analysis of the background to peak noise ratios. The observed ratios at all locations were very high for an urban area (Figure 7) and can result in relevant autonomous cardiovascular reactions during sleep [38,52,56]. The analysis indicated also a clear difference between "old" and "new" trams (Figure 6), which was not distinguishable with the A-weighted approach and further supports not to use A-weighting for this environmental health risk assessment.

The citizen's simultaneous exposure to low frequency noise, which also features high sharpness values, raises another question, since those characteristics can be understood as opposed noise phenomena. This question has to be answered by looking at the various noise sources of the complex system tramway. Whereas most of the low frequency noise stems from the rotating wheels on the rail track, the sharp sounds responsible for the high sharpness values are produced by both the pantograph and the corresponding transformer within the vehicle.

Overall the psychoacoustic analyses revealed a substantial variability in loudness, roughness and sharpness values across locations and the three tram types. In our view this high variability is one of the main determinant of the citizen complaints. The large variation in time makes the emissions not only well perceptible and intrusive but inhibits also habituation and impairs the adaption of the exposed persons. This view is supported by the older noticeability research, which demonstrated that annoyance was observed to be directly proportional to the detectability of the sounds [57–59]. Other research on traffic flow found rapidly alternating patterns of pass-by noise responsible for anomalies in annoyance [60]. Furthermore, changes in temporal and spectral signal features are other factors for an enhanced annoyance response found in laboratory and field studies [61–63]. These results are in compliance with neuro-biological and hearing research on the spectrotemporal filter mechanism of auditory attention [64–67]. If permanent changes of the temporal and frequency features occur the auditory system has difficulties to habituate and adapt—especially during nighttime.

In her multicomponent approach Preis [68] has summarized the main determinants of annoyance: the time-averaged difference between the loudness of the noise and that of the background noise (annoying loudness), the time-averaged difference between the sharpness of the noise and that of the background noise (called intrusiveness) and the distortion of the informational content. All those features were present in this case study.

A notable annoying feature in this context was the large differences observed with the indicator sharpness—especially at higher speed levels.

The control-study with trams from a comparable sized city revealed both: higher sharpness values and a wider spread in intensity for the "new" tramways in Graz (Figure 14).

Particularly the high variability observed with the new tram type in most psychoacoustic indices underlines the difficulty of a straight interpretation of the acoustic situation based on a single indicator. Nevertheless, this observed variability in the emissions of the new tram (Variobahn) is the key for improvements by strict quality control. In Figure 14 the Variobahn shows a reasonable number of trips with sharpness values below two—even with speed up to 50 km/h. This means: when all new trams can be "reprofiled" to these levels, the noticeability would be significantly reduced. Currently, a small quality control study is conducted to shed more light on the possible general implementation of this feature.

One has further to consider that due to atmospheric absorption effects the parameters sharpness and roughness behave differently with increased distance to a sound source compared to sound levels measured in dBA [69,70]. Therefore, another substantial underestimation is to expect by using the A-weighting in cases like in Graz: you will notice the tram over longer distances and the affected population will be larger than estimated by classical indicators.

A recent review [71] concluded, that commonly used weighting curves (e.g., Wm in Austria) do not correctly reflect annoyance caused by vibrations with multiple frequency components. Furthermore, recent evidence from exposure response curves [72,73] suggest that the standards (e.g., [74] or [48]) may underestimate the potential effects on sleep during evening and night hours". Unfortunately, the exposure response information in these studies used different vibration dose estimation parameters. To make this exposure-response information utilizable a mathematical conversion of the observed vibration values based on [48] into the one used in those studies (Wk-weighted RMS (m/s^2) or $VDV_{b,24hr}$ $(m/s^{1.75})$ and fast weighted, 0.125 s) was necessary. This concerned conversion from Wm-weighting to Wk-weighting, from slow to fast integration time and the calculation of the final overall dose (RMS or VDV). A full explanation of this procedure is provided in [75] and the resulting exposure response assessment is added as supplementary Figure A1 (annoyance) and Figure A2 (sleep disturbance). Based on these recalculations and considering upper 95% confidence intervals for the investigated effects, we could expect to have up to 15% highly annoyed and up to 25% sleep disturbed by the observed vibration values in Graz. These calculated effects are also comparable to those reported from the Cargovibe meta-analysis project [73]. Nevertheless, as these estimated prevalences are derived from main rail vibration exposure a cautious interpretation is necessary.

However, taking into account the extraordinary high background to peak noise ratio at all investigated sites (Figure 7) this means that all perceptible exposures (sound and vibration) will be easier noticeable. Such an interpretation is supported by studies which had lower background levels of noise and showed a stronger mutual effect of noise and vibration on reported annoyance [24,45,76].

Therefore, although the mean observed vibration level at all locations remained below the national guideline values, a sufficient protection against potential health impacts may not be guaranteed in a situation of combined exposures under critical environmental conditions (multiple frequency vibration, low background noise, complex sound exposure). A recent pilot study investigating lower vibration values at low background noise (LAEq = 25 dB) suggested that alterations of sleep depth and cortical arousals may begin already at 0.3 mm/s [77].

Furthermore, the observed presence of strong low frequency components can induce further vibration perceptions through cross-modality interactions [78,79]. Such cross-over effects are not covered in typical "mono-sensory" guideline assessments, where primary and secondary airborne sound and ground vibration effects are assessed separately.

This study extends previous tram noise studies by using a broad based technical and integrated health approach to investigate the possible reasons for strong citizen complaints after the introduction of a new tram generation. There are also some constraints.

Due to the already emotionally heated community situation (no significant improvements over two years) we had to abstain from carrying out an accompanying field survey to get our own data on annoyance and sleep disturbance. Instead we used external annoyance and sleep disturbance reference data and referred our obtained exposure data to this established general information. As no tram field exposure response information was available for potential health effects we had to resort to an approximation by using main rail response data.

Eventually, due to budget limitations, we were unable conducting parallel indoor and outdoor measurements at each location. This could have given further insight into the tram noise transmission through wall and windows.

5. Conclusions

Emissions from trams are a multi-faceted problem and need to be treated as such. Otherwise, the assessment runs the risk to underestimate the overall effect on humans in real life situations.

Therefore, the simple application of available exposure response information for vibration [75] may only be valid when the ambient soundscape [80] and the other relevant environmental and social context mimics the conditions of the included surveys [28].

With the extended integrated approach in our case study in Graz we were able to pinpoint to a few critical issues, which can help to explain the supposed "overreaction" of the concerned citizens. In addition, the case study shows the limitations in health risk assessment when only separate, classical single sound and vibration guideline assessments are carried out.

It seems that the perceptible change of the tram emissions verified by psychoacoustic parameters and vibration measurements was accentuated in the presence of low background levels (higher than typical background to peak noise ratio) and strong low frequency components. Altogether, the interaction between these sensory changes (cross-modality effects) may have introduced a perceived step change in the annoyance response after the introduction of the new tramway types [41,42,45,46,81]. However, the observed high variance of vibration (Figure 5) and all psychoacoustic indicators (see Figures 9–14) for the same tram types at different measurement sites makes it difficult to determine the main trigger for the observed subjective change in the perception of inhabitants. Further quality control studies are needed with "reprofiled" tramways to implement systematic changes.

The results point also to the constraints of applying national standards in isolation, when the health risks of combined exposures need to be assessed. This study provides further support to the statement in the review by Trolle et al. 2015 [71] that typical vibration weighting used in standards (e.g., Wm) do not provide sufficient protection under certain circumstances. Furthermore, the required time weighting "slow" in the Austrian standard can lead to a slight underestimation of the exposure peaks at the perceptual level.

Eventually, the fact that tramways are not required to undergo vibration assessment during the approval process (in Austria) does neither fit with the need for more public transportation nor with the stricter requirement to protect the public against adverse health effects from transportation.

Acknowledgments: We thank the inhabitants for the good compliance with the indoor measurements. The current study was funded by the Holding Graz Linien, who also provided the commissioned vibration data from tappauf.consultants. Special thanks goes to the operations manager Tram Rene Rath for the continuous support over the two years.

Author Contributions: P.L. was commissioned to do this work; P.L. and M.C. conceived and planned the design of the study; M.C. and M.L. conducted the field work and made the post processing; M.C., P.L. and M.L. analyzed the data and agreed on its interpretation; P.L., M.C. and M.L. drafted the article; P.L., M.C. and M.L. critically revised the article; and all authors approved the final version.

Appl. Sci. **2016**, *6*, 398

Conflicts of Interest: The authors declare no conflict of interest.

Appendix A

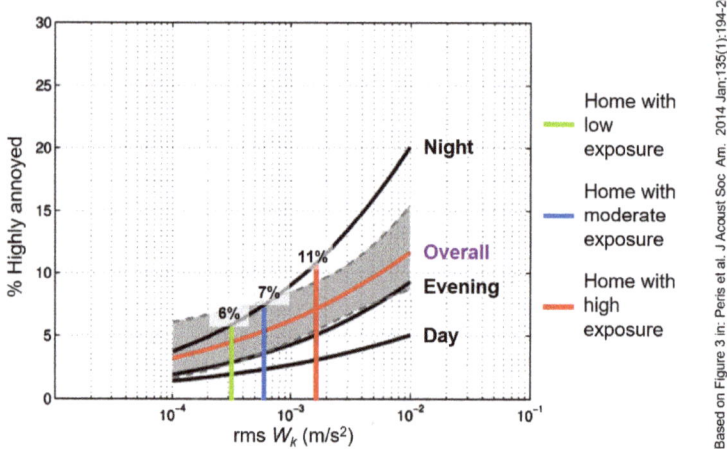

Figure A1. Comparison of the proportion of people reporting high annoyance (%HA) during the day, evening and night due to railway vibration (vertical vibration). Using the converted exposure data from the Graz immission survey (slow weighting).

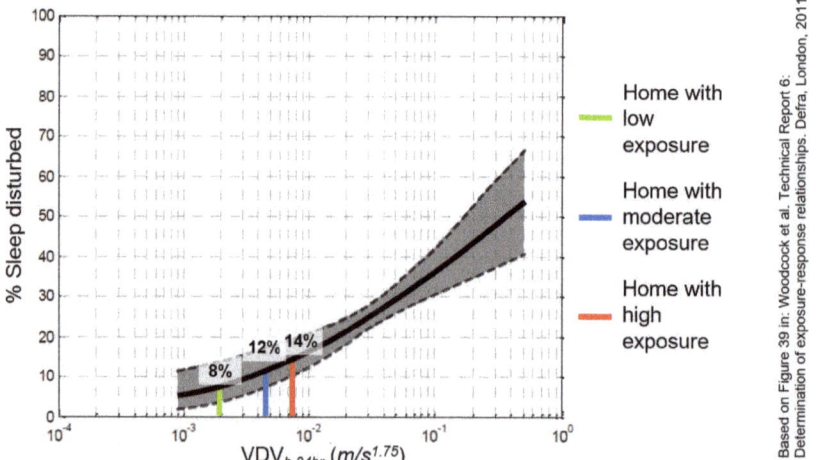

Figure A2. Exposure-response relationship showing the percentage of people reporting sleep disturbance for a given vibration exposure. Using the converted exposure data from the Graz immission survey (slow weighting).

Table A1. Vibration exposure of analyzed tramways by tram type and time weighting.

Measuring Points	Type of Tramway	Measured Tramways	Wm Weighted Peak Acceleration (SLOW) (m/s²) Mean	Wm Weighted Peak Acceleration (SLOW) (m/s²) SD	Wm Weighted Peak Acceleration (FAST) (m/s²) Mean	Wm Weighted Peak Acceleration (FAST) (m/s²) SD
Measuring point 1	New Tram	51	0.0046	0.0005	0.0070	0.0009
	Old Tram	14	0.0041	0.0002	0.0062	0.0003
Measuring point 2	New Tram	41	0.0041	0.0002	0.0063	0.0003
	Old Tram	19	0.0041	0.0002	0.0063	0.0003
Measuring point 3	New Tram	70	0.0061	0.0006	0.0091	0.0014
	Old Tram	2	0.0053	0.0004	0.0077	0.0001
Measuring point 4	New Tram	31	0.0066	0.0023	0.0099	0.0031
	Old Tram	18	0.0055	0.0011	0.0086	0.0021
Measuring point 5	New Tram	74	0.0069	0.0020	0.0099	0.0029
	Old Tram	45	0.0060	0.0013	0.0089	0.0021
Measuring point 6	New Tram	51	0.0050	0.0008	0.0076	0.0011
	Old Tram	26	0.0047	0.0007	0.0073	0.0009

Table A2. Maximum Sound Levels indoors during passing by tram type.

Type of tram	% above Threshold *	Lower 95% CI	Upper 95% CI
Variobahn ("new")	47%	41%	52%
CityRunner ("old")	20%	12%	29%
Series 500-600 ("very old")	32%	19%	49%

* Threshold ≥ 42 dBA, max indoors.

References

1. Hodgson, P.; Potter, S.; Warren, J.; Gillingwater, D. Can bus really be the new tram? *Res. Trans. Econ.* **2013**, *39*, 158–166. [CrossRef]
2. De Bruijn, H.; Veeneman, W. Decision-making for light rail. *Trans. Res. A Policy Pract.* **2009**, *43*, 349–359. [CrossRef]
3. Scherer, M. Is light rail more attractive to users than bus transit? *Trans. Res. Rec. J. Trans. Res. Board* **2010**, *2144*, 11–19. [CrossRef]
4. Mingardo, G. Transport and environmental effects of rail-based Park and Ride: Evidence from the Netherlands. *J. Trans. Geogr.* **2013**, *30*, 7–16. [CrossRef]
5. Wijnia, Y.K. Noise emission from trams. *J. Sound Vib.* **1988**, *120*, 281–286. [CrossRef]
6. Mandula, J.; Salaiová, B.; Kovalaková, M. Prediction of noise from trams. *Appl. Acoust.* **2002**, *63*, 373–389. [CrossRef]
7. Pallas, M.A.A.; Lelong, J.; Chatagnon, R. Characterisation of tram noise emission and contribution of the noise sources. *Appl. Acoust.* **2011**, *72*, 437–450. [CrossRef]
8. Van Ruiten, C.J.M. Mechanism of squeal noise generated by trams. *J. Sound Vib.* **1988**, *120*, 245–253. [CrossRef]
9. Vincent, N.; Koch, J.R.; Chollet, H.; Guerder, J.Y. Curve squeal of urban rolling stock—Part 1: State of the art and field measurements. *J. Sound Vib.* **2006**, *293*, 691–700. [CrossRef]
10. Kaczmarek, T. *Squeal Tram Noise Annoyance*; Euronoise: Tampere, Finland, 2006.
11. Kaczmarek, T.; Hafke, H.; Preis, A.; Sandrock, S.; Griefahn, B.; Gjestland, T. The tram bonus. *Arch. Acoust.* **2006**, *31*, 405–412.
12. Trollé, A.; Marquis-Favre, C.; Klein, A. Short-term annoyance due to tramway noise: Determination of an acoustical indicator of annoyance via multilevel regression analysis. *Acta Acust. United Acust.* **2014**, *100*, 34–45. [CrossRef]
13. Sandrock, S.; Griefahn, B.; Kaczmarek, T.; Hafke, H.; Preis, A.; Gjestland, T. Experimental studies on annoyance caused by noises from trams and buses. *J. Sound Vib.* **2008**, *313*, 908–919. [CrossRef]
14. Miedema, H.M.E.; van den Berg, R. Community response to tramway noise. *J. Sound Vib.* **1998**, *120*, 341–346. [CrossRef]

15. Philipps-Bertin, C.; Champelovier, P.; Lambert, J.; Trindade, C.; Legouis, T. Perception and annoyance due to tramway noise. In *INTER-NOISE and NOISE-CON Congress and Conference Proceedings*; Institute of Noise Control Engineering: Reston, VA, USA, 2007.

16. Trollé, A.; Marquis-Favre, C.; Klein, A. Acoustical indicator of noise annoyance due to tramway in in-curve operating configurations. In Proceedings of the 2013 3rd International Conference on Instrumentation Control and Automation, Meetings on Acoustics, Montreal, QC, Canada, 2–7 June 2013.

17. Kouroussis, G.; Connolly, D.P.; Verlinden, O. Railway-induced ground vibrations—A review of vehicle effects. *Int. J. Rail. Trans.* **2014**, *2*, 69–110. [CrossRef]

18. Maldonado, M.; Chiello, O.; Houédec, D. Propagation of Vibrations Due to a Tramway Line. In *Noise and Vibration Mitigation for Rail Transportation Systems*; Springer: Berlin/Heidelberg, Germany, 2008.

19. Real Herráiz, J.I.; Morales-Ivorra, S.; Zamorano Martín, C.; Soler Basauri, V. Analysis of Vibrations Generated by the Presence of Corrugation in a Modeled Tram Track. In *Mathematical Problems in Engineering*; Hindawi Publishing Corporation: Cairo, Egypt, 2015.

20. Jolibois, A.; Defrance, J.; Koreneff, H.; Jean, P.; Duhamel, D.; Sparrow, V.W. In situ measurement of the acoustic performance of a full scale tramway low height noise barrier prototype. *Appl. Acoust.* **2015**, *94*, 57–68. [CrossRef]

21. Lang, J. Ground-borne vibrations caused by trams, and control measures. *J. Sound Vib.* **1998**, *120*, 407–412. [CrossRef]

22. Kouroussis, G.; Pauwels, N.; Brux, P.; Conti, C.; Verlinden, O. A numerical analysis of the influence of tram characteristics and rail profile on railway traffic ground-borne noise and vibration in the Brussels Region. *Sci. Total Environ.* **2014**, *482–483*, 452–460. [CrossRef] [PubMed]

23. Connolly, D.P.; Marecki, G.P.; Kouroussis, G.; Thalassinakis, I.; Woodward, P.K. The growth of railway ground vibration problems—A review. *Sci. Total Environ.* **2016**, *568*, 1276–1282. [CrossRef] [PubMed]

24. Paulsen, R.; Kastka, J. Effects of combined noise and vibration on annoyance. *J. Sound Vib.* **1995**, *181*, 295–314. [CrossRef]

25. Waddington, D.C.; Woodcock, J.; Peris, E.; Condie, J.; Sica, G.; Moorhouse, A.T.; Steele, A. Human response to vibration in residential environments. *J. Acoust. Soc. Am.* **2014**, *135*, 182–193. [CrossRef] [PubMed]

26. Turunen-Rise, I.H.; Brekke, A.; Harvik, L.; Madshus, C.; Klaeboe, R. Vibration in dwellings from road and rail traffic—Part I: A new Norwegian measurement standard and classification system. *Appl. Acoust.* **2003**, *64*, 71–87. [CrossRef]

27. Klæboe, R.; Turunen-Rise, I.H.; Hårvik, L.; Madshus, C. Vibration in dwellings from road and rail traffic—Part II: Exposure–effect relationships based on ordinal logit and logistic regression models. *Appl. Acoust.* **2003**, *64*, 89–109. [CrossRef]

28. Peris, E.; Woodcock, J.; Sica, G.; Sharp, C.; Moorhouse, A.T.; Waddington, D.C. Effect of situational, attitudinal and demographic factors on railway vibration annoyance in residential areas. *J. Acoust. Soc. Am.* **2014**, *135*, 194–204. [CrossRef] [PubMed]

29. Sharp, C.; Woodcock, J.; Sica, G.; Peris, E.; Moorhouse, A.T.; Waddington, D.C. Exposure-response relationships for annoyance due to freight and passenger railway vibration exposure in residential environments. *J. Acoust. Soc. Am.* **2014**, *135*, 205–212. [CrossRef] [PubMed]

30. Smith, M.G.; Croy, I.; Ögren, M.; Waye, K.P. On the Influence of Freight Trains on Humans: A Laboratory Investigation of the Impact of Nocturnal Low Frequency Vibration and Noise on Sleep and Heart Rate. *PLoS ONE* **2013**, *8*, e55829. [CrossRef] [PubMed]

31. Croy, I.; Smith, M.G.; Waye, K.P. Effects of train noise and vibration on human heart rate during sleep: An experimental study. *BMJ Open* **2013**, *3*, e002655. [CrossRef] [PubMed]

32. Woodcock, J.; Moorhouse, A.T.; Waddington, D.C. A multidimensional evaluation of the perception and annoyance caused by railway induced groundborne vibration. *Acta Acust. United Acust.* **2014**, *100*, 614–627. [CrossRef]

33. Zapfe, J.A.; Saurenman, H.; Fidell, S. Ground-Borne Noise and Vibration in Buildings Caused by Rail Transit. Ground. Web-Only Document 48. Available online: http://onlinepubs.trb.org/onlinepubs/tcrp/tcrp_web-doc_48.pdf (accessed on 10 November 2016).

34. Peris, E.; Woodcock, J.; Sica, G.; Sharp, C.; Moorhouse, A.T.; Waddington, D.C. Guidance for new policy developments on railway noise and vibration. *Trans. Res. A Policy Pract.* **2016**, *85*, 76–88. [CrossRef]

35. Siemens, A.G. Avenio Tram—Munich, Germany. Available online: http://www.mobility.siemens.com/mobility/global/SiteCollectionDocuments/en/rail-solutions/trams-and-light-rail/avenio-muenchen-en.PDF (accessed on 10 November 2016).

36. Bombardier Transportation GmbH. Environmental Product Declaration—Flexity Outlook. Available online: http://www.bombardier.com/content/dam/Websites/bombardiercom/supporting-documents/Sustainability/Reports/BT/Bombardier-Transportation-EPD-FLEXITY-Valencia-en.pdf (accessed on 10 November 2016).

37. Alstom Transportation. Citadis Spirit—The Spirit That Moves Your City. Available online: http://www.alstom.com/Global/Transport/Resources/Documents/brochure2014/Citadis%20Spirit%20-%20Brochure%20-%20EN.pdf?epslanguage=en-GB (accessed on 10 November 2016).

38. Hume, K.I.; Brink, M.; Basner, M. Effects of environmental noise on sleep. *Noise Health* **2012**, *14*, 297–302. [CrossRef] [PubMed]

39. Kim, R.; van den Berg, M. Summary of night noise guidelines for Europe. *Noise Health* **2010**, *12*, 61–63. [CrossRef] [PubMed]

40. Griefahn, B. Sleep Disturbances Related to Environmental Noise. *Noise Health* **2002**, *4*, 57–60. [PubMed]

41. Ohrstrom, E. Effects of exposure to railway noise—A comparison between areas with and without vibration. *J. Sound Vib.* **1997**, *205*, 555–560. [CrossRef]

42. Gidlöf-Gunnarsson, A.; Ogren, M.; Jerson, T.; Ohrström, E. Railway noise annoyance and the importance of number of trains, ground vibration, and building situational factors. *Noise Health* **2012**, *14*, 190–201. [CrossRef] [PubMed]

43. Howarth, H.V.C.; Griffin, M.J. The annoyance caused by simultaneous noise and vibration. *J. Acoust. Soc. Am.* **1991**, *89*, 2317–2323. [CrossRef]

44. Lercher, P. Noise and Vibrations and other Interactions with the Environment. In *Proceedings of the International Workshop on "Combined Environmental Exposure: Noise, Air Pollutants and Chemicals"*; Kephalopoulos, S., Koistinen, K., Paviotti, M., Schwela, D., Kotzias, D., Eds.; Office for Official Publications of the European Communities: Ispra, Italy, 2007.

45. Lercher, P. Combined Noise Exposure at Home. In *Encyclopedia of Environmental Health*; Elsevier: Burlington, MA, USA, 2011; pp. 764–777.

46. Lee, P.J.; Griffin, M.J. Combined effect of noise and vibration produced by high-speed trains on annoyance in buildings. *J. Acoust. Soc. Am.* **2013**, *133*, 2126–2135. [PubMed]

47. Cik, M.; Lercher, P. Ground-borne vibrations, sounds and secondary airborne sounds from tramways: A psychoacoustic evaluation including health aspects. In Proceedings of the 43nd International Congress and Exhibition on Noise Control Engineering, Melbourne, Australia, 16–19 November 2014.

48. Beurteilung der Einwirkung von Schwingungsimmissionen des landgebundenen Verkehrs auf den Menschen in Gebäuden—Schwingungen und sekundärer Luftschall. ÖNORM S 9012. 1 February 2010.

49. Leventhall, H.G. Low frequency noise and annoyance. *Noise Health* **2004**, *6*, 59–72. [PubMed]

50. Messung und Bewertung Tieffrequenter Geräuschimmissionen in der Nachbarschaft. DIN 45680. March 1997; Deutsches Institut für Normung: Berlin, Germany.

51. Sottek, R. *Gehörgerechte Rauhigkeitsberechnung*; DAGA: Dresden, Germany, 1994.

52. World Health Organization Europe. *Night Noise Guidelines for Europe*; World Health Organization Europe: Geneva, Switzerland, 2009.

53. Kjellberg, A.; Tesarz, M.; Holmberg, K.; Landström, U. Evaluation of frequency-weighted sound level measurements for prediction of low-frequency noise annoyance. *Environ. Int.* **1997**, *23*, 519–527. [CrossRef]

54. Rushforth, I.; Moorhouse, A.; Styles, P. A case study of low frequency noise assessed using din 45680 criteria. *Noise Notes* **2004**, *3*, 3–18. [CrossRef]

55. Schomer, P.D. Criteria for assessment of noise annoyance. *Noise Contr. Eng. J.* **2005**, *53*, 132–144. [CrossRef]

56. Basner, M.; Brink, M.; Bristow, A.; de Kluizenaar, Y.; Finegold, L.; Hong, J. ICBEN review of research on the biological effects of noise 2011–2014. *Noise Health* **2015**, *17*, 57. [CrossRef] [PubMed]

57. Fidell, S.; Teffeteller, S. Scaling the annoyance of intrusive sounds. *J. Sound Vib.* **1981**, *78*, 291–298. [CrossRef]

58. Schomer, P.D.; Wagner, L.R. On the contribution of noticeability of environmental sounds to noise annoyance. *Noise Contr. Eng. J.* **1996**, *44*, 294–305. [CrossRef]

59. Sneddon, M.; Pearsons, K.; Fidell, S. Laboratory study of the notice-ability and annoyance of low signal-to-noise ratio sounds. *Noise Contr. Eng. J.* **2003**, *51*, 300–305. [CrossRef]

60. Roberts, M.J.; Western, A.W.; Webber, M.J. A theory of patterns of passby noise. *J. Sound Vib.* **2003**, *262*, 1047–1056. [CrossRef]

61. Bockstael, A.; Coensel, B.D.; Lercher, P.; Botteldooren, D. Influence of temporal structure of the sonic environment on annoyance. In Proceedings of the 10th International Congress on Noise as a Public Health Problem (ICBEN 2011), London, UK, 24–28 July 2011.

62. Coensel, B.D.; Botteldooren, D.; Muer, T.D.; Berglund, B.; Nilsson, M.E.; Lercher, P. A model for the perception of environmental sound based on notice-events. *J. Acoust. Soc. Am.* **2009**, *126*, 656–665. [CrossRef] [PubMed]

63. Klein, A.; Marquis-Favre, C.; Weber, R.; Trollé, A. Spectral and modulation indices for annoyance-relevant features of urban road single-vehicle pass-by noises. *J. Acoust. Soc. Am.* **2015**, *137*, 1238–1250. [CrossRef] [PubMed]

64. Lakatos, P.; Musacchia, G.; O'Connel, M.N.; Falchier, A.Y.; Javitt, D.C.; Schroeder, C.E. The Spectrotemporal Filter Mechanism of Auditory Selective Attention. *Neuron* **2013**, *77*, 750–761. [CrossRef] [PubMed]

65. Pérez-González, D.; Malmierca, M.S. Adaptation in the auditory system: An overview. *Front. Integr. Neurosci.* **2014**, *8*. [CrossRef] [PubMed]

66. Shamma, S.A.; Elhilali, M.; Micheyl, C. Temporal coherence and attention in auditory scene analysis. *Trends Neurosci.* **2011**, *34*, 114–123. [CrossRef] [PubMed]

67. Uppenkamp, S.; Röhl, M. Human auditory neuroimaging of intensity and loudness. *Hear. Res.* **2014**, *307*, 65–73. [CrossRef] [PubMed]

68. Preis, A. Noise annoyance and its components. *Arch. Cent. Sens. Res.* **1995**, *2*, 1–54.

69. Genuit, K.; Fiebig, A. Psychoacoustics and its benefit for the soundscape approach. *Acta Acust. United Acust.* **2006**, *92*, 952–958.

70. Cik, M.; Lienhart, M. Soundmapping approaches in a small suburban study area. In Proceedings of the 45th International Congress and Exhibition on Noise Control Engineering (Internoise 2016), Hamburg, Germany, 21–24 August 2016.

71. Trollé, A.; Marquis-Favre, C.; Parizet, E. Perception and annoyance due to vibrations in dwellings generated from ground transportation: A review. *J. Low Freq. Noise Vib. Act. Contr.* **2015**, *34*, 963–966. [CrossRef]

72. Peris, E.; Woodcock, J.; Sica, G.; Moorhouse, A.T.; Waddington, D.C. Annoyance due to railway vibration at different times of the day. *J. Acoust. Soc. Am.* **2012**, *131*, EL191–EL196. [CrossRef] [PubMed]

73. Woodcock, J.S.; Peris, E.; Moorhouse, A.T.; Waddington, D.C. *Guidance Document for the Evaluation of Railway Vibration*; CargoVibes: Salford, UK, 2014.

74. Mechanical vibration and shock—Evaluation of human exposure to whole-body vibration—Part 2: Vibration in buildings (1 Hz to 80 Hz). ISO 2631-2:2003. 2003.

75. Tappauf, B.; Cik, M.; Flesch, R.; Lercher, P. *The Use of Vibration Health Response Information in the Framework of Environmental Health Impact Assessments: Technical Issues of Implementation and Interpretation*; EuroNoise: Maastricht, The Netherlands, 2015.

76. Passchier-Vermeer, W.; Zeichart, K.; Gezondheid, T.; Preventie, N.O. *Vibrations in the Living Environment. Relationships between Vibration Annoyance and Vibration Metrics*; TNO: Leiden, The Netherlands, 1998.

77. Smith, M.G.; Ögren, M.; Hammar, O.; Persson-Waye, K. *Physiological Reaction Thresholds to Vibration during Sleep*; EuroNoise: Maastricht, The Netherlands, 2015.

78. Takahashi, Y. A study on the contribution of body vibrations to the vibratory sensation induced by high-level, complex low-frequency noise. *Noise Health* **2011**, *13*, 2–8. [CrossRef] [PubMed]

79. Takahashi, Y. Vibratory sensation induced by low-frequency noise: The threshold for "vibration perceived in the head" in normal-hearing subjects. *J. Low Freq. Noise Vib. Act. Contr.* **2013**, *32*, 1–10. [CrossRef]

80. Brooks, B.M.; Schulte-Fortkamp, B.; Voigt, K.S.; Case, A.U. Exploring our sonic environment through soundscape research & theory. *Acoust. Today* **2014**, *10*, 30–40.

81. Brown, A.L.; van Kamp, I. Response to a change in transport noise exposure: Competing explanations of change effects. *J. Acoust. Soc. Am.* **2009**, *125*, 905–914. [CrossRef] [PubMed]

Article

Validation of a Numerical Model for the Prediction of the Annoyance Condition at the Operator Station of Construction Machines

Eleonora Carletti * and Francesca Pedrielli

Institute for Agricultural and Earthmoving Machines of the National Research Council of Italy (C.N.R.-IMAMOTER), 44124 Ferrara, Italy; f.pedrielli@imamoter.cnr.it
* Correspondence: e.carletti@imamoter.cnr.it; Tel.: +39-0532-735635

Academic Editor: Jian Kang
Received: 21 September 2016; Accepted: 14 November 2016; Published: 18 November 2016

Abstract: It is well-known that the reduction of noise levels is not strictly linked to the reduction of noise annoyance. Even earthmoving machine manufacturers are facing the problem of customer complaints concerning the noise quality of their machines with increasing frequency. Unfortunately, all the studies geared to the understanding of the relationship between multidimensional characteristics of noise signals and the auditory perception of annoyance require repeated sessions of jury listening tests, which are time-consuming. In this respect, an annoyance prediction model was developed for compact loaders to assess the annoyance sensation perceived by operators at their workplaces without repeating the full sound quality assessment but using objective parameters only. This paper aims at verifying the feasibility of the developed annoyance prediction model when applied to other kinds of earthmoving machines. For this purpose, an experimental investigation was performed on five earthmoving machines, different in type, dimension, and engine mechanical power, and the annoyance predicted by the numerical model was compared to the annoyance given by subjective listening tests. The results were evaluated by means of the squared value of the correlation coefficient, R^2, and they confirm the possible applicability of the model to other kinds of machines.

Keywords: annoyance; noise; numerical model; earthmoving machines; sound quality

---

1. Introduction

It has been proved that sound levels, sound pressure, or even sound power, although properly weighted, are not able to assess the annoyance that a sound may generate [1]. This is true especially for high sound pressure levels due both to the great difference between the A-weighting filter and the equal loudness contour curve at these levels [2] and to the necessity of using parameters that account for the time structure and the spectral variation of the signals, such as the psychoacoustics parameters. Unfortunately, almost all legislation still refers to overall A-weighted levels (L_{Aeq}, L_{WA}, L_{pA}) aimed at checking the compliance of the products.

For earthmoving machines, the Directive 2000/14/EC [3] imposes limitations on the A-weighted sound power levels emitted by the machine while the Directive 2006/42/EC [4] requires information on the airborne noise emissions, in terms of A-weighted sound pressure level at the workstation, C-weighted peak instantaneous sound pressure value at the workstation, and A-weighted sound power level emitted by the machine. As the reduction of the noise levels is not strictly linked to the reduction of the annoyance, manufacturers are facing the problem of customers' complaints concerning the noise quality of the machines with increasing frequency.

In the last ten years, great efforts have been made by the authors to better understand the relationship between the multidimensional characteristics of the noise signals at the operator station of compact loaders in different working conditions and the relevant auditory perception of annoyance [5]. Compact loaders, indeed, are critical as far as noise emission is concerned because the operator station is located just above the engine compartment, which cannot be completely insulated from the outside due to overheating problems. As a consequence, noise and vibration levels at the operator station are extremely high, causing uncomfortable conditions for workers.

Moreover, compact loaders are widely used in dwelling areas for the activities of building construction and renovation, and the study of the quality of their noise emissions may be valuable to reduce their environmental noise impact.

Results of these studies showed that loudness and sharpness are the parameters primarily related to the annoyance perception of these noise signals [6,7]. In particular, S_5 (fifth sharpness percentile) and N_{50} (fiftieth loudness percentile) were found to be closely related to the annoyance perception when the machines were operating in dynamic conditions. As to the different perception occurring with sounds having different loudness and/or sharpness values, subjective listening tests indicated that the minimum differences which are subjectively perceived (just noticeable differences, JND) for the loudness and sharpness of these machines are 0.8 sone and 0.04 acum, respectively. Results highlighted also that the loudness JND becomes greater as the overall sound pressure level of the signal increases, while the sharpness JND has very small variations related to the overall level [8].

All of these studies followed the "product sound quality" approach that, although very powerful in relating the physical characteristics of the noise to the auditory perception of annoyance, requires repeated sessions of jury listening tests, which are time-consuming [9–12]. In this respect, an annoyance prediction model could be extremely valuable to assess the annoyance sensation perceived by operators of earthmoving machines at their workplaces without repeating the full sound quality assessment but using prior knowledge of these machines.

This approach has already been applied to many other products [13–16] as well as to construction machines and some of their components [17].

The authors developed an annoyance prediction model able to evaluate the grade of annoyance at the workplace of compact loaders using objective parameters only [18]. The model was developed by multi-regression analysis based on a relevant database of binaural noise signals recorded at the operator position. Results confirmed a very good correlation between the annoyance values predicted by the model and the subjective ratings resulting from jury tests.

This paper aims at verifying the feasibility of the developed annoyance prediction model when applied to other kinds of earthmoving machines. The basic idea guiding this study is that all earthmoving machines (excavators, back-hoe loaders, dozers, etc.) have common dominant noise sources: the internal combustion engine, the engine cooling system, and the hydraulic components. Consequently, the noise signals in different working conditions should have the same temporal and spectral characteristics irrespective of the type of machine. Then, the relationship between physical/psychoacoustics descriptors and annoyance auditory perception elicited by the sound stimuli should be the same. If this is confirmed, the annoyance prediction model developed for the compact loaders could be applied to other kind of earthmoving machines.

The several experiments and analyses performed in order to validate this thesis are extensively reported in the following sections.

2. The Annoyance Prediction Model for Compact Loaders

The annoyance prediction model was developed starting from measurements on 41 compact loaders belonging to six families both in dynamic and stationary conditions in order to represent all possible operations of such machines [18].

When the machine was in a stationary idle condition, the binaural signals were recorded by means of a head and torso simulator placed in the operator station. When the machine was performing a simulated work cycle (charging and discharging gravel or loam from a stockpile to another), the binaural signals were recorded by means of a binaural headphone with miniature microphones placed at the entrance of the operator's ear canals [19].

A total amount of 62 binaural noise signals were then available. The following acoustic and psychoacoustic parameters were calculated for all these signals, using the Pulse Sound Quality software (version 10, type 7698, Bruel & Kjaer, Nærum, Denmark): overall sound pressure levels, percentile values of the sound pressure levels, overall and percentile values of loudness (N) and sharpness (S), overall values of roughness (R), and fluctuation strength ($Fl.St.$).

This huge amount of sound stimuli was divided into nine groups; for each of them, the subjective assessment of annoyance was obtained by means of subjective listening tests carried out according to the paired comparison procedure [20].

Multiple regression analysis was then used for developing the prediction model as this technique is the most commonly used for analyzing multiple dependence between variables [21,22]. Six groups of noise stimuli were used in the development phase, while the remaining three groups were used for validation purposes.

The set of predictor variables which led to the highest R^2 (squared value of the correlation coefficient between the subjective scores and the predicted values of annoyance) when applied to the six groups of sound stimuli was (Peak, N_{50}, S_5), i.e., the sound pressure Peak level, in dB, the fiftieth percentile of loudness in sone, N_{50}, and the fifth percentile of sharpness in acum, S_5.

The multiple regression equations obtained for the set of variables (Peak, N_{50}, S_5) for each group of sound stimuli are listed in Table 1.

Table 1. Results of the multiple regression analysis for the predictor variables (Peak, N_{50}, S_5).

Noise Groups	Multiple Regression Equation	R^2
Group 1	$Y_1 = -9.310 + 0.057\,\text{Peak} + 0.184\,N_{50} + 0.216\,S_5$	0.79
Group 2	$Y_2 = -5.512 + 0.039\,\text{Peak} + 0.296\,N_{50} - 3.703\,S_5$	0.99
Group 3	$Y_3 = -5.322 + 0.038\,\text{Peak} + 0.057\,N_{50} + 0.412\,S_5$	0.89
Group 4	$Y_4 = -18.214 + 0.061\,\text{Peak} + 0.018\,N_{50} + 9.628\,S_5$	1.00
Group 5	$Y_5 = -4.241 + 0.030\,\text{Peak} + 0.046\,N_{50} + 0.289\,S_5$	0.96
Group 6	$Y_6 = 6.971 - 0.012\,\text{Peak} + 0.312\,N_{50} - 11.350\,S_5$	0.89

For each noise group, this set of variables accounted for at least 89% of the variation in the subjective scores, with the only exception of Noise Group 1.

Each regression equation was finally applied to the other five groups, and the predicted annoyance values were calculated for each equation. The correlation between these predicted annoyance values and the subjective ratings was evaluated for each noise group: the better the correlation, the higher the R^2 value. In such a way, the best annoyance prediction model was identified as the one that gave the maximum sum of R^2 over all the noise groups except for the one from which that model was issued.

According to this criterion, the regression equation referred to the Noise Group 3 gave the best results, and it was chosen as the numerical prediction model able to assess noise annoyance at the workplace of compact loaders:

$$Y_3 = 5.322 + 0.038\,\text{Peak} + 0.057\,N_{50} + 0.412\,S_5 \tag{1}$$

where Y_3 indicates the predicted annoyance value.

The validation process performed on the remaining three groups of sound stimuli confirmed the reliability of this model as an alternative and simpler way for manufacturers and customers to assess the grade of annoyance at the workplace of any compact loader.

3. Experimental Investigation on Different Kinds of Earthmoving Machines

3.1. Binaural Recordings and Objective Characterizations

Five brand new earthmoving machines, different in type, manufacturer, dimension, and engine mechanical power, were selected for this test: two excavators, a back-hoe loader (used both during loader and excavator operations), a dozer, and a skid steer loader. All the binaural recordings were performed at the operator working station in an open area while the machine, in stationary idle conditions, had the engine running at one of the rotational speeds corresponding to a typical operation for that specific type of equipment. Table 2 reports the list of the machines and the codes used hereinafter for their identification and the rotational speed values during the noise recordings.

Table 2. Earthmoving machines involved in the investigation.

Machine Type	Identification Code	Rotational Speed (rpm)
Skid steer loader	A	2350
Dozer	B	2350
Excavator	C	2350
Back-hoe loader (operating as loader)	D	2700
Excavator	E	2450
Back-hoe loader (operating as excavator)	F	1600

All the binaural measurements were performed at the operator station using the Cortex System MK1 head and torso simulator (NCI, Neutrik Cortex Instruments GMBH, Regensburg, Germany). The recordings corresponding to the left and right ears were then analyzed separately, and the same physical and psychoacoustic parameters as in the previous studies were evaluated. Figure 1 shows the 1/3 octave band sound pressure spectra of the six sound stimuli recorded at the right ear of the dummy head. Similar spectra were also detected at the left ear.

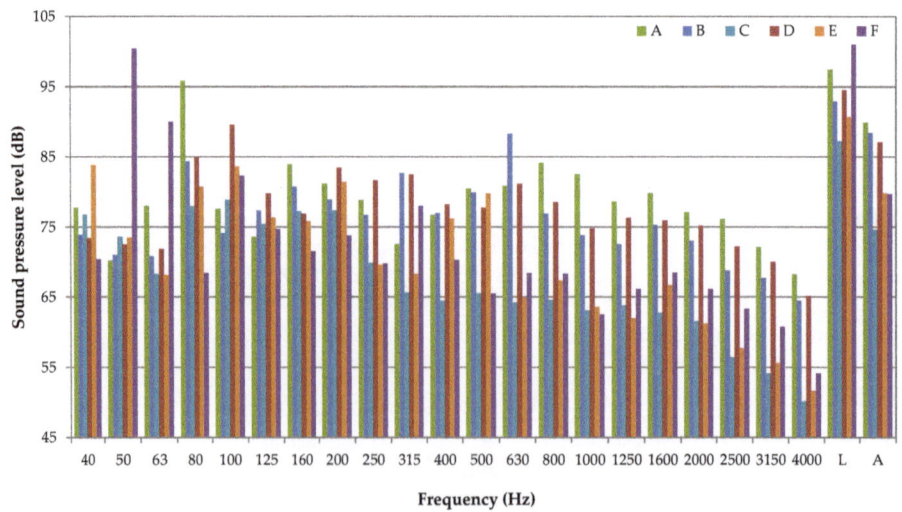

Figure 1. Sound pressure levels for all the six sound stimuli recorded at the right ear.

It is worth noting that all the noise signals except F have the first significant contribution at the engine firing frequency (80 Hz or 100 Hz depending on the rotational speed) and further significant noise contributions at higher frequencies. On the contrary, Signal F, which was recorded at 1600 rpm, still has the dominant contribution at the firing frequency (50 Hz), but this contribution is the only one responsible for the overall level. This noise spectrum feature is unusual for these kinds of machines, which generally have very similar frequency content due to the fact that most of the noise sources are the same [17,23,24].

Referring to the overall energy content of the signals, Signal F has the highest overall level, while A, D, B, E and C follow in decreasing order. Referring to the A-weighted overall level, A has the highest level and B, D, E, F and C follow in decreasing order.

Table 3 reports the most representative acoustic and psychoacoustic parameters for all the six sound stimuli.

Table 3. Acoustic and psychoacoustic parameters for the six sound stimuli.

Parameter		A	B	C	D	E	F
Peak (dB)	Left	106.0	103.0	100.0	105.0	101.0	106.0
	Right	107.0	104.0	98.2	106.0	101.0	107.0
L (dB)	Left	96.7	91.4	88.0	94.3	91.0	101.0
	Right	97.5	92.9	87.2	94.5	90.7	101.0
L_A (dB(A))	Left	89.1	84.9	76.2	86.3	78.3	79.9
	Right	89.9	88.4	74.6	87.1	79.8	79.7
N (sone)	Left	88.4	68.6	40.4	75.6	46.0	55.5
	Right	92.9	78.2	37.2	78.8	47.7	55.7
N_{50} (sone)	Left	88.8	68.9	40.6	76.0	45.9	56.0
	Right	93.4	78.6	37.3	79.2	47.8	56.0
S (acum)	Left	1.36	1.43	1.04	1.40	1.02	1.01
	Right	1.38	1.43	1.12	1.42	1.04	1.07
S_5 (acum)	Left	1.42	1.51	1.10	1.48	1.08	1.07
	Right	1.45	1.51	1.18	1.50	1.09	1.12
R (asper)	Left	1.63	1.34	1.78	1.40	1.53	1.55
	Right	1.40	1.59	1.49	1.43	1.26	1.63
Fl.St. (vacil)	Left	0.30	0.32	0.29	0.29	0.31	0.32
	Right	0.31	0.27	0.29	0.28	0.27	0.30

3.2. Listening Tests and Subjective Annoyance Scores

The six binaural noise recordings were organized in pairs, and all pairs were arranged in a random sequence according to the digram-balanced Latin square design to avoid any sequence effect. In addition, each sequence included at least the repetition of the first pair of the sound stimuli for checking purposes.

Thirty-five normal-hearing subjects (28 males and 7 females) were involved in the listening test. Fifty-eight percent of the subjects were aged less than 29 years, with 32% less than 50 and only 10% over 50. The group included experts of earthmoving machines (i.e., design engineers), experts of subjective listening tests, and scientists in acoustics. No earthmoving machine operators were included. The noise stimuli were presented to the subjects in a quiet environment through high-quality electrostatic headphones with a flat response in the 40–40,000 Hz frequency range after being modified to account for the transfer function of the headphones used for playing back. Each listening session started with a learning phase, during which the experimenter provided the instructions needed to understand the correct procedure for the test. The subjects had to choose, within the pair, the stimulus they considered more annoying. The rating was given by each subject after listening to each pair of sound stimuli as many times as necessary in order to increase the concentration and reduce the probability of inconsistent responses.

According to a procedure defined in Kendall and Babington Smith [20], the consistency for each subject and the agreement among the subjects were evaluated in order to guarantee the control of the variance due to the emotional state of the judging individuals [25]. Three subjects (2 males and 1 female <29 years) did not satisfy these consistency tests, and their ratings were not used in the data analysis. The subjective responses were then arranged in matrices whose overall value is shown in Table 4.

Table 4. Overall matrix of the sound stimuli as to the subjective annoyance score (SAS).

Machine	A	B	C	D	E	F	Subjective Annoyance Score		
							Sum	Rank	%
A	-	22	32	24	31	21	130	1	81.3
B	10	-	32	10	31	12	95	4	59.4
C	0	0	-	0	5	0	5	6	3.1
D	8	22	32	-	31	13	106	3	66.3
E	1	1	27	1	-	0	30	5	18.8
F	11	20	32	19	32	-	114	2	71.3

The number reported in each cell represents how many times the sound indicated on the left hand side of the row was judged more annoying than that heading the correspondent column. The subjective annoyance score (SAS) of the sound stimuli is shown in the last three columns in terms of (1) the overall value for each sound stimulus, with respect to all the others (Sum); (2) the ranking of the subjective scores (Rank); (3) the percentage value (%) normalized to the maximum score (160) that each stimulus could have obtained.

On the basis of the subjective judgements, the noise stimulus of Machine C (excavator at 2350 rpm) turned out to be the less annoying signal, while the signal of Machine A (skid steer loader) the most annoying. This result is in full agreement with the results of previous studies that showed the relevance of the overall energy level and the energy content in the 400–5000 frequency range on the auditory perception of annoyance [7].

On the contrary, the subjective annoyance score obtained by Signal F (back-hoe loader operating as excavator at 1600 rpm) seems only to partially fit the previous results. This stimulus was ranked second as regards the annoyance score. As reported in Table 3, it has the highest Peak level but all the other acoustic and psychoacoustic descriptors are lower than those of B or D signals that were judged less annoying. Probably such a high subjective annoyance judgement could be due to two combining features: the very high overall energy content of this signal and the very high tonal component at low frequency (50 Hz) without any other significant noise component at higher frequency.

4. The Applicability of the Prediction Model to Different Kinds of Earthmoving Machines

In order to verify whether the annoyance prediction model is able to assess the annoyance conditions at the work position of any kind of earthmoving machines, all six regression equations reported in Table 1 (those originally used to develop the model for compact loaders) were considered. For each equation, Y represents the predicted annoyance value that must be calculated using the objective parameters of the six noise stimuli.

These equations were applied to the six sound stimuli recorded from the different kinds of earthmoving machines listed in Table 2. The calculation was repeated for the left and the right noise stimuli, separately. As similar results were found for both, only those of the right noise stimulus will be presented hereinafter.

Figure 2 shows the predicted values of annoyance plotted against the observed values (subjective scores) for each equation. The match of the data (predicted vs. subjectively judged) was assessed by means of the squared value of the correlation coefficient (R^2): the better the correlation, the higher the R^2 value.

At first glance, all these results seem to be a kind of "compromise solution" as the R^2 values are all lower than 0.8. However, a more careful analysis shows that all these numerical prediction models lead to an incorrect assessment of annoyance for Stimulus F. This signal was ranked second as to the annoyance score given by the subjects, while all numerical predictions lead to lower annoyance values.

It is worth emphasizing that the frequency content of this signal is very unusual for earthmoving machines, as it has an unbalanced weight between the noise contributions at low (combustion process at 50 Hz) and medium-high (hydraulic and engine cooling systems at 400–4000 Hz) frequencies. This peculiarity could suggest considering Stimulus F as an "outlier" and to exclude it from the data set.

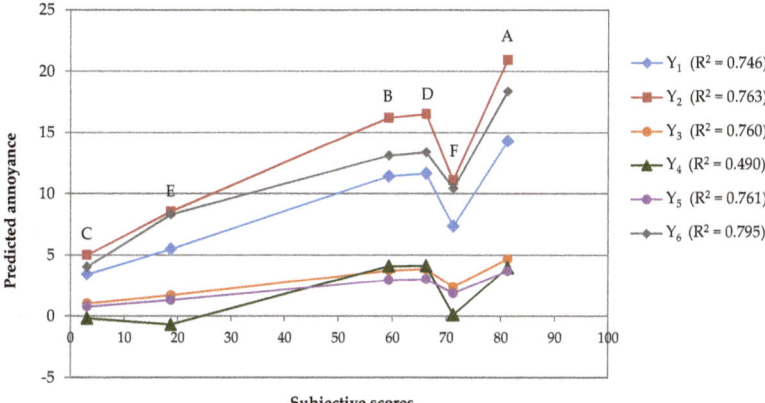

Figure 2. Comparison of the predicted and observed values of annoyance with different numerical regression models.

Figure 3 shows the regression curves and the R^2 values calculated with and without Stimulus F. This quantifies how good the relationship is between the annoyance calculated by means of a prediction model and that assessed by means of subjective evaluations. This is repeated for each of the equations in Table 1 (Y_1, Y_2, Y_3, Y_4, Y_5, Y_6).

Results show that all the regression equations lead to an R^2 value higher than 0.87 when the Signal F is not included in the data set. In particular, Y_3 and Y_5 both have very high values almost equal to 1 ($R^2 = 0.997$). On the basis of these considerations and results, it turns out that the annoyance prediction model developed for compact loaders (Y_3, see Equation (1)) offered a good assessment of noise annoyance at the workplace for other kinds of earth moving machines. Its validity should be further assessed with a larger number of machines.

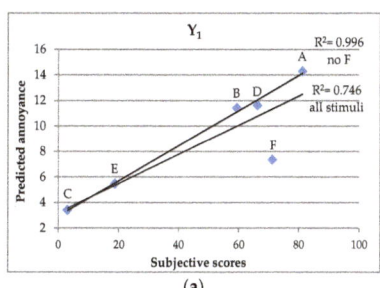

(a)

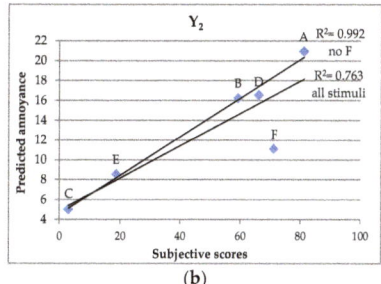

(b)

Figure 3. *Cont.*

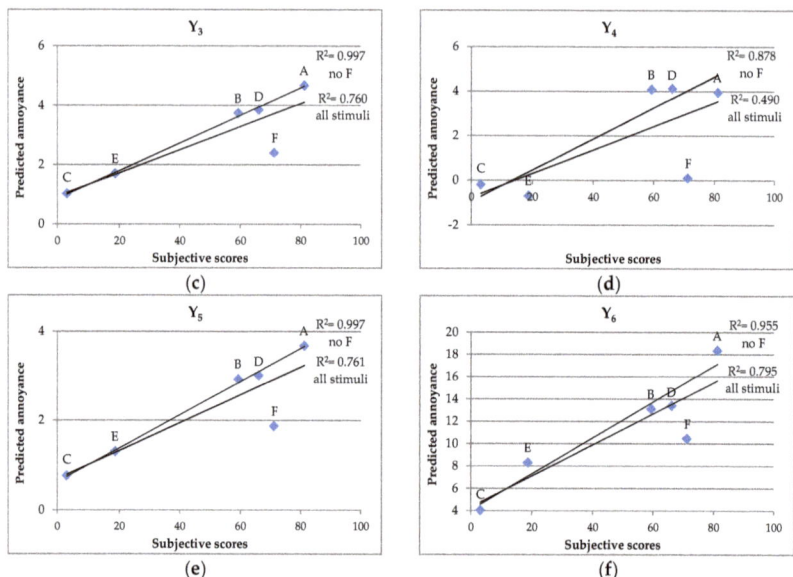

Figure 3. Comparison between the regressions obtained with and without Stimulus F, for each prediction model (**a**) Y_1; (**b**) Y_2; (**c**) Y_3; (**d**) Y_4; (**e**) Y_5; (**f**) Y_6.

Figure 4 shows a comparison between the annoyance values predicted by equation Y_3 and those obtained by subjective listening tests for all six stimuli. In order to make this comparison more understandable, the subjective annoyance values were previously normalized so that the predicted and the subjective results for the most annoying stimulus were the same. This graph shows that the prediction model leads to results in agreement with those obtained by subjective listening tests except for Stimulus F. In addition, the predicted annoyance values are slightly higher than the subjective ones. However, with the limitations due to the small number of machines under test, these results were considered satisfactory.

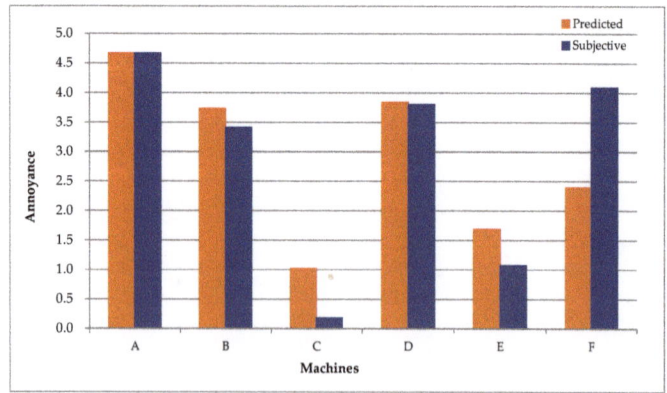

Figure 4. Comparison between the annoyance values predicted by Y_3 and those obtained by subjective listening tests.

5. Conclusions

This paper reports the results of a study aimed at verifying the feasibility of an annoyance prediction model developed for compact loaders when applied to other kinds of earth moving machines. For this purpose, six binaural noise signals were recorded at the workplace of five brand new earthmoving machines, different in type, manufacturer, dimension, and engine mechanical power: two excavators, a back-hoe loader (used both during loader and excavator operations), a dozer, and a skid steer loader.

The subjective annoyance scores of these noise stimuli were obtained by means of subjective listening tests performed according to the paired comparison procedure with more than 30 subjects. All the regression equations originally used to develop the model for compact loaders were then applied to these new binaural noise stimuli in order to obtain the annoyance predicted values. The match between the predicted annoyance and the subjective annoyance was finally assessed by means of the squared value of the correlation coefficient (R^2): the better the correlation, the higher the R^2 value.

Results showed that the regression equations led to quite low R^2 values (from 0.49 to 0.79). However, considering that Stimulus F has a frequency content very unusual for earth moving machines (a very high pick at low frequency and no significant contributions in the medium-high frequency range), it was considered as an "outlier" and excluded from the data set. This exclusion led to R^2 values higher than 0.87.

The regression equation chosen as numerical prediction model to assess noise annoyance at the workplace of compact loaders had the highest R^2 value ($R^2 = 0.997$). This model offered a good assessment of noise annoyance at the workplace and for other kinds of earth moving machines. It intrinsically reflected the main results of the sound quality approach although it was based on objective parameters only. Its validity should be further assessed with a larger number of machines.

Author Contributions: E.C. and F.P. conceived and designed the experiments; F.P. performed the experiments; E.C. and F.P. analyzed the data; E.C. and F.P. wrote the paper.

Conflicts of Interest: The authors declare no conflict of interest.

References

1. Hellman, R.; Zwicker, E. Why can a decrease in dB(A) produce an increase in loudness? *J. Acoust. Soc. Am.* **1987**, *82*, 1700–1705. [CrossRef] [PubMed]
2. Carletti, E.; Pedrielli, F. Subjective evaluation of the noise at the operator's ear position in earth moving machines: A preliminary investigation. In Proceedings of the 1998 ASME International Mechanical Engineering Congress and Exposition, Anaheim, CA, USA, 15–20 November 1998; ASME Noise Control and Acoustics Division: New York, NY, USA, 1998; Volume 25, pp. 151–156.
3. L162 Directive 2000/14/EC of the European Parliament and of the Council of 8 May 2000 on the Approximation of the Laws of the Member States to Noise Emission in the Environment by Equipment for Use Outdoors. Available online: http://eur-lex.europa.eu/legal-content/EN/TXT/?uri=uriserv: OJ.L_.2000.162.01.0001.01.ENG&toc=OJ:L:2000:162:TOC (accessed on 21 September 2016).
4. L157 Directive 2006/42/EC of the European Parliament and of the Council of 17 May 2006 on Machinery, and Amending Directive 95/16/EC (Recast). Available online: http://eur-lex.europa.eu/legal-content/EN/ TXT/?uri=uriserv:OJ.L_.2006.157.01.0024.01.ENG&toc=OJ:L:2006:157:TOC (accessed on 21 September 2016).
5. Carletti, E.; Pedrielli, F. From Noise Levels to Sound Quality: The Successful Approach to Improve the Acoustic Comfort. In *Noise Control, Reduction and Cancellation Solutions in Engineering*, 1st ed.; Siano, D., Ed.; InTech: Rijeka, Croatia, 2012; pp. 233–266. Available online: http://www.intechopen.com/books/noise-control-reduction-and-cancellation-solutions-in-engineering/ from-noise-levels-to-sound-quality-the-successful-approach-to-improve-the-acoustic-comfort (accessed on 21 September 2016).
6. Brambilla, G.; Carletti, E.; Pedrielli, F. Perspective of the sound quality approach applied to noise control in earth moving machines. *Int. J. Acoust. Vibr.* **2001**, *6*, 90–96. [CrossRef]

7. Carletti, E.; Casazza, C.; Pedrielli, F. Psychoacoustic characterisation of the noise at the operator position of a compact loader during real working conditions. In Proceedings of the 19th International Congress on Acoustics ICA, Madrid, Spain, 2–7 September 2007.

8. Pedrielli, F.; Carletti, E.; Casazza, C. Just noticeable differences of loudness and sharpness for earth moving machines. *J. Acoust. Soc. Am.* **2008**, *123*. [CrossRef]

9. Bowen, D.L.; Lyon, R.H. Mapping perceptual attributes of sound to product design choices. *Noise Control Eng. J.* **2003**, *51*, 271–279. [CrossRef]

10. Chatterley, J.J.; Blotter, J.D.; Sommerfeldt, S.D.; Leishman, T.W. Sound quality assessment of sewing machines. *Noise Control Eng. J.* **2006**, *54*, 212–220. [CrossRef]

11. Sottek, R.; Genuit, K. Sound quality evaluation of fan noise based on advanced hearing-related parameters. *Noise Control Eng. J.* **2009**, *57*, 384–390. [CrossRef]

12. Kang, J.; Hao, Y.; Yang, M.; Lavia, L. Soundscape evaluation and indicators for delivery sound environment. In Proceedings of the 22nd International Congress on Sound and Vibration ICSV22, Florence, Italy, 12–16 July 2015. Abstract Number 971.

13. Ih, J.-G.; Lim, D.-H.; Shin, S.-H.; Park, Y. Experimental design and assessment of product sound quality: Application to a vacuum cleaner. *Noise Control Eng. J.* **2003**, *51*, 244–252. [CrossRef]

14. Nor, M.J.M.; Fouladi, M.H.; Nahvi, H.; Ariffin, A.K. Index for vehicle acoustical comfort inside a passenger car. *Appl. Acoust.* **2008**, *69*, 343–353. [CrossRef]

15. Kim, E.-Y.; Shin, T.J.; Lee, S.-K. Sound quality index for assessment of sound quality of laser printers based on a combination of sound metrics. *Noise Control Eng. J.* **2013**, *61*, 534–546. [CrossRef]

16. Altinsoy, E.; Gül, M.; Kuyumcuoglu, A. Washing machine sound quality. In Proceedings of the 23rd International Congress on Sound and Vibration ICSV23, Athens, Greece, 28 September 2016. Abstract Number 868.

17. Khan, M.S.; Johansson, Ö.; Sundbäck, U. Development of an annoyance index for heavy-duty diesel engine noise using multivariate analysis. *Noise Control Eng. J.* **1997**, *45*, 157–167. [CrossRef]

18. Carletti, E.; Pedrielli, F.; Casazza, C. Development and validation of a numerical prediction model to estimate the annoyance condition at the operator station of compact loaders. *Int. J. Occup. Saf. Ergon. (JOSE)* **2011**, *17*, 233–240. [CrossRef] [PubMed]

19. Khan, M.S.; Dickson, C. Evaluation of sound quality of wheel loaders using a human subject for binaural recording. *Noise Control Eng. J.* **2002**, *50*, 117–126. [CrossRef]

20. Kendall, M.G.; Babington Smith, B. On the method of paired comparisons. *Biometrika* **1940**, *31*, 324–345. [CrossRef]

21. Kleinbaum, D.G.; Kupper, L.L.; Nizam, A.; Muller, K.E. *Applied Regression Analysis and Other Multivariable Methods*, 4th ed.; Duxbury Press: Belmont, CA, USA, 2007.

22. Dillon, W.R.; Goldstein, M. *Multivariate Analysis: Methods and Applications*, 1st ed.; John Wiley & Sons: New York, NY, USA, 1984.

23. Willemsen, A.M.; Poradek, F.; Rao, M.D. Reduction of noise in an excavator cabin using order tracking and ultrasonic leak detection. *Noise Control Eng. J.* **2009**, *57*, 400–412. [CrossRef]

24. Vardhan, H.; Karmakar, N.C.; Rao, Y.V. Experimental study of sources of noise from heavy earth-moving machinery. *Noise Control Eng. J.* **2005**, *53*, 37–42. [CrossRef]

25. Blauert, J.; Jekosch, U. Sound-quality evaluation—A multi-layered problem. *Acustica* **1997**, *83*, 747–753.

Chapter 2:
Building Acoustics and Room Acoustics

Review

A Review on Natural Ventilation-Enabling Façade Noise Control Devices for Congested High-Rise Cities

Shiu-Keung Tang

Department of Building Services Engineering, The Hong Kong Polytechnic University, Hong Kong, China;
shiu-keung.tang@polyu.edu.hk

Academic Editor: Tribikram Kundu
Received: 14 December 2016; Accepted: 6 February 2017; Published: 13 February 2017

Abstract: This review summarizes the current status of the research and development of natural ventilation-enabling noise control devices for use on the façades of high-rise residential buildings in congested cities. These devices are important for a sustainable urbanized city, as they are supposed to offer good acoustical protection to citizens, allowing for an acceptable level of natural ventilation inside residential units; energy for mechanical ventilation can then be saved. From the information presented in the existing literature, it is concluded that protrusive devices, such as lintels and balconies, are not effective noise screening devices, even if they are installed with sound absorbers and/or reflectors, under the effect of city reverberation. On the contrary, plenum windows and similar structures, which are plenum structures with a staggered air inlet and outlet, are interesting alternatives that are worth rigorous considerations.

Keywords: noise reduction; traffic noise; natural ventilation; building façade

1. Introduction

Excessive exposure to noise is hazardous to human health. Kang et al. [1] stated that, "prolonged exposure to noise, even at a level lower than statutory limits, can cause serious physiological and psychological symptoms". A recent report of the World Health Organization illustrates that noise has become the second most important environmental cause of death and disability in Western Europe [2]. Although no similar survey has been conducted outside of Europe, to the knowledge of the author, it is believed that noise pollution has become a worldwide problem.

The major source of noise pollution in a densely populated high-rise city, is ground traffic. However, controlling traffic noise exposure in such a city is never an easy task. It cannot be solved by simply migrating citizens, so that they live in sub-urban or even relatively rural areas, as the transportation network necessary for this migration will significantly disturb the originally quiet environment. Noise attenuation devices which are stronger than those used in the urban areas, may be required to reduce the annoying effect of the intrusive noises emitted by the relatively intermittent vehicles, in a low background noise environment [3]. Greenery views and sea views are able to moderate human noise annoyance responses [4–6]. It has also been found that the visibility of noise sources can affect human noise annoyance (for instance, Zhang et al. [7] and Aletta et al. [8]). However, such views cannot help when the traffic noise levels that have to be dealt with, can easily exceed 80 dBA.

Urban re-development, with the aim of creating residential spaces, is essential for a densely populated city with limited land that is suitable for residential purposes. However, such development is also making the, already very challenging noise control, even more challenging. This is because the targeted areas were not categorized for residential land use in the past and are mostly uninhabited, because of unacceptable noise levels. Since more and more people will be living in cities in the future [9], urban noise mitigation has become increasingly important in town planning. Effective noise mitigation measures urgently need to be developed.

Roadside noise barriers and enclosures are very common, as well as traditional noise mitigation measures [10]. They reduce the citizens' exposure to traffic noise by obstructing the direct-line-of-sight between the traffic and the residential units in their shadow zones. There have been extensive studies on their applications and performances (for instance [11,12]). However, these massive structures occupy relatively large pieces of land, in order to accommodate their foundations. Also, it is undesirable to build residential units close to a barrier because of the risk of an adverse standing acoustic wave setup [13], and air movement restrictions. A noise enclosure tends to trap noise energy, and thus, the areas in the proximity of its exits/entrances are not suitable for residential purposes, due to the strong noise radiation which is emitted from the enclosure [14]. Furthermore, the high construction and land costs make them very cost ineffective for attenuating noise. Besides, the barriers and enclosures may have adverse visual impacts, so they are not always welcomed by the citizens. Moreover, they cannot be adopted in urban re-development projects, due to the lack of space in these very congested areas.

Setbacks and extended podia [15] can help reduce noise exposure, but again, these measures tend to sacrifice buildable land areas and spaces, reducing the number of residential units that can theoretically be created. In a congested city, noise barriers, enclosures, setbacks, and extended podia, are therefore not desirable noise pollution solutions. The use of noise insensitive buildings as noise barriers, and a more careful street canyon design, have been proposed [15–17], but these approaches are also not easy to implement in a densely built environment, again due to the shortage of land.

Closing the windows of a residential unit is perhaps the most straight-forward way to prevent noise intrusion. However, this is achieved at the expense of natural ventilation, and therefore, fixed windows are not realistic options in modern practice, even when air conditioning/mechanical ventilation is provided. Double and triple glazed windows [18], and those equipped with mechanical ventilators [19], are very effective façade devices for noise reduction. However, these devices either do not allow for natural ventilation, or they have to consume energy to provide the necessary ventilation. When considering the concept of sustainability, they can not be the preferred noise mitigation measures. The development of a device/measure which can satisfactorily attenuate noise and, at the same time, allow for a reasonable level of natural ventilation, has become the focus in recent years. Noise attenuation and natural ventilation provision are, however, in conflict. Without an acceptable strategy, the number of new residential units that can be created during urbanization or urban re-development, will be largely limited.

De Salis et al. [20] presented a review on the noise control strategies for naturally ventilated buildings in 2002, and there have been many updates on this topic since its publication. The present review summarizes the continuous effort made in recent years by the research community, to develop natural ventilation-enabling noise control devices that can be installed at, or near to, openings on the façade of a high-rise building. For the sake of completeness, relevant devices reviewed by De Salis et al. [20] are also included and updated. Section 2 discusses the acoustical performance of these devices. It is followed by a discussion on their limitations and future challenges, in Section 3. Section 4 concludes this review.

2. Natural Ventilation-Enabling Façade Noise Control Devices

The traffic noise reduction performance of the devices is the main concern of this review. Figure 1 shows the shapes of two commonly adopted traffic noise spectra [21,22], and some examples of those measured in-situ at building façades located between 10 m to 20 m above busy trunk roads, recorded by the author during busy traffic hours. Although the traffic noise spectral content varies between studies, it is believed that the shapes of these spectra within the most important frequency bands are somewhat similar. Normalized traffic noise spectra are presented here, as they are recommended by the international standard for quantifying the noise reduction property of a frequency-sensitive device [21].

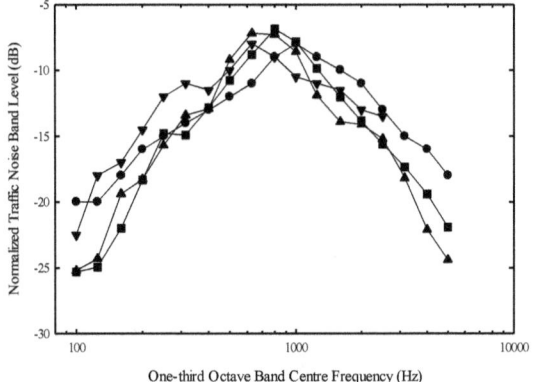

Figure 1. Examples of normalized traffic noise spectra. ●: EN1793-3 [21]; ▼: Delany et al. [22]; ■: in-situ measurement 1; ▲: in-situ measurement 2.

2.1. Fins, Lintels, Screens, and Similar Protrusions

The protrusions on the façade of a building next to a noisy road act as sound barriers and protect the windows behind them. Figure 2 illustrates the various forms of these devices which have previously been proposed by a number of researchers. As it is possible to open the windows, natural ventilation can be achieved. For a single apparatus of protrusion, the acoustical insulation may be calculated using the reduction in the view angle of the road seen by the receiver (windows/openings), as suggested in CRTN [23]. However, for a vertical fin, the protection will be largely limited because of the reflection by this fin, unless appropriate sound absorption is installed. When a window is located between two vertical fins, this situation is even worse, because of the multiple reflections between the fins. Janczu et al. [24] numerically illustrated the noise distribution within a vertical re-entrant region of a high-rise building facing a parallel road. The channel-like dual-fin structure resembles a re-entrant region, which tends to direct the noise energy to the upper floors. The maximum traffic noise protection which can be offered by a vertical fin, even with sound absorption, is believed to be less than 3 dB.

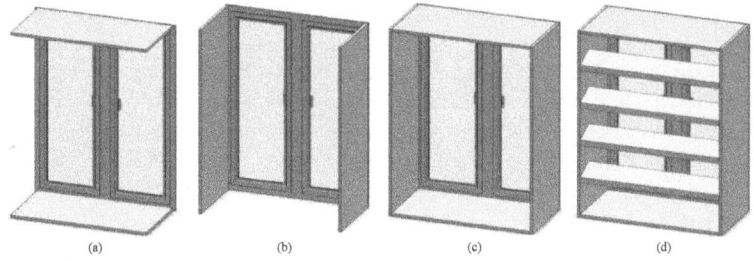

Figure 2. Examples of protrusive devices (excluding balconies). (**a**) Lintels; (**b**) vertical fins; (**c**) eaves; (**d**) eaves with louvers.

Lintels installed on building façades are horizontal canopies, as well as sound barriers when noise sources are located below them. Thus, they can theoretically help screen traffic noise. Tadeu et al. [25] numerically studied the sound attenuation achieved by the installation of thin rigid horizontal screens on building façades. The effect of the shapes of these screens on the acoustical protection was also examined. It was found that a circumference-arc-shaped screen performed better than a straight inclined screen, in terms of the acoustical protection, provided that the locations of the edges were unchanged. However, the screens were not found to be useful at the lower floors of a high-rise building, where the reflection from the screen of the immediate upper floor was significant enough to erase the sound barrier effect of the lower screen. Therefore, sound absorption needs to be installed on the reflecting surfaces of the screens [26]. However, these screens are not effective noise control devices when compared to balconies [27] (discussed later).

Eaves and louvers on the façade of a building can help reduce solar heat gain by providing shade. Sakamoto et al. [28] investigated the acoustical protection of different types of eaves and louvers, using scale model experiments. Similar to the results of the screens discussed above, the horizontal eaves/louvers did not provide meaningful acoustical protection, unless the sound incidence angle was large. Vertical louvers behaved in a similar way to vertical fins, and were less effective than the horizontal ones. Sound absorption was required in order to improve the overall acoustical performance (corresponding sound absorption coefficients were not provided). Sakamoto et al. [28] showed that the insertion losses of eaves, louvers, and their combinations, ranged from 1 to 10 dB. However, the sound incidence angle has to be as large as 80° for the insertion loss to be higher than 4 dB. Martello et al. [29] showed that the installation of sound absorption (7 mm thick polyurethane conglomerate of density 70 kg/m^3) onto the solar shading louvers, could help reduce the noise level by ~5 to 6 dB in the high frequency range (1.6 kHz to 5 kHz), when compared to those without absorption, for the case of a commercial building.

It should be noted that the above studies were completed without considering the reflections from neighbourhood buildings. In a congested city, the street canyon effect results in considerable city reverberation [30]. The acoustical protection of the abovementioned protrusions will be much reduced in the presence of random incident noises. However, recent research results show that external shading devices, like louvers, can help manipulate the various psycho-acoustical parameters [31]. This has a potential implication for future nuisance reduction strategies. Further research into this issue would be meaningful.

2.2. Resonant Devices

The use of resonators and similar devices, in conjunction with louvers and wall openings, has been proposed for attenuating external noise intrusion into indoor living environments. However, research in this direction has not been popular, mainly because of the limitations of these devices.

One example of these resonant devices is the tube array ventilator proposed by Field [32]. These tubes act as quarter wavelength resonators, which are able to stop the sound transmission by concerted resonance [33]. In his experiment, Field found that the weighted sound reduction index of his proposed device was around 22 dB. However, the proposed ventilator occupied a large area of the opening and was quite bulky, for improved broadband performance. Also, the ventilator opening size was small, and thus, the air speed inside the ventilator air passage will only be high enough to generate aerodynamic noise if a sufficient ventilation rate is achieved. Besides, the ventilator was oblique to light, so additional window glazing needs to be installed for daylight utilization.

Asakura et al. [34] investigated the use of a long duct-like ventilation shaft on the top of a fixed window glazing for sound attenuation. Resonators and coupled cavities (created by parallel fins) were installed inside the ventilation shaft, in order to improve its broadband sound attenuation performance. The difference between the noise levels across the corresponding fixed window was about 20 dB, which was just a few decibels above that of a closed window. Although the noise reduction was high, the small shaft openings, and the very long and narrow shaft design, results in unsatisfactory natural ventilation.

Nguyen et al. [35] studied the improvement of sound transmission loss across louvers/ventilation grilles, by installing cavity resonators inside the air passages within the louvers/grilles. These cavities had two openings for air penetration. The effects of their relative orientations on the sound attenuation were examined. These authors also predicted the corresponding sound transmission losses, by solving the wave equation. The sound attenuation of their prototypes varied between 2 and 9 dB, from the 500 Hz to the 8 kHz one-third octave bands. The performances of these devices at lower frequencies were not presented.

2.3. Balconies

A balcony on the façade of a building can provide an extended outdoor area with functionality, which cannot be achieved by indoor living spaces [36], and is very often welcomed by the residents. A balcony blocks the direct line-of-sight of a ground noise source from the receiver, while natural ventilation is possible. It has therefore attracted the attention of many researchers in the past few decades. A description of the various common balcony forms can be found in Tang [27]. These balcony forms are shown in Figure 3, for easy reference. The balcony was once regarded as a green design in terms of noise protection, but it is now understood that its acoustical protection is not obvious.

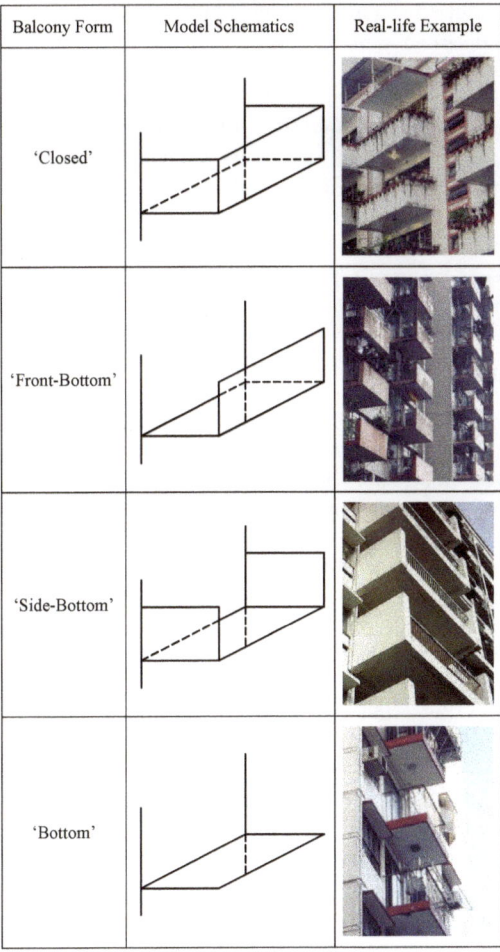

Figure 3. Common forms of high-rise building balconies (extracted from Tang [27]). Copyright Acoustical Society of America, 2005.

In an open space with a noise source on the ground, a standalone balcony on a building façade provides significant acoustical protection to the areas beyond it. Mohsen and Oldham [37] carried out a detailed experimental investigation, using a 1:10 scale model, to study the effects of source orientation, balcony form (in terms of depth and with and without parapet), window opening size, and locations, on the acoustical protection. On average, a ~5 dB insertion loss was recorded for a closed form balcony. Oldham and Mohsen [38] have also completed a theoretical analysis on the acoustical protection of a standalone balcony on a building façade.

Additionally, Oldham and Mohsen [39] suggested the use of a recessed building form for acoustical protection. The proposed recessed building form consisted of balconies arranged in the form of a terrace, reducing the jeopardizing reflection from the balcony ceiling, onto the windows or openings behind the balcony. The measured traffic noise reduction increased from ~5 dB at a very small effective path difference, to ~14 dB at an effective path difference of 1 m [39]. However, a recessed building form is not practical for a congested city, as it will largely reduce the number of residential units that can theoretically be built.

May [40] has performed a field measurement within the balconies of a high-rise building located next to a highway. Although a direct measurement of the balcony insertion loss could not be taken, his results show that the reflection from the balcony ceiling, as well as the multiple reflections within the balcony, can largely offset the noise screening effect of the balcony. Sound absorption is thus needed before a balcony on a high-rise building façade can be used as a noise screening device.

Conventional courtyards have high solid walls without ceilings, and thus, can offer high acoustical protection. Hammad and Gibbs [41,42] investigated the resultant acoustical protection when thnadners and splitters were applied to the courtyard wall, and the balcony front parapet facing the road traffic. A thnadner is a kind of shaped noise barrier [43]. For the courtyard cases, the use of a thnadner and splitter was shown to not significantly affect the acoustical protection, when compared to a solid wall, except at floor levels close to the ground/source. Hammad and Gibbs [41] showed that the protection of a courtyard with a thnadner ranged from 8 to 26 dB, depending on the depth of the courtyard and the height of the courtyard above the ground. The corresponding protection for the splitter cases, varied between 10 dB and 27 dB. Although the protection appears quite high, these devices have adverse effects on the natural ventilation. The multiple reflections inside a balcony with a ceiling tended to reduce the protection by ~3 dB, as shown by Hammad and Gibbs [42].

Recently, Tang [27,44] used a 3-storey scale model to study the effects of common high-rise building balcony forms on the acoustical insertion losses. The width-to-depth ratios of the adopted balconies were all 2:1. The source orientation, elevation angle, and source distance, were found to be well correlated to the insertion losses. Empirical formulae for the insertion loss prediction were also provided. Owing to the reflection of the balcony ceiling, noise amplification was found at an elevation angle of 30°, for all of the balcony forms tested, when the source was arranged parallel to the building façade. An even stronger amplification of ~2 dB could be recorded when the source was arranged parallel or perpendicular to the façade, when the elevation angle was further reduced to 15°. This was also the angle at which the horizontal canopy/screen failed to provide any acoustical protection. El-Dien [45] has also carried out a similar study with a standalone multi-storey building, using both a scale model and ray-tracing technique. A closed form balcony with a floor width-to-depth ratio of 5:1 was chosen, and noise reductions of 0.4 to 5 dB could be achieved. One should note that the noise reduction in El-Dien's study [44] was defined as the noise level difference between the parallel and non-parallel cases.

Furthermore, there have been efforts attempting to improve the acoustical protection of balconies. The installation of sound absorption appears to be the most straight-forward method. Although May [40] indicated that sound absorption (NRC 0.80) could help, the resulting balcony insertion losses in his study were not known, as the associated balconies could not be removed. Hothersall et al. [46] has carried out a two-dimensional simulation to study the effect of sound absorption on the insertion loss of balconies on a multi-storey building next to a road. The absorption adopted was a 100 mm thick fibrous material, with a flow resistance of 20,000 Ns·m^{-4}. In their simulations, the locations for sound absorption installation were the balcony ceiling, the rear wall, the internal surface of the parapet, and the building façade surface facing the road. It was found that the sound absorption installed on the balcony ceiling, was more effective in improving the balcony insertion loss, than those installed at the back of the front parapet and the rear wall. The simulated insertion loss ranged from 5 to 10 dB. The maximum elevation angle in their study was ~60°. Kropp and Bérillon [47] further confirmed the improvement of balcony insertion losses by the installation of sound absorption in the balcony void. The absorption used was a 15 mm thick fibrous material. Their results are basically in-line with those of Hothersall et al. [46], and illustrate that the balcony ceiling and the rear wall are the most effective locations for installing sound absorption. Their results also show that the insertion loss of their model balcony, when installed with sound absorption, ranged from 4 to 7 dB.

A full scale experimental study on the insertion loss of a balcony-like structure in the presence of sound absorption, has been completed by Tong et al. [48], inside a dual-chamber laboratory facility built for the ISO140-3 test. High density 1-inch thick fibreglass was used as the sound absorption. The sound source was a ~4 m long loudspeaker array, and the sound incidence angle was ~23°. They found that the balcony ceiling was the most appropriate location for the installation of the artificial sound absorption, in order to improve the broadband insertion loss. This conclusion is similar to that of Hothersall et al. [46]. However, the side walls were found to be the second best location for such installation. The maximum insertion loss was 7 dB. Tong et al. [48] also indicated the importance of acoustic modes in shaping the insertion loss spectra.

The effects of the shapes of a balcony ceiling and parapet on the sound insertion loss, have also attracted the attention of many researchers. El-Dien and Woloszyn [49,50] studied this using the pyramid tracing method, as well as a scale model, to show how the balcony ceiling's inclination and depth, and the front parapet design, could all affect the overall balcony sound insertion loss. They observed that the balcony insertion loss showed an increasing trend with increasing balcony depth. However, the effect of floor height on the insertion loss did not show a well-defined trend, most probably because of the "incident angle sensitive" reflections; the ceiling inclination angle also resulted in no trend being indentified. The balcony insertion loss was found to vary between 0.5 to 6 dB. However, the maximum insertion loss found was 2, 4, and 6 dB, for a balcony depth of 1 m, 2 m, and 3 m, respectively, when the front parapet remained vertical [49]. It was also found that an inclined front parapet could result in an additional 0.5 to 4 dB noise attenuation [50]. However, a 3 m deep balcony is by no means common in a congested high-rise city.

Lee et al. [51] illustrated the combined effects of the ceiling inclination, sound absorption, and front parapet design, on reducing the noise inside a high-rise building balcony, using a 1:50 sixteen-storey scale model building and simulations. They used 3 mm thick dense polystyrene as the sound absorption material. They found that the noise reduction could be as high as 23 dB. It should be noted that the noise reduction defined by Lee et al. [51] was the difference in the noise level inside the balcony, with and with the abovementioned special treatments. However, there was only one measurement on the rear wall of the balcony, and thus, the uncertainty in their study could be high. Kan et al. [52] summarized an experience of improving the balcony insertion loss by using sound absorption (NRC 0.60) and a small inclined screen at the balcony edge. A real 40-storey building next to a busy traffic trunk road was chosen for their study. The measured insertion losses with sound absorption installed on the ceiling and side-walls, were within 4 to 5 dB.

In general, sound absorption is not preferred by the users, due to the difficulty in maintaining it. Ishizuka and Fujiwara [53] proposed the use of specially designed hard surface reflectors on the balcony ceiling, in order to reflect incident noise back into open space. The amount of transmitted acoustical energy was thus reduced. By using a site measurement, they showed that the reflectors, when properly oriented, could provide an additional noise reduction of 7 to 10 dB, when compared to that which can be achieved by a conventional balcony. However, the reflectors have to be carefully designed and positioned. A large ceiling height is also required.

It can be concluded that balconies on a high-rise building do not offer much acoustical protection, unless sound absorption and/or proper ceiling reflectors can be installed. However, reverberation within the street canyons of a high-rise city will largely erase the acoustical protection of the balconies. Nash et al. [54] further illustrated that there would be a drop in speech intelligibility inside the balcony of a high-rise building located within a street canyon, after the installation of sound absorption.

2.4. Active Noise Control

The technique of active noise control, which uses a secondary sound to cancel unwanted noise, has been successfully implemented in confined areas (for instance, Trinder and Nelson [55]). Such a system has also been proposed for controlling the noise intrusion into a building's interior, through a ventilation opening [56]. Kwon and Park [57] carried out numerical simulation and experiments, in order to study the effectiveness of an active window system in reducing the noise intrusion through an opened window. Their system consisted of outdoor reference microphones and secondary sources at the window edge facing the building interior. With the appropriate acoustic transfer functions known, no error sensor was required, and the overall sound attenuation between 400 Hz to 1 kHz in their study, could be as high as 10 dB. However, such a system may not work properly when the building interior is occupied. The transfer functions first have to be determined. The outdoor wind condition can also affect the active control performance.

An acoustic shield design was proposed by Nishimura et al [58]. The idea was to use secondary sources in the ventilation opening, to protect against the intruding sound. In their experiment, a maximum noise reduction of 10 dB was observed within the frequency range of 500 Hz to 2 kHz. However, the sizes of the control sources were quite large, resulting in a relatively large blockage of the ventilation opening. In conclusion, an active control technique is not often adopted in residential buildings, probably because of system complexity, maintenance issues, and an uncertain reliability, due to the constantly varying living environmental conditions, both indoors and outdoors.

2.5. Plenum Windows/Double-Wall Structures with Staggered Air Inlet and Outlet

Although double glazing windows do not allow for natural ventilation, a partially opened one will allow for some degree of air movement across it, while the sound transmission loss may still be acceptable. Ford and Kerry [59] carried out a series of tests on the sound transmission losses across slightly opened double glazing windows. The two window openings in their experiment were staggered, and the air gap between the two window glass panes formed an air passage. A window design with a width of 2.4 m, a window frame separation of 200 mm, and an opening size of 30 mm, could provide a 9 dB higher traffic noise reduction than an opened single window.

Although the 30 mm opening width of Ford and Kerry [59] is far too small for meaningful natural ventilation, this window type has recently attracted attention. It is now commonly referred to as a ventilation window or plenum window [60,61] (hereinafter referred to as plenum window). This device is a double-walled (usually glass panes) plenum structure, with a staggered air inlet and outlet. The plenum window can be categorized into the horizontal and vertical type, according to the orientation of the openings, as shown in Figure 4. However, the corresponding noise reduction mechanisms are basically the same. In order to provide meaningful air movement across the window for acceptable natural ventilation, the sizes of the openings have to be increased. Søndergaard and Legarth [62] conducted both laboratory and site tests on an air supply window in Denmark. Their window type was of the vertical plenum window type, without sound absorption material. The opening sizes of their vents, though larger than those of Ford and Kerry [59], were still small compared to the physical length of the window, probably because of the Scandinavian climate. The corresponding noise reduction $R_w + C_{tr}$ ranged from 16 to 24 dB. However, such a window design is not suitable for use in tropical or sub-tropical regions. Bajraktari et al. [63] showed that their double-facade system, which was basically a plenum window setup, could offer a noise reduction, R_w, of between 18 to 26 dB, when no sound absorption material was applied.

A parametric study on the sound insertion loss of a horizontal type plenum window was carried out by Tong and Tang [61], using 1:4 scale model experiments. The effect of the window orientation, relative to the sound source, θ, was also tested. Their results show that, for a fixed overall window width L, the insertion loss of a plenum window generally increased with increasing overlapping length G, but decreased with increasing window opening sizes (W_1 and W_2), or gap width D. In their study, the overall window width, L, equals $G + W_1 + W_2$ and $W_1 = W_2 = W$. The maximum and minimum traffic noise insertion loss increases, achieved by replacing an opened casement window with a plenum window of the same overall window size, where $0.1 \leq G/L \leq 0.2$, $0.1 \leq W/L \leq 0.5$ and $-90° \leq \theta \leq 90°$ were 15 dB and 5 dB, respectively. The maximum insertion loss was recorded within $-30° \leq \theta \leq 30°$, while the minimum wasrecorded at $\theta = -90°$ or $90°$. The effect of the window height was not examined, as this height should be more or less fixed in practice.

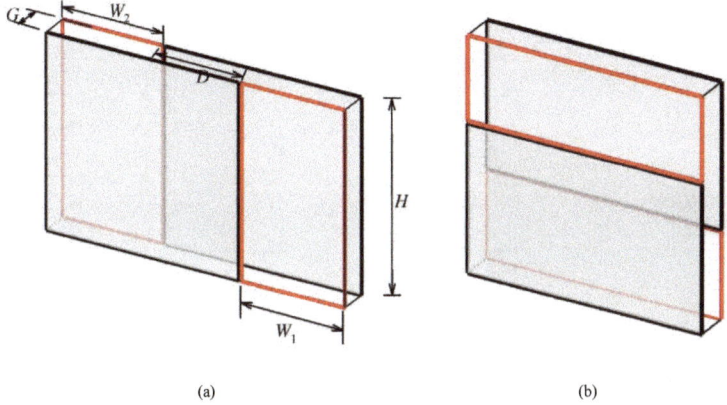

(a)   (b)

Figure 4. Basic plenum window schematics and nomenclature. (**a**) Horizontal type; (**b**) vertical type. Red lines: boundaries of window openings; grey shaded areas: glass panes.

The insertion losses of the horizontal type plenum windows were further tested using a site mockup, whose façade was next to and parallel to a busy trunk road [64]. In this mockup, two side-by-side standard residential units of a Hong Kong public housing estate, were constructed. One of them was equipped with plenum windows, while the other represented normal provision (side-hung casement windows). Measurements inside and outside these units were conducted simultaneously, such that the acoustical benefit of replacing the side-hung casement windows with plenum windows, could be estimated in-situ. Figure 5 illustrates the dimensions of the two plenum windows tested. The insertion losses of both the individual plenum windows and their combined version, were measured. The results, after correcting for the room reverberation effect, show that there was an additional 7 to 9 dB traffic noise reduction when adopting plenum windows. The gap widths of these windows were small, at 175 mm, but the computed natural ventilation rate met the local statutory requirement of 1.5 air-change per hour.

Furthermore, there have been proposals for improving the insertion loss of a plenum window. Kang and Brocklesby [60] conducted a detailed experimental investigation on the benefit of using micro-perforated absorbers in acoustic chambers. Many different ways of installing the micro-perforated absorber were included. Their results suggest that the application of micro-perforated absorbers inside a plenum window air gap, could increase the average sound level difference (arithmetic average from 500 to 8000 Hz) across a plenum window, by approximately 2 to 6 dB. The extent of this improvement increased with an increasing gap width, and the average sound level differences ranged from ~29 to 33 dB. The spectral average sound level differences roughly varied between 15 to 40 dB, within the 125 Hz to 8 kHz one-third octave bands. Their results also indicate that an air speed of 2 m/s inside the air passage did not affect the noise reduction capacity of the plenum windows.

Another example has been produced by Kang and Li [65], who carried out finite-element simulations in an attempt to further understand the sound transmission characteristics of plenum windows. Apart from the effect of sound absorption lining on the glass panes, discussed in Kang and Brocklesby [60], it was found that sound absorptive louvers and a hood, hung at the outdoor opening, could significantly improve the noise reduction performance of the windows. Their computed spectral sound level differences roughly varied between 22 to 50 dB, within the 125 Hz to 1 kHz one-third octave bands, in the presence of absorptive louvers. The hood resulted in spectral sound level differences which fluctuated between 8 to 40 dB. In general, the longer the vertical hood length was, the higher the sound level difference was. However, the resonance significantly affected the shapes of the sound level difference spectra.

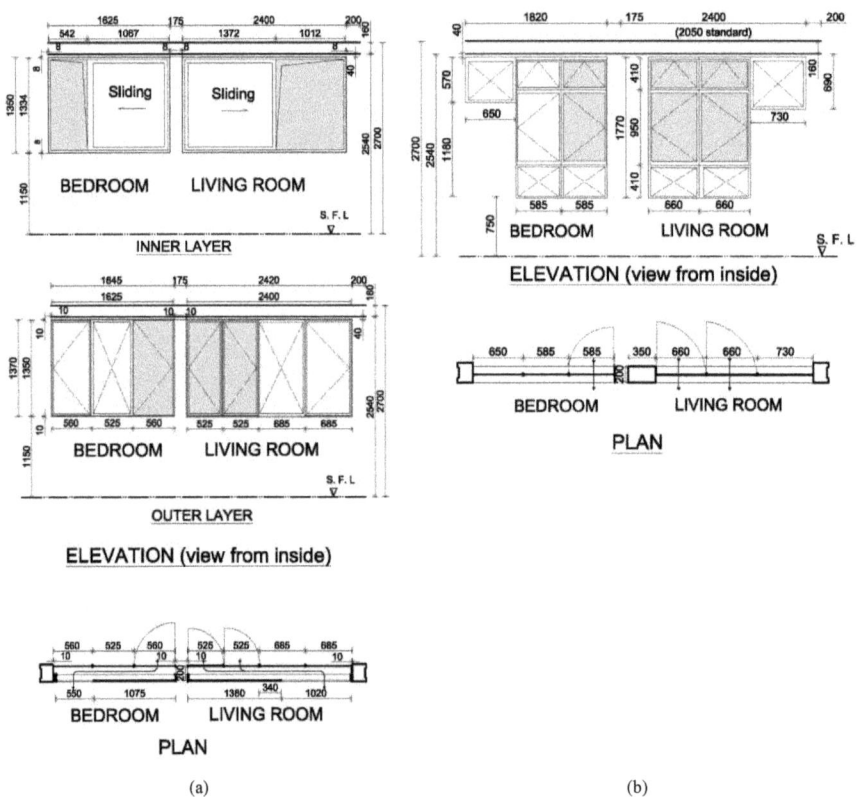

(a)   (b)

Figure 5. Dimensions and configurations of the plenum windows and casement windows tested previously by the author (extracted from [64]). (**a**) Plenum windows; (**b**) casement windows. Copyright Elsevier, 2015.

Site measurement, involving a vertical plenum window, was pursued at a student hostel in Hong Kong, in order to investigate the acoustical benefit that could be achieved by lining sound absorption over the different internal surfaces of a plenum window [66]. The dimensions of the tested window were similar to those of Kang and Brocklesby [60]. The sound absorption materials used were two-inch thick high density fibreglass (NRC 1.00), and micro-perforated absorbers with a 50 mm air gap between them and the glass panes (NRC 0.45). Without any additional sound absorption inside the window, the difference between the average indoor sound level and that at 1 m from the outer glass pane, was 19 dB. The maximum improvement in noise reduction was 23 dB, which was achieved with all of the concrete/tile surfaces, when the outer surface of the indoor window glass pane was lined with the fibreglass and micro-perforated absorbers.

Tang [67] further studied how the noise reduction of the plenum window of Tang [66] would be affected by tilting the indoor glass pane, using a 1:4 scale model. Owing to the limited gap width, the tilt angles could only be varied from −5° to 5°. The source was arranged parallel to the model façade, and no sound absorption was applied. The effects of the sound incident angle (7° to 35°) were also examined. It was found that the direction of tilting had no significant effect on the noise reduction. The noise reduction improvement varied from 0 to 4 dB.

More recently, Lee [68] discussed the sound transmission loss of, and the air ventilation across, double-skin curtain façades. He also computed the air temperature distributions inside the curtain wall cavities. This design can be regarded as a plenum window of a much larger physical dimension than those discussed above. Glass fins could be installed within the air cavities of these structures. The sound transmission class (STC) of the tested curtain walls ranged from 30 to 40, depending on the air cavity width and the fin thickness.

There have also been efforts to explore the use of active noise control for the improvement of plenum window noise reduction. Through the use of scale model experiments, Huang et al. [69] showed that the control was only satisfactory at frequencies below the cut-on frequency of the first odd mode in the gap direction. They found that there was a 20 dB additional noise reduction when the active control was applied. Qiu et al. [70] built a prototype plenum window, with a window cavity that was divided into two rectangular channels, using a horizontal glass pane to test the performance of the active noise control. They showed that their active control system could improve the noise reduction by an average of 12 dB, over a frequency range of 200 to 800 Hz. Tang et al. [71] carried out a full-scale model active control test with a horizontal plenum window and a single compact primary source, in the laboratory. They found that two secondary loudspeakers, installed symmetrically above the horizontal plenum window centreline, inside the window directly facing the incoming sound, were sufficient enough to provide the control. In addition, they indicated that a better active control performance could be achieved when the receiver room was less reverberant. However, the additional noise reduction due to the active control was found to be limited to below 5 dB, except at some individual frequencies, at which the noise reduction was above 10 dB. In addition, as in the study of Huang et al. [69], noise reduction improvement could only be found at frequencies below the first gap mode cut-on.

The performance of a plenum window is, in general, not affected by city reverberation. However, the air movement, and thus the associated natural ventilation effectiveness, largely depend on the availability of outdoor wind. The current window design tested by the author may thus not be applicable in areas where the air is stuffy for most of the year. Also, the level of natural ventilation depends on the possibility of cross ventilation inside the residential units equipped with plenum windows.

3. Remarks and Current Challenges

Table 1 summarizes the performance of the natural ventilation-enabling noise control devices, reviewed in Section 2. Their limitations are also reviewed. It can be seen that protrusive devices, such as lintels, eaves, fins, and balconies, are not effective noise screening devices for use in a congested high-rise living environment. Active noise control systems and resonance-based devices are also not desirable noise control solutions.

Table 1. Acoustical Performances of Natural Ventilation-enabling Noise Control Devices.

Device	Indicative References	Noise Reduction	Comments and Remarks
Fins, lintels, screens and similar protrusions	Janczu et al. [24]	3 dB max.	Not suitable for use in high-rise buildings unless significant sound absorption and/or reflectors can be installed at appropriate locations.
	Tadeu et al. [25]	−0.2–7 dB at 1 kHz	Performance can be affected by sound incidence angle and relative orientations of the windows to noise sources.
	Sakamoto et al. [28]	1 to 10 dB, but sound incidence angle has to be as large as 80° for the insertion loss to be higher than 4 dB	
	Martello et al. [29]	Façade sound insulation index (window closed): 20 to −40 dB from 100 to 5 kHz 1/3 octave bands	City reverberation will reduce noise reduction capacities.
Resonant devices	Field [32]	$R_w = 22$ dB	Bulky device. Tends to block air ventilation passage Not suitable for congested cities
	Asakura et al. [34]	Noise level difference between two sides of the associated window: ~20 dB	
	Nguyen et al. [35]	2–9 dB, 500 Hz to 8 kHz octave bands	
	Mohsen and Oldham [37]	~5 dB traffic noise insertion loss on average for a closed form balcony	Massive structures, but relatively weak noise reduction.
	Oldham and Mohsen [39]	Traffic noise reduction: −5 dB—14 dB for recessed building	Not suitable for use in high-rise buildings unless significant sound absorption and/or reflectors can be installed at appropriate locations.
	Hammad and Gibbs [41]	Courtyard with thmadner: 8–26 dBCourtyard with splitter: 10–27 dB	Floor height limits the use of reflectors in many cases.
	El-Dien [45]	Closed form balcony: 0.4–5 dB	Performance is affected by sound incidence angle and relative orientation of the windows to noise sources.
Balconies	Hothersall et al. [46]	Insertion loss: 5–10 dB (2D simulation)	City reverberation will reduce noise reduction capacities.
	Kropp and Bérillon [47]	Insertion loss: 4–7 dB	Use of sound absorption will lower down speech intelligibility inside balconies.
	Tong et al. [48]	Insertion loss: 7 dB max.	Courtyard/recessed building design could result in poor natural ventilation. Less number of residential units can be built.
	El-Dien and Wolnszyn [49,50]	Insertion loss: 0.5–6 dB	
	Kan et al. [52]	Insertion loss: 4–5 dB	
	Ishizuka and Fujiwara [53]	7–10 dB higher noise reduction than conventional balconies	
Active noise control	Kwon and Park [57]	10 dB max., 400 Hz to 1 kHz	Active control installation usually results in bulky systems. Tends to block air ventilation passage in some cases.
	Nishimura et al. [58]	10 dB max., 500 Hz to 2 kHz	Its effectiveness is affected by parameters which cannot be controlled. Not reliable for building façade application.
Plenum windows/ Double-wall plenum structures with staggered air inlet and outlet	Kang and Brocklesby [60]	Average sound level differences across window: −29–33 dB	Able to provide noise protection and enable reasonable natural ventilation.
	Tong and Tang [61]	Traffic noise insertion loss: 5–15 dB	Can be used together with the above devices or other measures for enhanced noise screening performance.
	Søndergaard and Legarth [62]	$R_w + C_{tr}$: 16–24 dB	Performance can be affected by sound incidence angle and relative orientation of the windows to noise sources.
	Bajraktari et al. [63]	R_{gl}: 18–26 dB	Performance is not much affected by city reverberation.
	Tong et al. [64]	Traffic noise insertion loss: 7–9 dB	Have rooms for further improvements and research
	Tang [66]	Traffic noise level differences across window: 19–23 dB	
	Lee [[68]]	Plenums with fin: STC 30–40	

On the contrary, double-wall plenum structures with a staggered air inlet and outlet, especially the plenum windows, are found to provide noise protection, and at the same time, allow air movement across them to enable natural ventilation. They can also be used together with other noise mitigation measures, such as sound absorbers and active noise control, for an enhanced noise reduction performance. Their performances are much less affected by city reverberation. All of these properties make this type of devices very useful for congested high-rise cities, especially those in tropical and sub-tropical climates. They have been attracting worldwide attention in recent years. Efforts have also been focused on the prediction of plenum window acoustical performances (for instance, Yu et al. [72]).

Plenum windows have been adopted in several housing estates in Hong Kong. However, as the less noisy areas are becoming increasingly inhabited, one has to work with more difficult sites. There are at least two questions to be answered. Can one obtain a stronger noise reduction without affecting the natural ventilation, or vice versa? And, can one improve both the natural ventilation and the noise reduction at the same time? Further studies for improving the acoustical performance of plenum windows are currently being carried out by the author.

4. Conclusions

A review has been pursued in an attempt to summarize the continuous efforts of researchers in the research and development of natural ventilation-enabling noise control devices. These devices have been proposed for use in high-rise buildings in congested cities with serious traffic noise pollution. This review also updates the relevant parts of a previous review completed in 2002 by another research team, with the addition of more recent information and new developments.

In general, protrusive devices, such as balconies, lintels, and fins, are not effective noise screening devices for high-rise buildings in congested cities, even when sound absorbers and/or reflectors are installed, due to city reverberation. Together with sound absorbers, they are only useful in semi-enclosed or open environmental conditions, where the multi-reflections from nearby buildings are either absent or insignificant. However, their screening effects are still limited, especially at lower floors which are closer to the ground traffic.

Active control installation and resonance-based devices usually result in bulky systems. The air ventilation passage can be seriously blocked in some cases. The active control effectiveness can also be affected by parameters which cannot be controlled, making such complicated systems unreliable for building façade application.

Plenum windows and other similar double-wall plenum structures with a staggered air inlet and outlet, are found to be useful as natural ventilation-enabling noise control devices, on building façades in the tropical and sub-tropical climatic regions. Based on the results in existing literature and the experience of the author and others, this window type should be useful in high-rise environments, even when considerable city reverberation exists. They have been adopted in several housing projects in Hong Kong. However, since one has to work with more extreme sites in the near future, as the less nosy sites will gradually be used up, it is time to start investigating the ways to improve both the noise reduction of, and the air movement across, these plenum structures.

Acknowledgments: This review study is financial supported by The Research Grant Council, The Hong Kong Special Administration Region Government under Project number GRF 152164/15E.

Conflicts of Interest: The author declares no conflict of interest.

References

1. Kang, J.; Chourmouziadou, K.; Sakantamis, K.; Wang, B.; Hao, Y. *Soundscape of European Cities and Landscapes*; COST-TD0804; Soundscape-COST: Oxford, UK, 2013.
2. Burden of Disease from Environmental Noise. *Quantification of Healthy Life Years Lost in Europe*; World Health Organization: Bonn, Germany, 2011.
3. Scholes, W.E. Traffic noise criteria. *Appl. Acoust.* **1970**, *3*, 1–21. [CrossRef]

4. Li, H.N.; Chau, C.K.; Tang, S.K. Can surrounding greenery reduce noise annoyance at home? *Sci. Total Environ.* **2010**, *408*, 4376–4384. [CrossRef] [PubMed]

5. Dzhambov, A.M.; Dimitrova, D.D. Green spaces and environmental noise perception. *Urban For. Urban Green.* **2015**, *14*, 1000–1008. [CrossRef]

6. Van Renterghem, T.; Botteldooren, D. View on outdoor vegetation reduces noise annoyance for dwellers near busy roads. *Landsc. Urban Plan.* **2016**, *148*, 203–215. [CrossRef]

7. Zhang, B.; Shi, L.; Di, G. The influence of the visibility of the source on the subjective annoyance due to its noise. *Appl. Acoust.* **2003**, *64*, 1205–1215.

8. Aletta, F.; Masullo, M.; Maffei, L.; Kang, J. The effect of vision on the perception of the noise produced by a chiller in a common living environment. *Noise Control Eng. J.* **2016**, *64*, 363–378. [CrossRef]

9. *World Urbanization Prospects: The 2014 Revision, Highlights*; Department of Economic and Home Affairs, United Nations, 2014.

10. Kurze, U.J.; Anderson, G.S. Sound attenuation by barriers. *Appl. Acoust.* **1971**, *4*, 35–53. [CrossRef]

11. Okubo, T.; Fujiwara, K. Efficiency of a noise barrier on the ground with an acoustically soft cylinder edge. *J. Sound Vib.* **1998**, *216*, 771–790. [CrossRef]

12. Hart, C.R.; Lau, S.K. Active noise control with linear control source and sensor arrays for a noise barrier. *J. Sound Vib.* **2012**, *331*, 15–26. [CrossRef]

13. Li, K.M.; Tang, S.H. The predicted barrier effects in the proximity of tall buildings. *J. Acoust. Soc. Am.* **2003**, *114*, 821–832. [CrossRef] [PubMed]

14. Takagi, K.; Miyake, T.; Yamamoto, K.; Tachibana, H. Prediction of road traffic noise around tunnel mouth. In Proceedings of the 29th International Congress and Exhibition on Noise Control Engineering, Nice, France, 27–30 August 2000.

15. *Hong Kong Planning Standard and Guidelines*; Environmental Protection Department, The HKSAR Government: Hong Kong, China, 1990.

16. Öhrström, E.; Skånberg, A.; Svensoon, H.; Gidlöf-Gunnarsson, A. Effects of road traffic noise and the benefit of access to quietness. *J. Sound Vib.* **2006**, *295*, 40–59. [CrossRef]

17. Echevarria Sanchez, G.M.; van Renterghem, T.; Thomas, P.; Botteldooren, D. The effect of street canyon design on traffic noise exposure along roads. *Build. Environ.* **2016**, *97*, 96–110. [CrossRef]

18. Tadeu, A.J.B.; Mateus, D.M.R. Sound transmission through single, double and triple glazing. Experimental evaluation. *Appl. Acoust.* **2001**, *62*, 307–325. [CrossRef]

19. Asdrubali, F.; Buratti, C. Sound intensity investigation of the acoustics performances of high insulation ventilating windows integrated with rolling shutter boxes. *Appl. Acoust.* **2005**, *66*, 1088–1101. [CrossRef]

20. De Salis, M.H.F.; Oldham, D.J.; Sharples, S. Noise control strategies for naturally ventilated buildings. *Build. Environ.* **2002**, *37*, 471–484. [CrossRef]

21. BS EN1793-3. *Road Traffic Noise Reducing Devices—Test Methods for Determining the Acoustic Performance—Part 3. Normalized Traffic Noise Spectrum*; ISO: London, UK, 1998.

22. Delany, M.E.; Rennie, A.J.; Collins, K.M. *Scale Model Investigation of Traffic Noise Propagation*; National Physical Laboratory: Teddington, UK, 1972.

23. Department of Transport, Welsh Office. *Calculation of Road Traffic Noise*; HMSO: London, UK, 1988.

24. Janczu, J.; Walerian, E.; Czechowicz, M. Façade shaping as local means protecting against traffic noise. *Acta Acust. United Acust.* **2011**, *97*, 769–778. [CrossRef]

25. Tadeu, A.; Antónia, J.; Amado Mendes, L.; Godinho, L. Sound pressure level attenuation provided by thin rigid screens coupled to tall buildings. *J. Sound Vib.* **2007**, *304*, 479–496. [CrossRef]

26. Szokolay, S.V. *Introduction to Architectural Science: The Basis of Sustainable Design*; Architectural Press: Oxford, UK, 2008.

27. Tang, S.K. Noise screening effects of balconies on a building façade. *J. Acoust. Soc. Am.* **2005**, *118*, 213–221. [CrossRef] [PubMed]

28. Sakamoto, S.; Ito, K.; Asakura, T. Experimental study on the noise shielding effects of eaves attached on building façade. In Proceedings of the 37th International Congress and Exposition on Noise Control Engineering, Shanghai, China, 26–29 October 2008.

29. Zuccherini Martello, N.; Fausti, N.; Santoni, P.; Secchi, S. The use of sound absorbing shading systems for the attenuation of noise on building façades. An experimental investigation. *Buildings* **2015**, *5*, 1346–1360. [CrossRef]

30. Ko, N.W.M. Reverberation time in a high-rise city. *J. Sound Vib.* **1978**, *56*, 459–461. [CrossRef]
31. Zuccherini Martello, N.; Aletta, F.; Fausti, P.; Kang, J.; Secchi, S. A psychoacoustic investigation on the effect of external shading devices on building façades. *Appl. Sci.* **2016**, *6*, 429. [CrossRef]
32. Field, C. The latest developments of an attenuator for naturally ventilated buildings. In Proceedings of the 33rd International Congress and Exposition on Noise Control Engineering, Prague, Czech Republic, 22–25 August 2004.
33. Tang, S.K. Narrow sidebranch arrays for low frequency duct noise control. *J. Acoust. Soc. Am.* **2012**, *132*, 3086–3097. [CrossRef] [PubMed]
34. Asakura, T.; Sakamoto, S.; Rikitake, H.; Higuchi, Y.; Sakamoto, Y.; Satoh, F.; Tachibana, H. Development of duct-like ventilation system with high sound insulation. In Proceedings of the 35th International Congress and Exposition on Noise Control Engineering, Honolulu, HI, USA, 3–6 December 2006.
35. Nguyen, Q.H.; Takashima, Y.; Nishimura, T.; Nishimura, S.; Nishimura, Y. Wave analysis of soundproofing ventilation grille. In Proceedings of the 41st International Congress and Exposition on Noise Control Engineering, New York, NY, USA, 19–22 August 2012.
36. Eveno, C. A balcony in a city—Imagination in architecture. *Archit. d'Aujourd'hui* **1995**, *299*, 3.
37. Mohsen, E.A.; Oldham, D.J. Traffic noise reduction due to the screening effect of balconies on a building façade. *Appl. Acoust.* **1977**, *10*, 243–257. [CrossRef]
38. Oldham, D.J.; Mohsen, E.A. The acoustical performance of self-protecting buildings. *J. Sound Vib.* **1979**, *65*, 557–581. [CrossRef]
39. Oldham, D.J.; Mohsen, E.A. A technique for predicting the performance of self-protecting buildings with respect to traffic noise. *Noise Control Eng. J.* **1980**, *15*, 11–19. [CrossRef]
40. May, D.N. Freeway noise and high-rise balconies. *J. Acoust. Soc. Am.* **1979**, *65*, 699–704. [CrossRef]
41. Hammad, R.N.S.; Gibbs, B.M. The acoustic performance of building façades in hot climates: Part I—Courtyards. *Appl. Acoust.* **1983**, *16*, 121–137. [CrossRef]
42. Hammad, R.N.S.; Gibbs, B.M. The acoustic performance of building façades in hot climates: Part II—Closed balconies. *Appl. Acoust.* **1983**, *16*, 441–454. [CrossRef]
43. Writ, L.S. The control of diffracted sound by means of thnadners (shaped noise barriers). *Acta Acust. United Acust.* **1979**, *42*, 73–88.
44. Tang, S.K. Scale model study of balcony insertion losses on a building façade with non-parallel line sources. *Appl. Acoust.* **2010**, *71*, 947–954. [CrossRef]
45. Hussain El-Dien, H. The influence of an inclined line source close to building façades with balconies. *Noise Control Eng. J.* **2012**, *60*, 363–373. [CrossRef]
46. Hothersall, D.C.; Horoshenkov, K.V.; Mercy, S.E. Numerical modeling of the sound field near a tall building with balconies near a road. *J. Sound Vib.* **1996**, *198*, 507–515. [CrossRef]
47. Kropp, W.; Bérillon, J. A theoretical model to consider the influence of absorbing surfaces inside the cavity of balconies. *Acta Acust. United Acust.* **2000**, *86*, 485–494.
48. Tong, Y.G.; Tang, S.K.; Yeung, M.K.L. Full-scale model investigation on the acoustical protection of a balcony-like façade device. *J. Acoust. Soc. Am.* **2011**, *130*, 673–676. [CrossRef] [PubMed]
49. Hussain El-Dien, H.; Woloszyn, P. Prediction of the sound field into high-rise building façades due to balcony ceiling form. *Appl. Acoust.* **2004**, *63*, 431–440. [CrossRef]
50. Hussain El-Dien, H.; Woloszyn, P. The acoustical influence of balcony depth and parapet form: Experiments and simulations. *Appl. Acoust.* **2005**, *66*, 533–551. [CrossRef]
51. Lee, P.J.; Kim, Y.H.; Jeon, J.Y.; Song, K.D. Effects of apartment building façade and balcony design on the reduction of exterior noise. *Build. Environ.* **2007**, *42*, 3517–3528. [CrossRef]
52. Kan, J.; Chan, I.; Ng, I.; Yeung, M.; Tang, S.K.; Lo, P. Study of noise reduction effect of acoustic balconies in high-rise buildings. In Proceedings of the 44th International Congress and Exposition on Noise Control Engineering, San Francisco, CA, USA, 9–12 August 2015.
53. Ishizuka, T.; Fujiwara, K. Traffic noise reduction at balconies on a high-rise building façade. *J. Acoust. Soc. Am.* **2012**, *131*, 2110–2117. [CrossRef] [PubMed]
54. Naish, D.A.; Tan, A.C.C.; Demirbilek, F.N. Speech interference and transmission on residential balconies with road traffic noise. *J. Acoust. Soc. Am.* **2013**, *133*, 210–226. [CrossRef] [PubMed]
55. Trinder, M.C.J.; Nelson, P.A. Active noise control in finite length ducts. *J. Sound Vib.* **1983**, *89*, 95–105. [CrossRef]

56. Anai, K.; Shiki, T. Improving sound insulation capacity at a ventilation opening using active noise control: Improving sound insulation performance degraded by living sound. In Proceedings of the 37th International Congress and Exposition on Noise Control Engineering, Shanghai, China, 26–29 October 2008.

57. Kwon, B.; Park, Y. Interior noise control with an active window system. *Appl. Acoust.* **2013**, *74*, 647–652. [CrossRef]

58. Nishimura, M.; Ohnishi, K.; Kanamori, N.; Ito, K. Basic study on active acoustic shielding. In Proceedings of the 37th International Congress and Exposition on Noise Control Engineering, Shanghai, China, 26–29 October 2008.

59. Ford, R.D.; Kerry, G. The sound insulation of partially open double glazing. *Appl. Acoust.* **1972**, *6*, 57–72. [CrossRef]

60. Kang, J.; Brocklesby, M.W. Feasibility of applying micro-perforated absorbers in acoustic window systems. *Appl. Acoust.* **2005**, *66*, 669–689. [CrossRef]

61. Tong, Y.G.; Tang, S.K. Plenum window insertion loss in the presence of a line source—A scale model study. *J. Acoust. Soc. Am.* **2013**, *133*, 1458–1467. [CrossRef] [PubMed]

62. Søndergaard, L.S.; Legarth, S.V. Investigation of sound insulation for a supply air window—Field measurements and occupant responses. In Proceedings of the 43rd International Congress and Exposition on Noise Control Engineering, Melbourne, Australia, 16–19 November 2014.

63. Bajraktari, E.; Lechleitner, J.; Mahdavi, A. Estimating the sound insulation of double facades with openings for natural ventilation. *Energy Procedia* **2015**, *78*, 140–145. [CrossRef]

64. Tong, Y.G.; Tang, S.K.; Kang, J.; Fung, A.; Yeung, M.K.L. Full scale field study of sound transmission across plenum windows. *Appl. Acoust.* **2015**, *89*, 244–253. [CrossRef]

65. Kang, J.; Li, Z. Numerical simulation of an acoustic window system using finite element method. *Acta Acust. United Acust.* **2007**, *93*, 152–163.

66. Tang, S.K. Acoustical protection of a plenum window installed with sound absorptions. In Proceedings of the 44th International Congress and Exposition on Noise Control Engineering, San Francisco, CA, USA, 9–12 August 2015.

67. Tang, S.K. Sound transmission across plenum windows with non-parallel glass panes. In Proceedings of the 45th International Congress and Exposition on Noise Control Engineering, Hamburg, Germany, 21–24 August 2016.

68. Lee, J. Ventilation and sound attenuation potential of double-skin façades in urban high-rises. *CTBUH J.* **2016**, *1*, 32–37.

69. Huang, H.H.; Qiu, X.J.; Kang, J. Active noise attenuation in ventilation windows. *J. Acoust. Soc. Am.* **2011**, *130*, 176–188. [CrossRef] [PubMed]

70. Qiu, X.J.; Huang, H.H.; Lin, Z. Progress in research on natural ventilation ANC windows. In Proceedings of the 40th International Congress and Exposition on Noise Control Engineering, Osaka, Japan, 4–7 September 2011.

71. Tang, S.K.; Tong, Y.G.; Tsui, K.L. Sound transmission across a plenum window with an active noise cancellation system. *Noise Control Eng. J.* **2016**, *64*, 423–432. [CrossRef]

72. Yu, X.; Lau, S.K.; Cheng, L.; Cui, F. A numerical investigation on the sound insulation of ventilation windows. *Appl. Acoust.* **2017**, *117*, 113–121. [CrossRef]

Article

A Psychoacoustic Investigation on the Effect of External Shading Devices on Building Facades

Nicolò Zuccherini Martello [1,*], Francesco Aletta [2], Patrizio Fausti [1], Jian Kang [2] and Simone Secchi [3]

[1] Engineering Department, University of Ferrara, 44122 Ferrara FE, Italy; patrizio.fausti@unife.it
[2] School of Architecture, University of Sheffield, Sheffield S10 2TN, UK; f.aletta@sheffield.ac.uk (F.A.); j.kang@sheffield.ac.uk (J.K.)
[3] Industrial Engineering Department, University of Florence, 50139 Firenze, Italy; simone.secchi@unifi.it
* Correspondence: nicolo.zuccherinimartello@unife.it; Tel.: +39-0532-974-879

Academic Editor: Gino Iannace
Received: 10 October 2016; Accepted: 5 December 2016; Published: 14 December 2016

Abstract: Due to energetic and natural lighting factors, building facades often present external shading devices, but the acoustic properties of such devices have not yet been well studied. This study was carried out using a full-scale model of a portion of a shading device, in a semi-anechoic chamber, using traditional and sound absorbing louvres. The psychoacoustic effects produced by the shading system were evaluated through comparisons between averaged values of loudness, roughness and sharpness levels, as well as sound pressure levels as reference. Results highlighted that the sound absorbing shading device offers good attenuation in terms of loudness, roughness and sound pressure level, with a small reduction in sharpness. The traditional shading system studied does not efficiently reduce the analysed parameters, or even worsens the situation. Several analyses of variance were carried out, one for each situation studied. The sound source position and the louvres' tilt angle both produce statistically significant effects on almost all of the variations of the parameters studied. The analyses of the partial eta squared factors highlighted that source position and louvre tilt angle affect the variations of the parameters studied to a different degree in respect of the two types of louvres.

Keywords: building shading devices; insertion loss; psychoacoustics; loudness; roughness; sharpness

1. Introduction and Objectives

Traffic noise is a major sound pollutant in densely populated cities. It has been largely demonstrated that long-term and short-term exposure to noise has a strong impact on human health and behaviour [1].

There are many possibilities to mitigate traffic noise inside dwellings in crowded cities, using noise barriers between traffic lanes and buildings, or enhancing the facade sound insulation. The efficacy of the noise barriers, of various types and shapes, has also been studied [2–6]. Recent research funded by the European Union's Seventh Framework Programme (FP7/2007-2013—HOSANNA [7]) studied the optimisation of green areas and surfaces, in order to reduce noise propagation in urban areas. Noise barriers often present installation problems due to lack of space between the noise source and the buildings to be protected. If the noise barrier installation is not possible or not effective, the design of the building facade becomes very important. It is quite easy to obtain good performances in sound insulation of the opaque components of a building facade. Furthermore, its shape design represents a good opportunity to protect dwellings from external noise [8–13]. Since the windows represent the weak element in facade sound insulation, they have been widely studied: they represent the visual and the ventilating interface between the internal and the external space of a building. Kang and

Brocklesby [14] presented a laboratory study on the possibility to enhance the noise attenuation of windows, introducing transparent micro-perforated sound absorbing panels, in order to maintain natural ventilation and daylighting comfort. The results of similar experiments, both on a scale model and using a full-scale model, are respectively shown in [15,16].

Different issues arise in buildings with large glazed surfaces on the facade, such as curtain wall systems. For example, they force designers to use shading systems in order to avoid excessive solar irradiation, which can increase the energy consumption to cool the building, while reducing the discomfort due to thermal and glare effects perceived by the users. The efficiency of the external shading devices in terms of the reduction of energy consumption and visual comfort enhancement has been largely demonstrated [17–20], but their acoustic effects on the building facade have not yet been well studied. Some recent works have focused their attention on the acoustic effects of the shading devices on the buildings in terms of sound pressure level (SPL) differences over the building facade (insertion loss (IL), in dB), behind the louvres [21–23]. It has been demonstrated that the external louvres tend to increase the sound pressure level over the facades, since they receive not only the direct sound waves, but also the sound reflections that are generated by the louvres. In [23], a laboratory study was presented to acoustically optimise the louvres, applying to them a layer of sound absorptive material, in order to reduce the sound pressure level over the building facade: The insertion loss provided by the sound absorbing louvres is much higher if compared with the effect of the traditional shading system. The use of the insertion loss in dB is a commonly used procedure in the evaluation of the acoustic effects of a barrier or other building components. However, it has been demonstrated [24–26] that objective values in dB are not necessarily correlated to human perception in terms of the disturbing characteristics of noise. In [27], the airborne sound insulation was studied using a loudness model instead of making a traditional evaluation [28]. The study was conducted in order to introduce a procedure to find a subjective estimation for airborne sound insulation.

This paper presents analyses related to the effect over the building facade of a shading device in terms of variation of some psychoacoustic parameters, namely loudness, roughness and sharpness [29]. The aim of the present work is to study how averaged loudness, roughness, sharpness levels and SPL are modified by the presence of a traditional and an improved shading system considering different configurations of source position and louvres' tilt angle.

Designers can choose between many types of shading devices. The choice can depend both on technical and aesthetical reasons. The main function of these systems is obviously to reduce solar irradiation over the building facade and to improve daylight distribution in the interior; these aspects can affect both the dimensions and the spacing of the louvres. In this work the results of the measurements carried out on a model representative of typical devices extensively used by architects are presented. A 1:1 scale model of a portion of a shading system was tested in a semi-anechoic chamber. Both sound pressure levels and impulse responses measurements were conducted in order to evaluate the variations of the chosen psychoacoustic parameters derived from two noise signals convolved with the measured impulse responses.

The variations of sound pressure levels reported in this paper have been analysed in greater detail in [23].

2. Methodology

2.1. Experimental Set-Up

2.1.1. Model of the Shading System

The model is a portion of a shading device, 4 m × 4 m, with louvres measuring 2 m × 0.2 m, 0.018 m thick, spaced at 0.2 m from each other. The model was completely built from pine plywood slabs, with mullions measuring 2 m × 0.1 m, 0.02 m thick. The model was placed on the floor of the semi-anechoic chamber, simulating a glazed facade. Indeed, the shading devices are usually installed over the glazed surface of the buildings, and glass and concrete have comparable sound absorption properties. The semi-anechoic chamber has a net volume of 796 m³ (10.1 m × 9.5 m, height 8.3 m): The chamber respects the requirements of Annex A of the ISO 3745:2012 [30], with a low cut-off frequency under 50 Hz and a high frequency above 10 kHz. The top of the model was demarcated by the sound absorbing wedges of the chamber, while the other three sides were delimited by a boundary of polyester fibres, 0.25 m thick and 1 m wide. The absorbing boundary was used in order to reduce as much as possible the sound diffraction through the lateral mullions of the structure. The position of the model inside the semi-anechoic chamber and some dimensional data are shown in Figure 1.

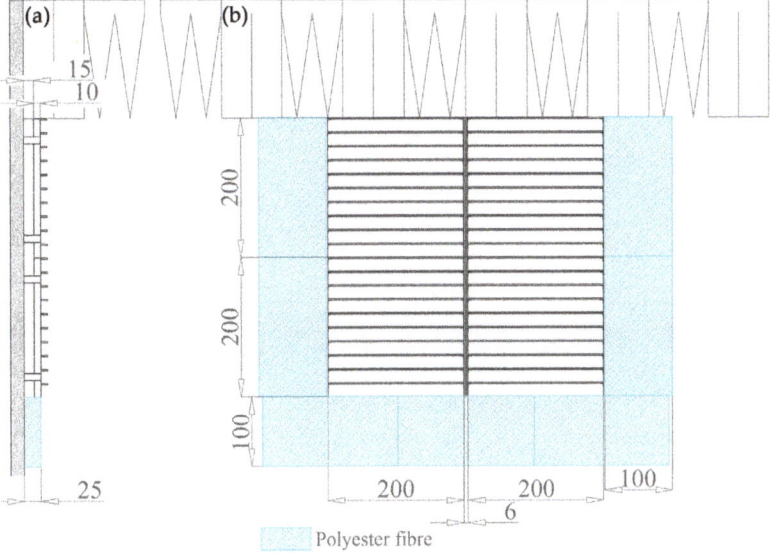

Polyester fibre

Figure 1. Side (**a**) and plan (**b**) views of the model of the shading devices in the semi-anechoic chamber. Dimensions are expressed in cm.

The study was carried out with two different types of shading device: traditional louvres were used for the first set of measurements, while modified sound-absorbing louvres were used for the second set, in order to evaluate the possibility of an enhancement in the acoustic performance of the system. In order to give sound absorption properties to the shading device, a 3 cm thick layer of expanded melamine was used, fixed to the back of each louvre (Figure 2c). The sound absorption coefficient of the used melamine was measured in impedance tubes [31], with diameters of 4.5 cm and 10.0 cm, respectively: Results are shown in Figure 3. The shading system was analysed with three different tilt angles of the louvres (0°, 30°, 45°) toward the sound source. Measurements were carried out also with the blank floor of the semi-anechoic chamber (Figure 2a,d), in order to find out the reference values to be compared with the effects of the shading system. From now on, the floor of the semi-anechoic room will be called *"facade"*, in order to simplify the reading of the text. Figure 4 shows the three configurations of the facade: without the shading system (Figure 4. Configuration A), with the traditional louvres (Figure 4. Configurations B) and with the sound absorbing ones (Figure 4. Configurations C). The values obtained with configuration A were used as reference in the evaluation of the acoustic effect of the shading system.

(a)   (b)   (c)   (d)   (e)

Figure 2. (**a**) The blank floor of the semi-anechoic room simulating the plain facade; (**b**) the traditional shading system; (**c**) the sound absorbing louvres; (**d**) the 12-microphones array used in the measurements without the shading system model; and (**e**) the microphones placed on the plane below the model.

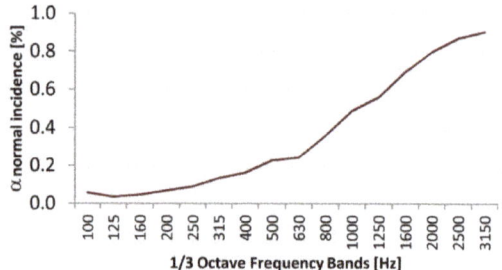

Figure 3. Normal incidence sound absorption coefficient (α) of the material (expanded melamine layer) used in the shading device.

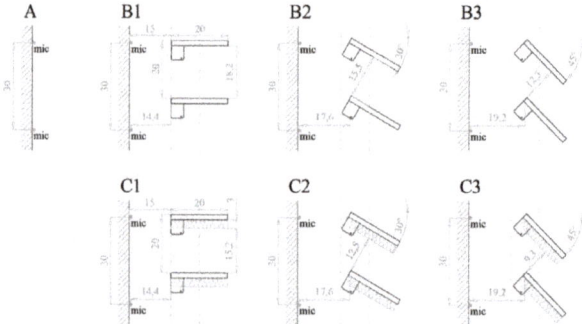

Figure 4. Setup of the different configurations: (**A**) without shading system; (**B1–B3**) different tilt angles of the traditional shading system; and (**C1–C3**) different tilt angles of the shading system with absorbing material. The dimensions are given in cm.

2.1.2. Sound Source, Excitation Signals and Microphone Grid

A directive loudspeaker, in general utilised for facade sound insulation measurements [32], was used during the experiment. It is clear that the generated sound field is non-homogeneous on the studied surface of 16 m², but all the results are evaluated in terms of relative values, and it is possible to affirm that the differences should be the same in all the studied situations. The sound source was placed in three different positions (Figure 5a), in order to evaluate how the shading device behaves with three different angles of incidence of the sound field (30°, 45°, and 60°). The dimensions of the semi-anechoic chamber did not allow to move the source too far from the model, but the different source positions are intended to simulate the effect of the louvres with a fixed sound source position placed on the ground, producing noise toward three corresponding heights of a hypothetical building. Referring to Figure 5c, which shows a building section, the sound source positions S1, S2 and S3, respectively, correspond to the 3rd floor, a floor between the 1st and the 2nd, and the 1st floor.

The measurements were carried out using 12 half-inch pre-polarised condenser microphones PCB 377B02 (PCB® Piezotronics, Depew, NY, USA), with 426E01 ICP® microphone preamplifiers (PCB® Piezotronics, Depew, NY, USA). The microphones were mounted in an array, spaced 30 cm from each other. This array was moved in 10 positions under the model, spaced 40 cm from each other. The complete grid was set with a total of 120 microphone positions, with 12 rows and 10 columns, as shown in Figure 5b. Figure 2d,e shows the details of the microphone array on the floor of the semi-anechoic chamber and under the shading device. The signals of the microphones were acquired by the Sinus Samurai System (SINUS Messtechnik GmbH, Leipzig, Germany). The calibration procedure of the microphones was repeated before and after each measurement sessions. The SPLs were obtained from the described measurements set-up using a pink noise as source signal. The impulse responses (IRs) where obtained from a logarithmic sine sweep signal, with duration of 10 s and a frequency range from 50 Hz to 10,000 Hz.

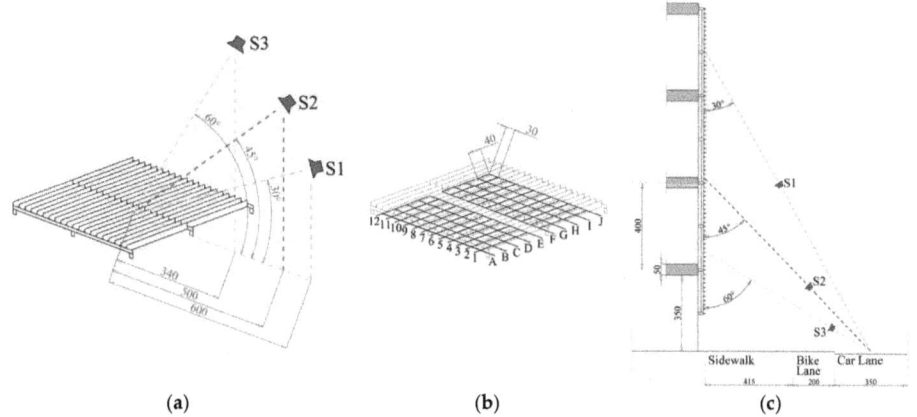

Figure 5. (a) The three positions of the sound source with respect to the model; (b) the grid of 120 microphone positions used in the measurements; and (c) section of a hypothetical building facade and a road. The source positions in the semi-anechoic chamber are shown as a fixed road lane. Dimensions are in cm.

2.2. Parameters Selection: SPL and Psychoacoustics Parameters

2.2.1. Sound Pressure Levels

Sound pressure level, in dB, describes the amount of the atmospheric pressure (Pa) variation, in logarithmic scale, due to an acoustic phenomenon. It is calculated with the following Equation (1), where p_{eff}, in Pa, is the effective gap of the atmospheric pressure from its equilibrium value and $p_{ref} = 2 \times 10^{-5}$ Pa.

$$\text{SPL} = 10 \times \log_{10}\left(\frac{p_{eff}^2}{p_{ref}^2}\right) \text{[dB]} \tag{1}$$

2.2.2. Loudness

Loudness (N) describes the human perception of the volume of a sound. Loudness level (L_N) is the intensity in dB of a 1-kHz tone perceived to be as loud as the sound being measured. The measurement unit of loudness is the sone, while the loudness levels are represented in phon. The relation between loudness and loudness level is expressed in Equation (2), where L_N is the loudness level in phon and N is the loudness in sone. The sone scale is linear, so as the loudness is doubled so is the perceived volume of a sound, while the same difference corresponds to 10 phon. The A-weighting curve, which is largely used in environmental noise evaluation, only describes the perception of a sound around 40 phons.

$$L_N = 40 + 10\log_2(N) \ [\text{phon}] \tag{2}$$

The perception of loudness depends on the time duration of the studied noise, on its spectral components and it is related to its sound pressure level in dB. In this study, two steady-state signals were used in order to avoid the time dependency of loudness. Loudness levels from the pink noise and the traffic noise signals were obtained using the software Artemis Suite v11 – Psychoacoustics Module (HEAD Acoustics GmbH, Herzogenrath, Germany), according to the DIN 45631:1991 [33].

2.2.3. Roughness

Roughness describes the annoyance of a sound due to its modulation frequency. The unit of roughness is the asper and it is defined with a 1 kHz tone with 60 dB in SPL, 100% modulated with a frequency of 70 Hz. Roughness is not strongly dependent on the sound pressure level. The minimum perceived change in roughness is an increment in the degree of modulation of around 10%, which corresponds to a relative variation of around 17%. For this reason, the variations in roughness were evaluated in terms of ratio (Equation (4)). Roughness was calculated with Artemis Suite software.

2.2.4. Sharpness

Sharpness measures the high frequency content of a sound: A high level at high frequency, with respect of the broad band sound, generates a high sharpness. The reverse sensation of sharpness is the sense of pleasantness of a sound, which depends on sharpness itself, as well as on roughness and loudness. The unit of sharpness is the acum, which corresponds to a narrow-band noise at 1 kHz having a level of 60 dB, and a width corresponding to one critical band. Sharpness in this study was evaluated using the Artemis Suite software, according to the DIN 45692:2009 [34], using the method presented by Aures in [35].

2.3. Experimental Measurements and Data Analysis

2.3.1. Measurement Procedure

Two different types of measurements were made in the semi-anechoic chamber. Sound pressure levels (SPL) and impulse response (IR) measurements were carried out in order to evaluate different acoustic performances of the shading device. The SPLs were used to calculate the sound attenuations in dB given by the louvres (already presented in [23]). The impulse response measurements were conducted in order to evaluate the variations of the chosen psychoacoustic parameters derived from two noise signals convolved with the measured impulse responses.

2.3.2. Convolution Process and Analysis of the Differences of the Studied Values

The two chosen signals to be convolved with the measured IRs are a broadband noise signal, the so-called "pink noise", and the standard traffic noise generated according to the indication of the standard EN 1793-3 [36]. Both signals were created in Adobe Audition 3.0 (Adobe Systems Incorporated, San Jose, CA, USA), as mono signals with a sample frequency of 96 kHz, with a duration of 10 s. The two signals were chosen because, due to their differences, it is possible to obtain different values for the chosen psychoacoustic parameters, which are better correlated to different real situations. Pink noise is a commonly used signal in facade sound insulation measurements, while standard traffic noise is an artificial signal that is used in the IL measurements of noise barriers. In particular, the spectral characteristics of the two signals can affect the loudness level calculations, as further shown by the results of this work.

The impulse response analysis and the following convolution process were carried out in Matlab® R2013a (MathWorks, Natick, MA, USA), using its in-built convolution function. Two normalization factors were applied to the two output signals, according to the scheme in Figure 6, in order to obtain values in Pascal (Pa) for the signals close to the unit. In this way the output signals respectively give comparable psychoacoustic parameters: For example, the loudness values obtained from the convolved pink noise are comparable.

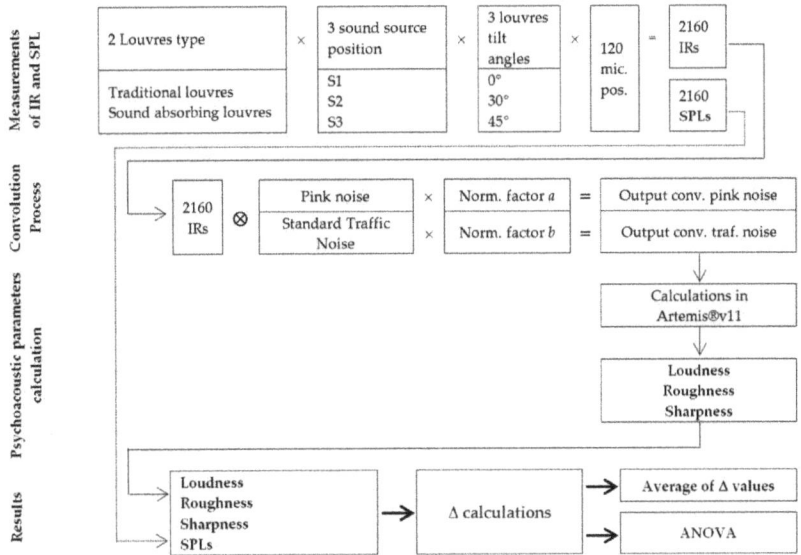

Figure 6. Flow-chart of the entire process to evaluate the acoustic effect of the shading device model: the measurements process with its variables, the convolution process with the two signals, the calculation of the psychoacoustic parameters and the evaluation of the variations over the facade in terms of average values and the statistical analysis of variance (ANOVA).

3. Results and Discussion

The first part of this section presents the averaged loudness, roughness and sharpness levels, as well as the sound pressure levels, in terms of their variations (Figures 7–10), caused by the presence of the shading system in its different configurations. The second sub-section is dedicated to the analyses of variance and their respective effects of size of the fixed parameters on the dependant variables.

The Δ calculations were conducted to evaluate the acoustic effect of the studied shading device on a building facade. All the psychoacoustic parameters studied and the sound pressure levels were analysed in terms of mutual variations, taking as reference the values coming from the measurements with the blank facade. The evaluation in terms of mutual comparisons, between the calculated values of SPL and psychoacoustic parameters, was chosen to avoid some issues deriving from the measurements. In fact, both the sound pressure levels and the impulse response measurements were affected by the sound source directivity. It is assumed that the diverted acoustic field reaches each microphone position in the same way during each measurement. For this reason, the differences in the acoustic field are attributed only to the presence of the shading device, in its various configurations (Figure 6, Section "Measurements of IR and SPL"). This method was chosen in order to avoid also the different sound absorption characteristics of the floor of the semi-anechoic chamber and a glazed facade.

The variations (Δ) in loudness, sharpness and sound pressure levels were calculated with Equation (3), in terms of simple difference. The ratios of roughness were instead obtained with Equation (4), because the ratio is more appropriate than a difference for the evaluation of roughness changes (see also Section 2.2.3).

According to Equations (3) and (4), the higher the values of the result, the better the effect of the shading device. Letters A, B and C refer to Figure 4, where A corresponds to the blank floor of the semi-anechoic chamber, B presents the traditional louvres and C the sound absorbing ones. Subscripts 1 to 10 and 1 to 12 refer respectively to the 10 columns and 12 rows of the microphone grid. The term Val in Equations (3) and (4) refers to the measurements of sound pressure levels (dB) and to the calculated psychoacoustic parameters. Equations (3) and (4) were alternatively repeated to separately evaluate the performance of the traditional louvres (B, in its configurations B1, B2, and B3) and of the sound absorbing louvres (C, in its configurations C1, C2 and C3).

$$\left(\Delta_{N,Sharp,SPL}\right)_{12,10} = \begin{bmatrix} (Val_{B,C})_{1,1} & \cdots & (Val_{B,C})_{1,10} \\ \vdots & \ddots & \vdots \\ (Val_{B,C})_{12,1} & \cdots & (Val_{B,C})_{12,10} \end{bmatrix} - \begin{bmatrix} (Val_A)_{1,1} & \cdots & (Val_A)_{1,10} \\ \vdots & \ddots & \vdots \\ (Val_A)_{12,1} & \cdots & (Val_A)_{12,10} \end{bmatrix} \ [\text{phon, acum, dB}] \quad (3)$$

$$\left(\Delta_{Rough}\right)_{12,10} = \begin{bmatrix} \dfrac{(Val_{B,C})_{1,1}}{(Val_A)_{1,1}} & \cdots & \dfrac{(Val_{B,C})_{1,10}}{(Val_A)_{1,10}} \\ \vdots & \ddots & \vdots \\ \dfrac{(Val_{B,C})_{12,1}}{(Val_A)_{12,1}} & \cdots & \dfrac{(Val_{B,C})_{12,10}}{(Val_A)_{12,10}} \end{bmatrix} \ [\%] \quad (4)$$

3.1. Average Variations of Loudness, Roughness, Sharpness and Sound Pressure Level over the Building Facade

The variations of the analysed parameters are expressed as averages over all the 120 values coming from Equations (3) and (4). The averages have been repeated for each variable of the measurements set-up. Finally, the obtained values are expressed with respect to the two different louvres types, the three different sound source positions and the three tilt angles of the louvres (18 averages). The psychoacoustic parameters have as additional variable the signal used in the convolution process (pink noise and standard traffic noise), with 36 averages.

3.1.1. Average Loudness Differences: Traditional versus Sound Absorbing Louvres

The loudness levels do not significantly vary in the case of the traditional shading system, with all the source positions, with the louvres tilted at 0° and 30° toward the sound source. The situation changes when the louvres' tilt angle rises to 45°: The presence of the traditional louvres worsens the loudness situation, with an increase of up to 3.5 phons. This is a low variation, corresponding to less than a doubling in sone, but it constitutes a worsening of the loudness over the building facade, due to the presence of the shading devices. The differences are quite similar for the loudness calculated from both signals used. The sound absorbing shading system has a good effect on the average variation of the loudness levels over the portion of the studied facade. The loudness level reduction has a maximum value of 14 phons (standard traffic noise, sound source in position S1, un-tilted louvres—Figure 7). The minimum value of attenuation in terms of loudness is even positive, around 3 phon: It is again a low difference, but this time it represents a reduction in the loudness level. In general, it is possible to assume that, with reference to the loudness levels variations, the shading device has linear dependency on the sound source position: the protection increases inversely proportionally to the angle between the source and the facade plane. Referring to Figure 5c, the shading device offers greater protection in loudness for higher floors. Figure 7 shows a linear dependency even between the louvres' tilt angle and the given loudness level reduction. The effect of the shading device on the loudness level variations is more relevant when the standard traffic noise is studied: This is to be ascribed to the higher levels at higher frequencies in this type of signal. According to an equal-loudness contour [29], it is clear how a high frequency pure tone needs a lower sound pressure level to reach the same loudness as a low frequency pure tone.

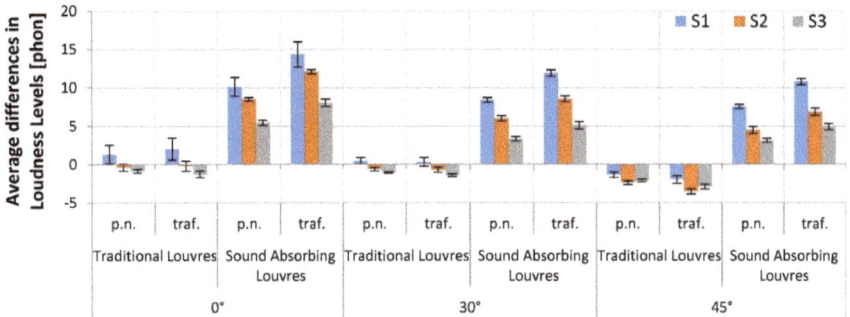

Figure 7. Average differences in Loudness levels due to the presence of the traditional louvres compared to the sound absorbing louvres. The bars in the figure are listed according to the source positions used for the measurements (S1, S2, and S3). Error bars report the doubled standard deviations for each average. The acronym "p.n." refers to the pink noise signal. The abbreviation "traf." refers to the standard traffic noise.

3.1.2. Average Roughness Differences: Traditional versus Sound Absorbing Louvres

Roughness variations were evaluated in terms of asper ratios, in percentage, so values below 1 correspond to a negative impact of the shading device. The performances of the traditional shading system to reduce the roughness sensation over a building facade are not relevant, with average ratio between the shaded situation and the blank facade not exceeding ±10% (0.9–1.1). Indeed, the minimum perceived change in roughness corresponds to an increment or a decrease of around 17% [29]. The roughness highly depends on the modulation of the signal: The traditional shading device seems not to interfere with the sound modulation in any of the studied configurations of the louvres, since they do not present particular performances in their sound absorption, no do they highly interact with the generated acoustic field. The sound absorbing shading louvres give a fair reduction of the roughness of both studied signals, up to a decrease of almost 40% (standard traffic noise, sound source in position S1, un-tilted louvres—Figure 8).

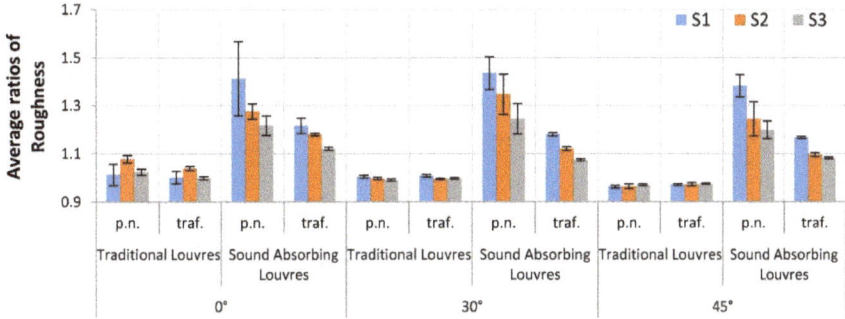

Figure 8. Average ratios of Roughness due to the presence of the traditional louvres compared to the sound absorbing louvres. The bars in the figure are listed according to the source positions used for the measurements (S1, S2, and S3). Error bars report the doubled standard deviations for each average. The acronym "p.n." refers to the pink noise signal. The abbreviation "traf." refers to the standard traffic noise.

3.1.3. Average Sharpness Differences: Traditional versus Sound Absorbing Louvres

The standard shading device has a small impact on the variations of the sharpness over the studied facade. It is however possible to affirm that the sound absorbing shading system behaves better in reducing the sharpness over the building facade, with reductions of up to around 0.6 acum (traffic noise, S1, un-tilted louvres, Figure 9). In the same case, even the sound absorbing shading system is practically ineffective in reducing sharpness, when the sound source position is in S3 (Figure 5a), corresponding to the lower floor of a hypothetical building (Figure 5c). The most effective configuration of the shading device to reduce sharpness is with the sound source in S1 and with un-tilted louvres.

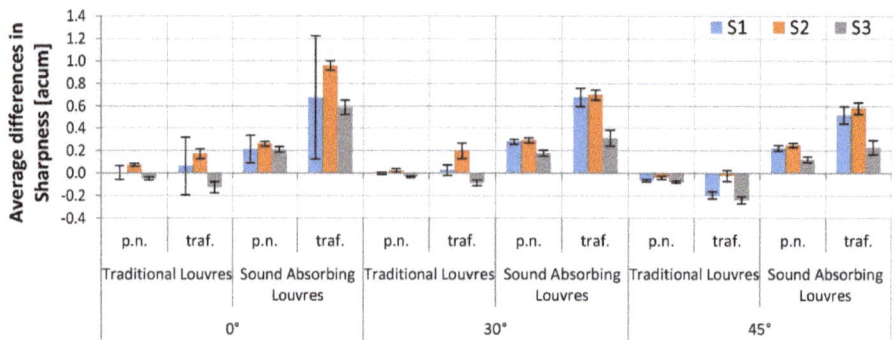

Figure 9. Average differences in Sharpness due to the presence of the traditional louvres compared to the sound absorbing louvres. The bars in the figure are listed according to the source positions used for the measurements (S1, S2, and S3). Error bars report the doubled standard deviations for each average. The acronym "p.n." refers to the pink noise signal. The abbreviation "traf." refers to the standard traffic noise.

3.1.4. Average SPL Differences: Traditional versus Sound Absorbing Louvres

The SPL differences in dB are expressed as single frequency broadband values, calculated between 100 Hz and 3150 Hz. A more detailed explanation of the SPL variations over a building facade due to the presence of a shading device can be found in [23]. The shading system plays quite an important role in the SPL changes over a facade. While the traditional louvres can enhance the SPL over the facade by up to 2 dB, the sound absorbing shading device gives a sound attenuation by up to 9 dB. The differences in SPL have a similar behaviour to the loudness levels, regarding the sound source position and the louvres' tilt angle. This fact is easily understood because loudness depends on spectral content at medium-high frequencies, which is the same range of efficacy as the melamine used in the experiment. The dependences of the SPL reductions on the sound source position and the louvres' tilt angle (Figure 10) is again similar to what was observed for the difference in loudness.

3.2. Analysis of Variance: Significance and Fixed Factors Effects

An analysis of variance test (ANOVA) was conducted over the calculated Δs values of loudness, roughness, sharpness and sound pressure levels. The statistical analyses were conducted on the line averages of the results given by Equations (3) and (4), as explained in Equation (5).

$$\left(\Delta_{avg}\right)_{12,1} = \begin{bmatrix} avg(\Delta_{1,1}, & \cdots & , \Delta_{1,10}) \\ & \vdots & \\ avg(\Delta_{12,1}, & \cdots & , \Delta_{12,10}) \end{bmatrix} \tag{5}$$

The input of the ANOVA analyses using as dependant variable the line averages obtained from Equation (5) and the fixed factor were the sound source position and the louvres tilt angle.

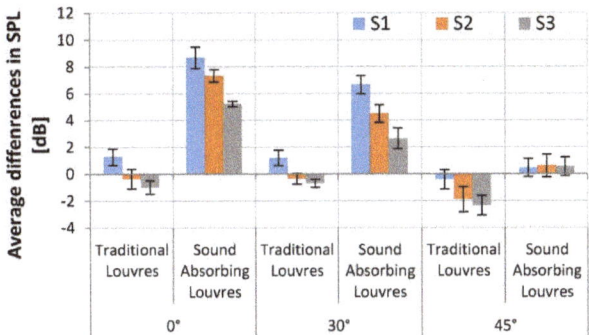

Figure 10. Average differences in Sound Pressure Levels (Insertion Loss in dB) due to the presence of the traditional louvres compared to the sound absorbing louvres. The bars in the figure are listed in function of the source positions used for the measurements (S1, S2, and S3). Error bars reports the doubled standard deviations for each average.

The ANOVA tests are necessary to verify that the variations between the various studied situations are statistically significant, and do not occur due to random factors. A p-value under 0.05 has been considered as significant. The ANOVA tests were completed with the calculation of the effect of size (η_p^2) in order to evaluate which factor has a greater effect between the sound source position and the louvres' tilt angle on the Δs of the studied parameters. The ANOVA tests were separately carried out for each data set of the calculated differences: each ANOVA is referred to a single case study. The dependant variable in each ANOVA was the Δ in terms of loudness, roughness, sharpness, sound pressure level, due to the presence of the shading device, in its two main configurations (traditional and sound absorbing). The sound source positions and the louvres' tilt angles were considered as fixed factors. The sound source position is important to determine the acoustic protection as a function of the building height (Figure 5c), while the louvres' tilt angle is a parameter that is more closely related to the energy saving needs of the buildings, and can be decided directly by the designer or by the user. tab:applsci-06-00429-t001 reports the p-values of the ANOVA tests. Figure 11 shows the effect of size of the sound source position and of the louvres' tilt angles. The complete report of all the ANOVA is in Appendix A (Tables A1–A4). The statistical analyses were conducted with the software IBM-SPSS Statistics v23 (IBM Corp., Armonk, NY, USA).

Table 1. p-values calculated from the analysis of the variance for each data set of the calculated Δs. The term "Interaction" is to be intended as the interaction between the sound source position and the louvres' tilt angle.

ANOVA Fixed Factors		Δ in Loudness Levels		Δ in Roughness		Δ in Sharpness		Δ in SPL
		p.n.	traf.	p.n.	traf.	p.n.	traf.	-
Traditional Louvres	Sound source pos.	$p < 0.001$	$p < 0.001$	0.021	0.048	$p < 0.001$	$p < 0.001$	$p < 0.001$
	Louvres tilt angle	$p < 0.001$	$p < 0.001$	$p < 0.001$	$p < 0.001$	$p < 0.001$	$p < 0.001$	$p < 0.001$
	Interaction	0.205	0.071	0.001	$p < 0.001$	0.025	0.668	0.766
Sound Absorbing Louvres	Sound source pos.	$p < 0.001$	$p < 0.001$	$p < 0.001$	$p < 0.001$	$p < 0.001$	$p < 0.001$	$p < 0.001$
	Louvres tilt angle	$p < 0.001$	$p < 0.001$	0.348	$p < 0.001$	0.044	$p < 0.001$	$p < 0.001$
	Interaction	0.067	0.123	0.985	0.004	0.215	0.369	0.977

3.2.1. Analysis of Variance and Effect of Size of the Loudness Comparisons

The differences in loudness levels are statistically significant, looking at both the effects given by the louvres' tilt angle and the sound source position, while the interaction between the two factors is never significant. This result is repeated for both differences given by the traditional and the sound absorbing louvres. This means that the shading device plays an important role in the variations of the loudness levels, and both the sound source position and the louvres' tilt angle are important.

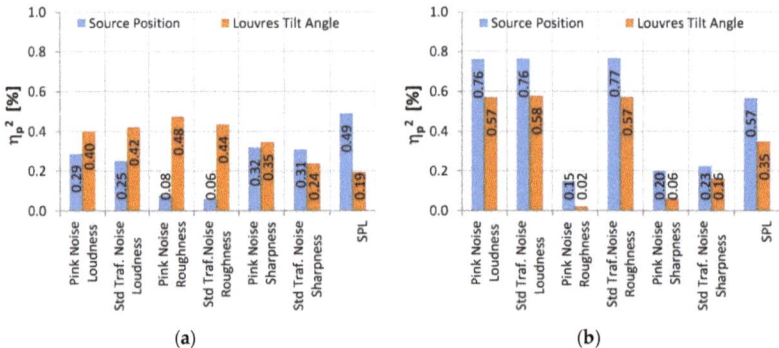

Figure 11. The effect of size for the group mean differences; partial eta squared factor for the mean differences referred to the variances of Loudness Levels, Roughness, Sharpness and SPL: (**a**) traditional louvres; and (**b**) sound absorbing louvers.

The comparison of the effect of size ($\eta_p{}^2$) on the loudness differences (Figure 11) shows that the louvres' tilt angle of the standard louvres has a greater effect on the loudness variations compared to the sound source position, while the opposite behaviour is observed for the sound absorbing louvres. The loudness level attenuation given by the traditional louvres is quite poor, if not negative (Figure 7). Tilting the louvers produces greater effects on the façade loudness levels than changing the sound source position, because they become transparent to the generated acoustic field (Figure 11a). The reverse situation observed with the sound absorbing louvres (Figure 11b) is due to the fact that the sound absorbing material plays an important role independently of the louvres' tilt angle, because the material quantity in the shading system does not change. In this case the sound source position seems to have a greater effect because the free space between the louvres, seen from the position of the sound source, becomes smaller as the angle between the loudspeaker and the facade plane is reduced (Figure 5a,c). Similar behaviours in $\eta_p{}^2$ are observed for both studied signals.

3.2.2. Analysis of Variance and Effect of Size of the Roughness Comparisons

The ANOVA carried out on the Δ_s in roughness shows that the fixed factors play a statistically significant role on the roughness variation on the facade, even in their interaction. Only two exceptions were found when the sound absorbing device is observed, with pink noise: The louvres' tilt angle and the interaction of the two fixed factors are not statistically significant. This fact can be more easily understood looking at the averages ratios, reported in Section 3.1.2: The values slightly vary due to the tilt angle, and the standard deviation is quite high. This is ascribed to the fact that roughness strongly depends on the degree of modulation. Both the traditional and the sound absorbing shading device can vary the modulation frequency only by attenuating some components of the sound spectrum, which modulate more: this can depend on the sound absorption and sound screening effects of the used materials, which do not change with the louvres' tilt angles nor with the sound source position. The $\eta_p{}^2$ has a similar behaviour to what was observed for the differences in loudness levels.

3.2.3. Analysis of Variance and Effect of Size of the Sharpness Comparisons

The sound source position and the louvres' tilt angle have a statistical significance on the variation of the sharpness over the studied facade portion, with both studied signals. Their interaction is not statistically significant, except when the standard louvres in presence of pink noise are observed.

The η_p^2 has an unclear behaviour with similar values for each factor. The results of both the ANOVA and the analyses of η_p^2 are to be ascribed to the characteristic of sharpness itself, which depends on the high frequency content of the studied signal. The shading system acts as a great diffuser/absorber and it is impossible to evaluate if the source position or the louvres' tilt angle plays a more important role on the sharpness variations. The sound absorbing system mainly works at high frequency (Figure 3) and subsequently the sharpness is reduced.

3.2.4. Analysis of Variance and Effect of Size of the SPL Comparisons

The ANOVA highlighted statistically significant variations in sound pressure levels due to the separate actions of the sound source position and the louvres' tilt angle, but similarly to what was observed for the loudness levels, their interaction is not statistically significant.

The η_p^2 analysis shows that the SPL variations over the facade, in both cases with standard and sound absorbing louvres, are mainly influenced by the sound source position. This is an important finding that means that the noise protection given by the shading device increases faster with the building height than with the louvres' tilt angle. This aspect is ascribed to the fact that at higher floors the louvres appear closer to each other and denser, with respect to the noise source placed at the bottom.

4. Summary and Conclusions

This work represents a first approach to the evaluation of the variability of some psychoacoustic parameters over a building facade, due to the presence of a shading device, both with traditional and sound absorbing louvres. The experimental data were obtained during a measurements campaign conducted on a 1:1 scale model of a portion of a shading device to be installed over a building facade in a semi-anechoic chamber. The acoustic insertion loss given by the shading device model has been discussed in greater detail in [23]. The large amount of impulse response measurements were convolved with two different noise signals in order to calculate loudness, roughness and sharpness, which were evaluated with mutual comparison between the situation with the shading device, in its various configurations, and the blank facade (the floor of the laboratory).

The results of the measurements and post-processing procedures generated a large amount of data, which were investigated with an analysis of variance to evaluate the statistical significance of the variations of the sound pressure levels and of the chosen psychoacoustic parameters. The ANOVA tests carried out on the different data-sets highlight that in general the measured differences are statistically significant, with respect to the variations of the sound source position and the louvres' tilt angles. The combination of the two factors is in general not statistically significant. There is a significant difference in the behaviour of the η_p^2 in the separate analysis of the psychoacoustic parameters deriving from the presence of the traditional or the sound absorbing shading system. The effects of the louvres' tilt angle seem to be more relevant with respect to the sound source positions in the data set related to the standard louvres, while the tendency is reverse when the sound absorbing louvres are observed. It is possible to ascribe this fact to the poor sound absorption properties of the standard louvres made of simple plywood: for this reason they play an important role as a barrier when they are un-tilted and they can intercept the acoustic field that comes from below. The opposite tendency is observed for the sound absorbing shading system: this can be attributed to the fact that the expanded melamine used in the experiment modifies the content in frequencies of the sound pressure field arriving on the facade and the louvres' tilt angles are less relevant, in view of the quantity of sound absorbing material. The generated sound field is intercepted by the same amount of material with a small consideration of the louvres' tilt angle, while varying the sound source position.

In conclusion, it is possible to affirm that the shading device plays an important role in the variations of sound pressure level and loudness, has quite a good effect on roughness, while it has practically no effect on sharpness. It is possible to say that the traditional shading system has a negative effect as it increases both the sound pressure levels and the loudness over the studied facade portion.

The sound absorbing shading device, on the contrary, can reduce both the loudness and the sound pressure level, respectively, by up to 14 phons and 8 dB. The loudness reduction given by the sound absorbing louvres represents an important result, since loudness is a subjective acoustic parameter, more related to human noise perception, if compared with the sound pressure level in dB, or in dB(A).

The external shading devices have an important role both in controlling the internal comfort of the building for its users and in reducing the cooling energy consumption. This research highlights that an acoustic optimisation of the louvres can additionally play an important role in reducing not only the sound pressure levels over the building facade, but in particular the magnitude perception of the noise. An accurate research activity is needed in order to study in greater detail the psychoacoustic analysis of the shading devices. Further investigations should optimise the louvres' materials, their tilt angle, their spacing and dimensions, in order to simultaneously maximise energy saving, daylighting distribution and the acoustic and psychoacoustic protection of the building facade.

Acknowledgments: The research leading to these results was partially funded by the grant "Young Researchers 2016", provided by the University of Ferrara (IT). The grant derives by the 5‰ part of the Italian tax return (2013), assigned to the University of Ferrara.

Author Contributions: The study of the acoustic behaviour of the external shading devices began as a collaboration between the University of Florence (Simone Secchi) and the University of Ferrara (Patrizio Fausti). It was then continued at the University of Sheffield (Jian Kang) where Nicolò Zuccherini Martello carried out a period of research. Nicolò Zuccherini Martello designed and built the shading device model. Together with Patrizio Fausti and Simone Secchi, he carried out the measurements in the semi-anechoic chamber of the University of Ferrara and made the post-processing of the collected data. Nicolò Zuccherini Martello elaborated the impulse responses in order to analyse the psychoacoustics parameters. Francesco Aletta provided useful hints for the psychoacoustic and for the statistical analysis of the data-set of the variations of sound pressure levels, loudness, roughness and sharpness. Jian Kang supervised the whole process for the evaluation of the psychoacoustic parameters and the statistical analysis.

Conflicts of Interest: The authors declare no conflict of interest.

Appendix

Table A1. Two-way Factorial ANOVAs results referred to the differences in Loudness.

ANOVA Fixed Factors	Dependent Variable: Differences in Loudness Levels	
	Traditional Louvres	**Sound Abs. Louvres**
Sound Source Position (p.n.)	$F_{(2, 99)} = 20$, $p = 5.07 \times 10^{-8}$, $\eta_p^2 = 0.29$	$F_{(2, 99)} = 157.22$, $p = 1.87 \times 10^{-31}$, $\eta_p^2 = 0.76$
Sound Source Position (traf.)	$F_{(2, 99)} = 16.75$, $p = 5.43 \times 10^{-7}$, $\eta_p^2 = 0.25$	$F_{(2, 99)} = 159.88$, $p = 9.93 \times 10^{-32}$, $\eta_p^2 = 0.76$
Louvres Tilt Angle (p.n.)	$F_{(2, 99)} = 33.11$, $p = 9.76 \times 10^{-12}$, $\eta_p^2 = 0.40$	$F_{(2, 99)} = 65.67$, $p = 7.01 \times 10^{-19}$, $\eta_p^2 = 0.57$
Louvres Tilt Angle (traf.)	$F_{(2, 99)} = 35.96$, $p = 1.83 \times 10^{-12}$, $\eta_p^2 = 0.42$	$F_{(2, 99)} = 152.59$, $p = 2.82 \times 10^{-19}$, $\eta_p^2 = 0.58$
Factors Interaction (p.n.)	$F_{(4, 99)} = 1.51$, $p = 0.20$, $\eta_p^2 = 0.06$	$F_{(4, 99)} = 2.27$, $p = 0.07$, $\eta_p^2 = 0.08$
Factors Interaction (traf.)	$F_{(4, 99)} = 2.23$, $p = 0.07$, $\eta_p^2 = 0.08$	$F_{(4, 99)} = 4.20$, $p = 0.12$, $\eta_p^2 = 0.07$

Table A2. Two-way Factorial ANOVAs results referred to the differences in Roughness.

ANOVA Fixed Factors	Dependent Variable: Differences in Roughness	
	Traditional Louvres	**Sound Abs. Louvres**
Sound Source Position (p.n.)	$F_{(2, 99)} = 4.04$, $p = 0.021$, $\eta_p^2 = 0.075$	$F_{(2, 99)} = 8.59$, $p = 3.63 \times 10^{-4}$, $\eta_p^2 = 0.148$
Sound Source Position (traf.)	$F_{(2, 99)} = 3.13$, $p = 0.048$, $\eta_p^2 = 0.06$	$F_{(2, 99)} = 162.48$, $p = 5.39 \times 10^{-32}$, $\eta_p^2 = 0.77$
Louvres Tilt Angle (p.n.)	$F_{(2, 99)} = 44.86$, $p = 1.35 \times 10^{-14}$, $\eta_p^2 = 0.475$	$F_{(2, 99)} = 1.066$, $p = 0.35$, $\eta_p^2 = 0.021$
Louvres Tilt Angle (traf.)	$F_{(2, 99)} = 38.14$, $p = 5.23 \times 10^{-13}$, $\eta_p^2 = 0.43$	$F_{(2, 99)} = 66.13$, $p = 5.77 \times 10^{-19}$, $\eta_p^2 = 0.57$
Factors Interaction (p.n.)	$F_{(4, 99)} = 5.10$, $p = 0.001$, $\eta_p^2 = 0.171$	$F_{(4, 99)} = 0.09$, $p = 0.98$, $\eta_p^2 = 0.04$
Factors Interaction (traf.)	$F_{(4, 99)} = 6.65$, $p = 8.81 \times 10^{-5}$, $\eta_p^2 = 0.21$	$F_{(4, 99)} = 4.10$, $p = 0.004$, $\eta_p^2 = 0.14$

Table A3. Two-way Factorial ANOVAs results referred to the differences in Sharpness.

ANOVA Fixed Factors	Dependent Variable: Differences in Sharpness	
	Traditional Louvres	Sound Abs. Louvres
Sound Source Position (p.n.)	$F(2, 99) = 23.19, p = 5.47 \times 10^{-9}, \eta_p^2 = 0.32$	$F(2, 99) = 12.2, p = 1.84 \times 10^{-5}, \eta_p^2 = 0.198$
Sound Source Position (traf.)	$F(2, 99) = 22.13, p = 1.14 \times 10^{-8}, \eta_p^2 = 0.31$	$F(2, 99) = 15.00, p = 1.91 \times 10^6, \eta_p^2 = 0.23$
Louvres Tilt Angle (p.n.)	$F(2, 99) = 26.26, p = 7.07 \times 10^{-10}, \eta_p^2 = 0.35$	$F(2, 99) = 3.22, p = 0.04, \eta_p^2 = 0.06$
Louvres Tilt Angle (traf.)	$F(2, 99) = 15.48, p = 1.41 \times 10^{-6}, \eta_p^2 = 0.24$	$F(2, 99) = 9.87, p = 1.20 \times 10^{-4}, \eta_p^2 = 0.16$
Factors Interaction (p.n.)	$F(4, 99) = 2.92, p = 0.02, \eta_p^2 = 0.10$	$F(4, 99) = 1.47, p = 0.21, \eta_p^2 = 0.06$
Factors Interaction (traf.)	$F(4, 99) = 0.59, p = 0.67, \eta_p^2 = 0.02$	$F(4, 99) = 1.08, p = 0.37, \eta_p^2 = 0.04$

Table A4. Two-way Factorial ANOVAs results referred to the differences in Sound Pressure Levels.

ANOVA Fixed Factors	Dependent Variable: Differences in Sound Pressure Levels	
	Traditional Louvres	Sound Abs. Louvres
Sound Source Position	$F(2, 99) = 47.58, p = 3.31 \times 10^{-15}, \eta_p^2 = 0.49$	$F(2, 99) = 64.67, p = 1.07 \times 10^{-18}, \eta_p^2 = 0.57$
Louvres Tilt Angle	$F(2, 99) = 11.91, p = 2.32 \times 10^{-5}, \eta_p^2 = 0.19$	$F(2, 99) = 26.53, p = 5.93E{-}10, \eta_p^2 = 0.35$
Factors Interaction	$F(4, 99) = 0.46, p = 0.77, \eta_p^2 = 0.02$	$F(4, 99) = 0.11, p = 0.98, \eta_p^2 = 0.005$

References

1. Fritschi, L.; Brown, A.L.; Kim, R.; Schwela, D.; Kephalopolous, S. *Burden of Disease from Environmental Noise—Quantification of Healthy Life Years Lost in Europe*; The World Health Organization, Regional Office for Europe: Copenhagen, Denmark, 2011.

2. Grubesa, S.; Jambrosic, K.; Domitrovic, H. Noise barriers with varying cross-section optimized by genetic algorithms. *Appl. Acoust.* **2012**, *73*, 1129–1137. [CrossRef]

3. Koussa, F.; Defrance, J.; Jean, P.; Blanc-Benon, P. Acoustic performance of gabions noise barriers: Numerical and experimental approaches. *Appl. Acoust.* **2013**, *74*, 189–197. [CrossRef]

4. Oldham, D.J.; Egan, C.A. A parametric investigation of the performance of multiple edge highway noise barriers and proposals for design guidance. *Appl. Acoust.* **2015**, *96*, 139–152. [CrossRef]

5. Van Renterghem, T.; Attenborough, K.; Maennel, M.; Defrance, J.; Horoshenkov, K.; Kang, J.; Bashir, I.; Taherzadeh, S.; Altreuther, B.; Khan, A.; et al. Measured light vehicle noise reduction by hedges. *Appl. Acoust.* **2014**, *78*, 19–27. [CrossRef]

6. Van Renterghem, T.; Forssen, J.; Attenborough, K.; Jean, P.; Defrance, J.; Hornikx, M.; Kang, J. Using natural means to reduce surface transport noise during propagation outdoors. *Appl. Acoust.* **2015**, *92*, 86–101. [CrossRef]

7. Hosanna—Greener-Cities. Available online: www.greener-cities.eu (accessed on 14 September 2016).

8. Tang, S.K. Noise screening effects of balconies on a building facade. *J. Acoust. Soc. Am.* **2005**, *118*, 213–221. [CrossRef] [PubMed]

9. El Dien, H.H.; Woloszyn, P. The acoustical influence of balcony depth and parapet form: Experiments and simulations. *Appl. Acoust.* **2005**, *66*, 533–551. [CrossRef]

10. Lee, P.J.; Kim, Y.H.; Jeon, J.Y.; Song, K.D. Effects of apartment building facade and balcony design on the reduction of exterior noise. *Build. Environ.* **2007**, *42*, 3517–3528. [CrossRef]

11. Busa, L.; Secchi, S.; Baldini, S. Effect of Facade Shape for the Acoustic Protection of Buildings. *Build. Acoust.* **2010**, *17*, 317–338. [CrossRef]

12. Ishizuka, T.; Fujiwara, K. Full-scale tests of reflective noise-reducing devices for balconies on high-rise buildings. *J. Acoust. Soc. Am.* **2013**, *134*, 185–190. [CrossRef] [PubMed]

13. Tang, S.K.; Ho, C.Y.; Tso, T.Y. Insertion losses of balconies on a building facade and the underlying wave interactions. *J. Acoust. Soc. Am.* **2014**, *136*, 213–225. [CrossRef] [PubMed]

14. Kang, J.; Brocklesby, M.W. Feasibility of applying micro-perforated absorbers in acoustic window systems. *Appl. Acoust.* **2005**, *66*, 669–689. [CrossRef]

15. Tong, Y.G.; Tang, S.K. Plenum window insertion loss in the presence of a line source—A scale model study. *J. Acoust. Soc. Am.* **2013**, *133*, 1458–1467. [CrossRef] [PubMed]

16. Tong, Y.G.; Tang, S.K.; Kang, J.; Fung, A.; Yeung, M.K.L. Full scale field study of sound transmission across plenum windows. *Appl. Acoust.* **2015**, *89*, 244–253. [CrossRef]

17. Cellai, G.; Carletti, C.; Sciurpi, F.; Secchi, S. Transparent Building Envelope: Windows and Shading Devices Typologies for Energy Efficiency Refurbishments. In *Building Refurbishment for Energy Performance, Green Energy and Technology*; Magrini, A., Ed.; Springer: Cham, Switzerland, 2014; pp. 61–118.

18. Secchi, S.; Sciurpi, F.; Pierangioli, L.; Randazzo, M. Retrofit strategies for the improvement of visual comfort and energy performance of classrooms with large windows exposed to East. *Energy Procedia* **2015**, *78*, 3144–3149. [CrossRef]

19. Yun, G.; Yoon, K.C.; Kim, K.S. The influence of shading control strategies on the visual comfort and energy demand of office buildings. *Energy Build.* **2014**, *84*, 70–85. [CrossRef]

20. Cho, J.; Yoo, C.; Kim, Y. Viability of exterior shading devices for high-rise residential buildings: Case study for cooling energy saving and economic feasibility analysis. *Energy Build.* **2014**, *82*, 771–785. [CrossRef]

21. Sakamoto, S.; Aoki, A. Numerical and experimental study on noise shielding effect of eaves/louvers attached on building façade. *Build. Environ.* **2015**, *94*, 773–784. [CrossRef]

22. Zuccherini Martello, N.; Fausti, P.; Santoni, A.; Secchi, S. The Use of Sound Absorbing Shading Systems for the Attenuation of Noise on Building Facades. An Experimental Investigation. *Buildings* **2015**, *5*, 1346–1360. [CrossRef]

23. Zuccherini Martello, N.; Fausti, P.; Secchi, S. Acoustic Measurements on a 1:1 Scale Model of a Shading System for Building Facade in a Semi-Anechoic Chamber. In Proceedings of the Inter-Noise 2016, Hamburg, Germany, 21–24 August 2016; pp. 3813–3824.

24. Genuit, K.; Fiebig, A. Prediction of psychacoustic paramenters. In Proceedings of the Noise-Con 2005, Minneapolis, MN, USA, 17–19 October 2005.

25. Salomons, E.M.; Janssen, S.A. Practical Ranges of Loudness Levels of Various Types of Environmental Noise, Including Traffic Noise, Aircraft Noise, and Industrial Noise. *Int. J. Environ. Res. Public Health* **2011**, *8*, 1847–1864. [CrossRef] [PubMed]

26. Sottek, R.; Genuit, K. Models of signal processing in human hearing. *AEU—Int. J. Electron. Commun.* **2005**, *59*, 157–165. [CrossRef]

27. Neubauer, R.O.; Kang, J. Airborne sound insulation in terms of a loudness model. *Appl. Acoust.* **2014**, *85*, 34–45. [CrossRef]

28. ISO 16283-1:2014. *Acoustics—Field Measurement of Sound Insulation in Buildings and of Building Elements—Part 1: Airborne Sound Insulation*; International Organization for Standardization: Geneva, Switzerland, 2014.

29. Fastl, H.; Zwicker, E. *Psychoacoustics: Facts and Models*, 3rd ed.; Springer: Berlin, Germany, 2007.

30. ISO 3745:2012. *Acoustics—Determination of Sound Power Levels and Sound Energy Levels of Noise Sources Using Sound Pressure–Precision Methods for Anechoic Rooms and Hemi-Anechoic Rooms*; International Organization for Standardization: Geneva, Switzerland, 2012.

31. ISO 10534-2:1998. *Acoustics—Determination of Sound Absorption Coefficient and Impedance in Impedance Tubes—Part 2: Transfer-Function Method*; International Organization for Standardization: Geneva, Switzerland, 1998.

32. ISO 16283-3:2016. *Acoustics—Field Measurement of Sound Insulation in Buildings and of Building Elements—Part 3: Façade Sound Insulation*; International Organization for Standardization: Geneva, Switzerland, 2016.

33. DIN 45631:1991. *Procedure for Calculating Loudness Level and Loudness*; Deutsches Institut für Normung: Berlin, Germany, 1991.

34. DIN 45692:2009. *Measurement Technique for the Simulation of the Auditory Sensation of Sharpness*; Deutsches Institut für Normung: Berlin, Germany, 2009.

35. Aures, W. Berechnungsverfahren fur den sensorischen Wohlklang beliebiger Schallsignale (A model for Calculating the Sensory Euphony of Various Sounds). *Acustica* **1985**, *59*, 130–141.

36. EN 1793-3:1997. *Acoustics—Road Traffic Noise Reducing Devices. Test Method for Determining the Acoustic Performance. Part 3: Normalized Traffic Noise Spectrum*; European Committee for Standardization: Bruxelles, Belgium, 1997.

Article

Advanced Rating Method of Airborne Sound Insulation

Reinhard O. Neubauer

IBN Bauphysik GmbH & Co. KG, Theresienstr. 28, 85049 Ingolstadt, Germany;
in@ibn.de or dr.neubauer@ibn.de; Tel.: +49-841-34173

Academic Editor: Gino Iannace
Received: 15 September 2016; Accepted: 20 October 2016; Published: 26 October 2016

Abstract: This paper describes an advanced calculation scheme based on the loudness level linked to the specific fluctuation strength yielding a weighted normalized loudness level difference as a single number value. This advanced rating method is a useful tool investigating airborne sound insulation. Evidence has been presented that a simple level difference is not a suitable method to exhibit the effects of a given signal to the airborne sound insulation. Additionally, while using a weighted normalized loudness level difference, the effect of different test signals results in a significant influence in the single number value. By analyzing the difference between the standard airborne sound insulation value and the weighted normalized loudness level difference, the sound pressure level that is transmitted through a partition is demonstrated to contain important details concerning the subjective assessment. This study supports findings in the literature that airborne sound insulation performance is significantly dependent on what type of sound signal is used. This paper investigates six different thicknesses of a sand-lime brick using five different sound samples. The study indicates that no single number value can be modeled at this time in relation to a certain construction to fulfill comparable results related to a hearing sensation.

Keywords: airborne sound insulation; subjective assessment; loudness; sound signal; level difference; transmission loss; weighted sound reduction index; assessment; noise awareness

---

1. Introduction

Acoustic comfort is assessed in general by subjective evaluation. It describes a condition that expresses satisfaction with the acoustical environment. In that sense, building acoustics is an important factor in building design; in particular, the interior walls, partitions, and floors need to be designed to prevent the intrusion of sound from one room into another. In general, rooms for residential purposes, flats, and dwelling houses are supposed to be designed and constructed with the aim to provide reasonable airborne sound insulation [1]. A measure to describe airborne sound insulation is the airborne sound reduction index or the sound level difference; both are descriptors defined in standards.

Protection against noise is such an essential requirement that it has been stated in the European Construction Product Regulation [2]. A major factor arises from disturbances between dwellings due to audible sounds perceived from neighbor activities. The basic characteristics of a sound field are now known; however, so far, how people perceive these measures has hardly been taken into considerations. It is, however, important to be aware of the fact that limits given in standards and regulations cannot guarantee that no unwanted sound transmission occur [3]. The main body of standards of sound insulation in dwellings originated in the early 1950s [4,5]. In Germany the first standard dated as early as 1938 [6]. Meanwhile, living standards have improved significantly. A consequence of this is, among others, that home entertainment systems and other domestic electrical appliances are extensively used. The quality of sound insulation in buildings is generally described as a single number rating of sound insulation.

Neubauer and Kang introduced a concept describing a frequency-dependent weighted normalized loudness level difference [7–9]. This concept is intended to be a connection between the objective measure of airborne sound insulation and the psychoacoustic measures of the loudness level and fluctuation strength.

This paper describes the advanced method and discusses the model of a weighted normalized loudness level difference. Some values of the measured and calculated airborne sound insulation for sand-lime bricks of different thicknesses are presented, and computed values of the weighted normalized loudness level differences of the respective sand-lime bricks using different sound samples are discussed. To assess the differences in the evaluation of source signals, electronic filters were generated. The investigation is based on the single number value of the weighted normalized loudness level difference.

2. Calculation Scheme and Method of Assessment

The advanced rating method as introduced by Neubauer and Kang is given as the frequency-dependent weighted normalized loudness level difference, as shown in Equation (1) and is described in detail in [8].

$$L_{nor,w}(f) = L_{nor(f)} \times w_{(f)},$$ (1)

where $L_{nor(f)}$ is the normalized level difference, and $w_{(f)}$ is a weighting factor

A method for determining a single value of a sound in terms of a loudness level is given in ISO 532 B [10] and in DIN 45631 [11]. The loudness level can be obtained for any sound [12]. The single number quantity for the normalized loudness level difference (L_{nor}) is written as the quotient of the differences of the total loudness levels (L_N), which yields the following:

$$L_{nor} = \frac{L_{N1} - L_{N2,m}}{L_{N1} - L_{N2,0}} = \frac{\Delta L_m}{\Delta L_0},$$ (2)

where the level difference of the idealized (i.e., hypothetical or computed) airborne sound insulation has subscript 0 and the measured has subscript m. The level L_{N1} is the loudness level in the source room, and L_{N2} is the loudness level in the receiving room.

The idealized airborne sound insulation to obtain ($L_{N2,0}$) may be found using a prediction model as provided by, e.g., EN 12354 [13], or by assuming a reference curve, e.g., ISO 717-1 [14].

The total specific fluctuation strength is calculated as the sum of all partial fluctuation strength yielding Fls'. The single number quantity of the weighting (w) is then the following:

$$w = \frac{Fls'_m}{Fls'_0}.$$ (3)

The multiplication of Equations (2) and (3) yields a single number quantity for the weighted normalized loudness level difference ($L_{nor,w}$) and is written as the following:

$$L_{nor,w} = L_{nor} \times w.$$ (4)

3. Measured and Calculated Values

3.1. Airborne Sound Insulation

To investigate a construction without the influence of a flanking transmission, measurements taken in a laboratory were used. In this study, six different sand-lime brick thicknesses were studied. The values of the measured and calculated weighted sound reduction index (R_w) for the sand-lime bricks of different thicknesses are shown in Table 1.

Table 1 shows measured and calculated R_w-values, the surface density m', the thickness of the sand-lime brick t, the critical frequency f_c, and the respective normalized and weighted normalized loudness level difference L_{nor} and $L_{nor,w}$ when using pink noise as a source signal. The standardised method assessing airborne sound insulation, which takes into account the dependence of sound insulation on the incident spectrum according to ISO 717-1, provides two basic spectrum adaptation terms, C and C_{tr}, which are also given in Table 1. C is the spectrum adaptation term for A-weighted pink noise, and the spectrum adaptation term for A-weighted urban traffic noise is C_{tr}.

Table 1. Calculated [1] and measured R- and R_w- values, and related values. Signal: pink noise.

t (mm)	70 mm		115 mm		150 mm		175 mm		240 mm		300 mm	
	Meas.	Calc.	Meas.	Calc.	Meas.	Calc.	Meas.	Calc.	Meas.	Calc.	Meas.	Calc.
R_w (dB)	43	42	46	45	54	51	56	54	60	59	63	63
C (dB)	−1	−1	−1	0	−1	0	−1	−1	−1	−1	−2	−1
C_{tr} (dB)	−5	−3	−4	−3	−5	−4	−5	−5	−5	−5	−5	−6
m' (kg/m²)	130		180		285		341		475		614	
f_c (Hz)	-	423	-	237	-	200	-	173	-	127	-	104
L_{nor} (-)	1.029		0.969		1.057		1.064		1.025		1.018	
w (-)	1.047		0.996		0.889		0.858		0.841		0.889	
$L_{nor,w}$ (-)	1.078		0.964		0.940		0.912		0.862		0.905	

[1] The calculation of the respective airborne sound insulation was performed using the software INSUL 8.0.

3.2. Sound Signals

To quantify the sound insulation effect of different sound signals and to allow a numerical investigation of the results, a series of measurements were carried out. The influence using different signals was investigated via two categories of signals, namely, steady-state and non-steady-state signals.

The steady-state signals are the broadband noise signals, "pink noise" (PN) and "white noise" (WN). These signals were chosen because they are recommended in the standards for measuring airborne sound insulation.

The non-steady-state signals, i.e., the transient signals, were music samples, namely, rap (Eminem: "Lose Yourself") (E) and classic music (Beethoven: Symphony Nr. 9: "Poco Allegro, Stringendo Il Tempo, Sempre Piu Allegro—Prestissimo") (B). This type of music has also been investigated earlier [15–17].

Additionally, a sound sample called "party sound" was used as a source signal. This sound was a combination of people talking and laughing and dance music.

The time spectra of the used signals are shown in Figure 1.

For the investigated sound source signals, the psychoacoustic parameters loudness level and specific fluctuation strength were calculated, and the results are listed below in Table 2.

Table 2. Psychoacoustic factors of the unprocessed signals: sound pressure level (L), loudness level (L_N), and specific fluctuation strength (Fls') [1].

Sound Sample	L (dB)	L_N (Phon)	Fls' (Vacil)
White Noise	85	98.5	0.0166
Pink Noise	85	99.1	0.0225
Beethoven	85	97.2	0.1182
Eminem	85	94.8	0.223
Party Sound	85	94.8	0.129

[1] The calculations of the respective loudness level (L_N) and specific fluctuation strength (Fls') were done using the software ArtemiS V11, HEAD acoustics.

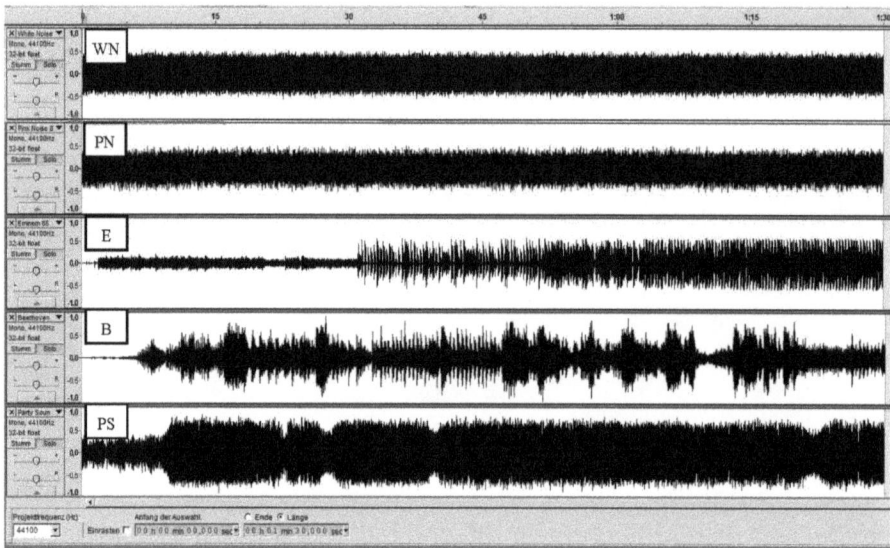

Figure 1. Time signal of white noise (WN), pink noise (PN), Eminem (E), Beethoven (B), and Party Sound (PS) with equivalent continuous sound pressure level of 85 dB and duration of 90 s.

3.3. Sound Level of Interest

After transmission of the source signal (L_1) through a structure or partition (R_w, D_{nT}), the sound heard by a listener is the receiving sound signal (L_2). The filtered level (L_2) contains all the information of the airborne sound insulation characterized by the weighted apparent sound reduction index (R'_w) as it is the transmitted sound signal. The sound level of interest (L_2) is, in this study, the electronically filtered sound sample, which is obtained using a filter function representing the sound insulation (R_w) of interest. The filter function, i.e., the transfer function used in the software, is generated by modeling the R-values as the coefficients of a built transfer function. The phon is a unit of perceived loudness level (L_N), which is a subjective measure of the strength of a sound so that the measure of sound insulation is written in terms of a loudness level. Thus, the heard sound, which is the sound level of interest (L_2), is assessed in terms of a loudness level L_N.

If the loudness level (L_N) of the sound signals used in this study is calculated for different sound pressure levels, it is observed that there is no linear correlation between both measures. This is illustrated in Figure 2, where the loudness level is depicted over sound pressure level.

From Figure 2, it is seen that the loudness level is not linearly related to the sound pressure level and is dependent on the type of signal. Even for an equal sound pressure level, the calculated loudness level differs in its absolute value depending on the type of signal. Inspection of this data shows that varying the sound signal, i.e., using a broadband noise signal and a transient signal, leads to somewhat different results, allowing the sound pressure level to remain constant. This means that the loudness of a broadband sound and that of a transient signal are different. This is in agreement with the literature [12].

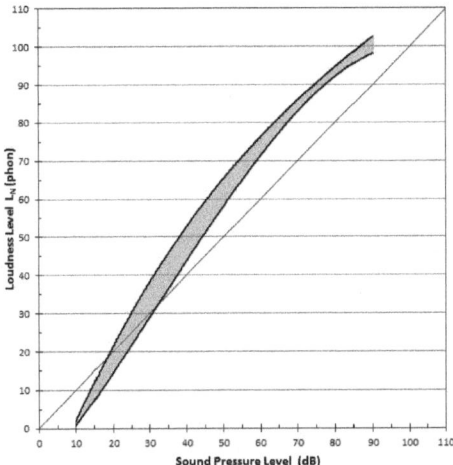

Figure 2. Loudness level (L_N) as a function of sound pressure level for different sound signals including transient and steady state signals. The shaded area characterizes the region for the loudness level (L_N). The straight line corresponds to the following relationship: sound pressure level = loudness level.

The calculated psychoacoustic parameter specific fluctuation strength (*Fls'*) is also not a linear function and is also dependent on the type of signal and on the level of the sound signal. In Figure 3, the region of the specific fluctuation strength (*Fls'*) of the sound signals used in this study is depicted as a function of sound pressure level.

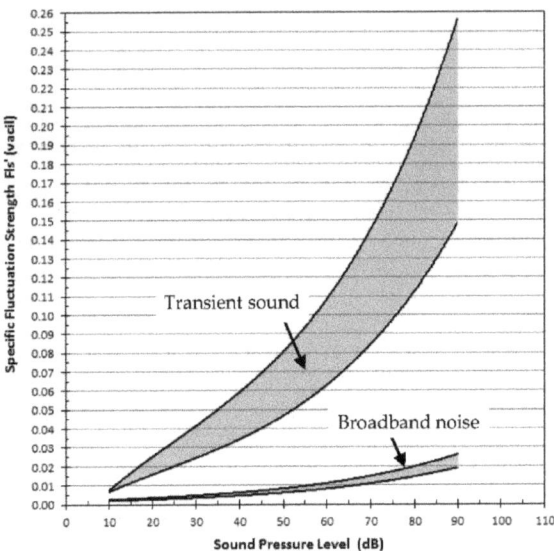

Figure 3. Specific fluctuation strength (*Fls'*) as a function of sound pressure level. The shaded area characterizes the region for the specific fluctuation strength (*Fls'*).

It is seen that the broadband noise signal has little specific fluctuation strength, whereas the transient signal, i.e., music-type signal, spreads with increasing sound pressure level. This means that the specific fluctuation strength depends on the level of the signal. For very low sound pressure levels, i.e., below approximately 10 dB, both signal types tend to be close to zero. The smallest values are observed using white noise, and the maximum values are identified for the music-type signal E. The deviation of the studied signal types, i.e., the difference between a broadband noise signal and a music-type signal, was observed to be as large as a factor of approximately 100.

3.4. Weighted Normalized Loudness Level Difference

The computed normalized loudness level difference (L_{nor}) for different sound samples is presented in Figure 4. Analyzing Equation (2), it is clear that a value greater than 1 indicates that the measured airborne sound insulation (R_w) performs better than the calculated insulation.

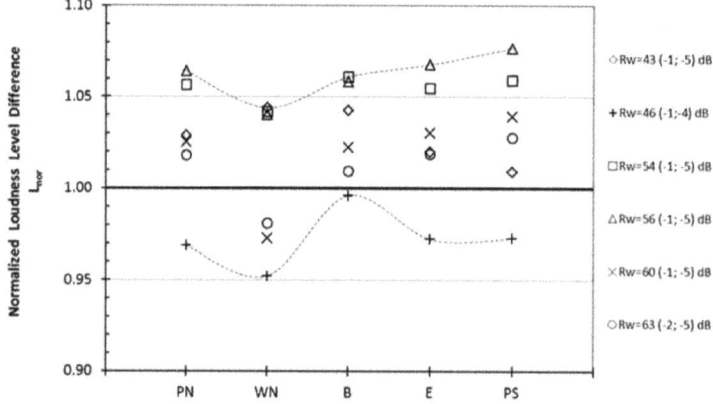

Figure 4. Normalized loudness level difference (L_{nor}) for different sound samples calculated for a single wall construction of sand-lime brick of thickness ranging from 70 to 300 mm and calculated sound reduction index R_w (C; C_{tr}). The upper and lower dotted grey lines indicate the region for the individual results. PN stands for pink noise, WN for white noise, B for Beethoven, E for Eminem, and PS for Party Sound.

The computed values of the weighted normalized loudness level differences of the respective sand-lime bricks of different thicknesses are presented in Table 3, and the results are depicted graphically in Figure 5.

Table 3. Calculated weighted normalized loudness level differences. The different signal types are indicated by PN for pink noise, WN for white noise, B for Beethoven, E for Eminem, and PS for Party Sound.

Thickness mm	Weighted Normalized Loudness Level Difference ($L_{nor,w}$) for Different Thicknesses and Different Sound Signals				
	WN	PN	E	B	PS
70	1.060	1.078	1.041	0.987	1.079
115	0.901	0.964	1.005	0.996	1.069
150	0.929	0.940	0.987	0.983	1.009
175	0.925	0.912	0.977	0.998	0.970
240	0.897	0.862 [1]	0.990	1.004	0.975
300	1.033	0.905	1.038	1.010	1.081 [1]
Mean	0.957	0.943	1.006	0.996	1.030
Standard deviation	0.071	0.074	0.027	0.010	0.052

[1] The bold and italic numbers in Table 3 are the minimum and maximum values.

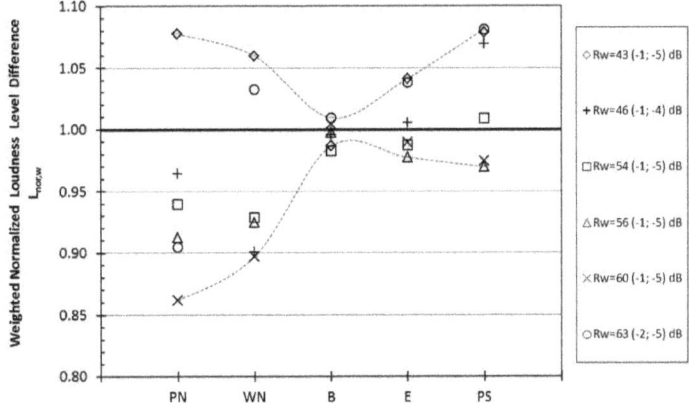

Figure 5. Weighted normalized loudness level difference ($L_{nor,w}$) for different sound samples calculated for a single wall construction of sand-lime brick of thickness ranging from 70 to 300 mm and calculated sound reduction index R_w (*C*; *Ctr*). The upper and lower dotted grey line indicates the region for the individual results. PN stands for pink noise, WN for white noise, B for Beethoven, E for Eminem, and PS for Party Sound.

Table 3 shows the $L_{nor,w}$-values for different thicknesses of the sand-lime brick, and different sound signals.

Figure 5 shows the weighted normalized loudness level difference ($L_{nor,w}$) for different sound samples. Analyzing Equation (4) reveals that results greater than 1 indicate a tendency that theoretical values are overestimated in comparison to measurements.

4. Analysis of Results

The range of measured weighted sound reduction index (R_w) with surface density 130–614 kg/m^2 varies between 43–63 dB (Table 1). The range of respective spectrum adaptation terms (*C*; C_{tr}) is −1 dB. A comparison with calculated values reveals that there is a maximum difference in airborne sound insulation of 3 dB.

The time signals used to compute the loudness level had a sound pressure level of 85 dB and duration of 90 s. In theory, it should be clear that computing the airborne sound insulation using different sound signals should reveal no difference. This is only true if sound pressure level differences or even loudness level differences are concerned [8].

Comparing results in Table 3 where the weighted normalized loudness level difference is depicted reveals that a minimum value (0.862) was observed using pink noise insulated by a construction of sand-lime brick with a thickness of 240 mm, while a maximum value (1.081) was observed for the "party sound" sample insulated by a construction of sand-lime brick with a thickness of 300 mm. It is seen in Table 3 that the "party sound" sample, followed by the music sample E, yielded the highest mean values. The broadband noise samples (pink and white noise) yielded the smallest values.

In Figure 5, it is seen that the music sound sample B yielded the smallest values, whereas the broadband noise signal "pink noise" showed large variation in response. This is also indicated by the calculated standard deviation of the mean for pink noise, which was ±0.074, whereas B yielded the smallest standard deviation: ±0.010 (Table 3). This result showed clearly that different sounds yield different weighted normalized loudness level differences indicating a large scattering of measured and predicted results.

5. Discussion

The results of Figure 4 (normalized loudness level difference) indicate that the measured airborne sound insulation (R_w), for most of the investigated constructions, performs better than indicated by the calculation. This result turns completely if we analyze results in Figure 5 (weighted normalized loudness level difference), which reveals that for most of the investigated constructions, theoretical values tend to be overestimated in comparison to measurements. This indicates that a loudness level difference does not adequately describe the effect of a transient signal in a hearing related measure. From comparing the psychoacoustic values of loudness level and specific fluctuation strength, it is clear that no linear relation exists for a specific sound sample. This means that no single number value can be modeled at this time in relation to a certain construction. This becomes very clear by inspection of Figure 5. The main reason for this is that the sound signal (i.e., the type of signal) plays a major part in the perception of a sound sample (as demonstrated by psychoacoustic data), although, as was shown in this study, a construction can be found for a particular sound signal and sound insulation.

6. Conclusions

This paper showed the effects of different sound signals on airborne sound insulation by relating objective measures of a sound pressure level difference and subjective related measures, i.e., loudness level and specific fluctuation strength. The study supports results presented earlier [8] that an index of sound insulation expressed as a single number rating (such as the weighted sound reduction index) cannot provide a reliable measure of the perceived efficacy of the insulation.

The computed efficacy of airborne sound insulation was investigated, revealing that an objective measure of efficacy is dependent on the type of sound signal. As shown by the comparison of calculated values with experimental results, the difference in weighted normalized loudness level demonstrated dependence on signal characteristics and on the type of airborne sound insulation.

This study supports the advanced calculation scheme of a loudness-based model. It has been shown that it is feasible to transform the objective measure of a sound pressure level into a loudness level and form, together with the specific fluctuation strength, a subjectively related evaluation. This new measure of a weighted normalized loudness level difference permits evaluating a construction in terms of an objective and subjectively related measure.

Conflicts of Interest: The author declares no conflict of interest.

References

1. The Building Regulation. Approved Document E. UK Regulation, into force since 1 July 2003. Available online: https://www.gov.uk/government/publications/resistance-to-sound-approved-document-e (accessed on 15 September 2016).
2. Construction Products Regulation (CPR). Regulation No. 305/2011 of the European Parliament and of the European Council of 9 March 2011, Official Journal of the European Communities. 4.4.2011. L 88/5. Available online: http://eur-lex.europa.eu/legal-content/EN/TXT/HTML/?uri=CELEX:32011R0305&from=EN (accessed on 15 September 2016).
3. Noise. Technical Handbooks 2013 Domestic—Noise, The Scottish Government Publications. Section 5—Noise. Available online: http://www.gov.scot/Resource/0045/00459728.pdfhttp://eur-lex.europa.eu/legal-content/EN/TXT/HTML/?uri=CELEX:32011R0305&from=EN (accessed on 15 September 2016).
4. Rasmussen, B.; Rindel, J.H. Concepts for Evaluation of Sound Insulation of Dwellings—From Chaos to Consensus? In Proceedings of the 4th European Congress on Acoustics (Forum Acusticum), Budapest, Hungary, 29 August–2 September 2005.
5. Neubauer, R.O.; Scamoni, F. Die Akustische Klassifikation in Italien und Deutschland: Perspektiven und Möglichkeiten. (In German). In Proceedings of the Conference on Acoustics EUROREGIO, Merano, Italy, 22 March 2013; pp. 1–4.

6. DIN 4110:1938. *Technische Bestimmung für die Zulassung neuer Bauweisen. (Technical Specification for the Approval of New Construction Methods)*; Beuth Verlag: Berlin, Germany. (In German)

7. Neubauer, R.O.; Kang, J. Airborne Sound Insulation Based on a Model of Loudness. In Proceedings of the 21st International Congress on Sound and Vibration (ICSV), Beijing, China, 13–17 July 2014.

8. Neubauer, R.O.; Kang, J. Airborne sound insulation in terms of a loudness model. *Appl. Acoust.* **2014**, *85*, 34–45. [CrossRef]

9. Neubauer, R.O.; Kang, J. A Model Based on Loudness Level to Describe Airborne Sound Insulation. In Proceedings of the 43rd International Congress on Noise Control Engineering (InterNoise), Melbourne, Australia, 16–19 November 2014.

10. ISO 532/R. *Acoustics- Method for Calculating Loudness Level*; International Organization for Standardization: Geneva, Switzerland, 1975. (Standard confirmed in 2012).

11. DIN 45631/A1:2010-03. *Berechnung des Lautstärkepegels und der Lautheit aus dem Geräuschspektrum-Verfahren nach E. Zwicker-Änderung 1: Berechnung der Lautheit zeitvarianter Geräusche*; Beuth Verlag: Berlin, Germany. (In German)

12. Fastl, H.; Zwicker, E. *Psychoacoustics: Facts and Models*, 3rd ed.; Springer: Berlin, Germany, 2007.

13. EN 12354-1:2000. *Building Acoustics. Estimation of Acoustic Performance in Buildings from the Performance of Elements (Part 1: Airborne Sound Insulation between Rooms)*; European Committee for Standardization (CEN): Brussels, Belgium, 2016.

14. ISO 717-1:2013. *Acoustics—Rating of Sound Insulation in Buildings and of Building Elements, Part 1: Airborne Sound Insulation*; International Organization for Standardization: Geneva, Switzerland, 2013.

15. Neubauer, R.O.; Kang, J. What Describes the Airborne sound Insulation in Technical and Subjective Regard? In Proceedings of the 6th Forum Acusticum, Aalborg, Denmark, 26 June–1 July 2011; pp. 1783–1787.

16. Neubauer, R.O.; Kang, J. Time Structure of the Signal in Airborne Sound Insulation. In Proceedings of the 9th European Conference on Noise Control (EuroNoise), Prague, Czech Republic, 10–13 June 2012.

17. Neubauer, R.O.; Kang, J. Airborne Sound Insulation as a Measure for Noise Annoyance. In Proceedings of the 21st International Congress on Acoustics (ICA), Montréal, QC, Canada, 2–7 June 2013.

Article

Field Measurements of Water Supply and Drainage Noise in the Bathrooms of Korea's Multi-Residential Buildings

Hong-Seok Yang [1], Hyun-Min Cho [2] and Myung-Jun Kim [2,*]

[1]   Land and Housing Institute, Korea Land and Housing Corporation, Daejeon 34047, Korea; acousticsyang@gmail.com
[2]   School of Architecture, University of Seoul, Seoul 02504, Korea; chunryou@nate.com
*   Correspondence: mjunkim@uos.ac.kr; Tel.: +82-2-6490-2761

Academic Editor: Jian Kang
Received: 7 October 2016; Accepted: 15 November 2016; Published: 22 November 2016

Abstract: In Korea, water supply and drainage noises result in one of the main noise complaints because more than 50% of people reside in multi-residential buildings. In this study, a series of field measurements were therefore carried out to examine the current noise situation. The noise levels were measured in the bathrooms of the upper and lower floors, as well as in habitable rooms. The measurement results for the bathrooms of the lower floor ($N = 113$) are 47.8 dBA (water closet), 42.7 dBA (basin), and 33.9 dBA (bathtub) for water drainage, while values vary between 33.7 dBA and 37.0 dBA for the water supply. The results suggest that the water drainage noise needs to be controlled first. The system bathroom (42.8 dBA) produced lower noise levels than the wet construction method (48.2 dBA) for all of the sanitary wares. The highest noise levels in the living rooms ($N = 11$) and bedrooms ($N = 8$) of the lower floor are 34.3 dBA and 39.1 dBA, respectively. The average noise level in the rooms ($N = 19$) is 37.8 dBA. The overall result suggests that it is necessary to develop an acoustic guideline to satisfy the higher Class of the 2nd ISO/CD 19488, although the current noise level satisfies Class C (living room) and Class D (bedroom).

Keywords: water supply and drainage noise; bathroom; multi-residential building; field measurement

1. Introduction

Due to their high expectations for the quality of their housing, the residents of multi-residential buildings demand regulations regarding the levels of indoor noise such as floor impact noise, airborne noise through walls, and water supply and drainage noises. Especially in Korea, the level of this requirement is higher than those of other countries because more than 50% of people reside in multi-residential buildings with high property prices. The Korean government has consequently enacted several noise regulations regarding the allowable indoor noise level and classifications for floor impact noise, the sound insulation of walls, and transport noise.

In contrast to the above noise regulations, water supply and drainage noises from bathrooms are evaluated by a Korean certification tool named G-SEED (Green Standard for Energy and Environmental Design) [1], which assigns different points for each tier in the evaluation of the sustainability of a building. In G-SEED, the sustainability of the water supply and drainage noises is mainly determined by whether pipes and construction methods that result in the generation of low noise levels have been applied or not, rather than the noise level.

The noise generated from sanitary wares such as a water closet is unpleasant for residents living on lower floors. In Korea, water supply and drainage noises result in one of the main noise complaints because the drain-pipe system is installed through the penetration of a slab between the upper and lower floors in most multi-residential buildings. The penetrated vertical pipe is then connected to horizontal pipes that are installed above the ceiling. The pipe system draining the fluctuating fluid consequently comprises a vulnerable structure that transmits sound energy with structure-borne and airborne paths [2–5].

In Korea, multi-residential buildings have been built with various floor plans. Generally, the number of bathrooms is one for floor plans with two bedrooms or fewer, while more than two are built for floor plans with more than three bedrooms. In housing units with more than two bathrooms, one bathroom is generally attached to a master bedroom. The water supply and drainage noises can therefore be transmitted easily through an adjacent bedroom, which causes noise annoyances during rest periods, as well as sleep disturbances at night.

In this study, a series of field measurements was therefore carried out to investigate the current situation regarding water supply and drainage noises in terms of the bathrooms and adjacent rooms of 14 types of floor plans for multi-residential buildings in Korea. This measurement campaign was conducted as a preliminary study for the proposal of an acoustic-design guideline so that a certain noise level can be satisfied for the water supply and drainage in the bathrooms and adjacent rooms of multi-residential buildings.

2. Literature Review on Noise Criteria and Regulations

2.1. Korea

In Korea, national regulations and recommendations for indoor noise levels with respect to water supply and drainage noises in multi-residential buildings are currently absent, although a KS (Korean Standard) [6,7] that is related to the method for measurement and evaluation has been issued. On the other hand, national regulations on acceptable indoor noise levels are implemented for floor impact noise and airborne noise from neighbors [8,9]. The minimum requirement for the indoor noise level from external traffic noise is also managed by a relevant national regulation [10]. As described in Table 1, the regulations for the indoor noise level in L_{eq} (equivalent continuous A-weighted sound-pressure level) during the daytime ranges between 43 dBA and 45 dBA, while the 5 dBA for night-time is stricter. Impulsive noise such as floor-impact noise is regulated at less than 57 dBA in L_{max} (maximum A-weighted sound-pressure level) during the daytime.

Table 1. Korean regulation on acceptable indoor noise level for different noise sources.

Type of Noise Sources	Noise Index	Indoor Noise Level (dBA)	
		Daytime (06:00 to 22:00)	Night-Time (22:00 to 06:00)
Structure-borne noise (e.g., floor-impact noise)	L_{eq}	43	38
	L_{max}	57	52
Airborne noise (e.g., TV noise from neighbor)	L_{eq}	45	40
Road traffic noise	L_{eq}	45	
Water supply and drainage noise	None	None	

The G-SEED is a Korean certification system that was created to accomplish the construction of environmental-friendly buildings. Within G-SEED, the measures for the reduction of water supply and drainage noises are assessed according to four tiers, as described in Table 2. The tier in Table 2 is determined by checking whether building elements and construction methods that generate low noise levels have been applied or not. The highest point is four, and is given to the construction method called "in-floor type", whereby the pipes on the slab are installed at the same floor.

In Korea, the field measurements of water supply and drainage noises are carried out based on KS F 2870 (supply noise) and KS F 2871 (drainage noise). The standards describe factors such as the location and height of microphones, room conditions, and background-noise correction. Alternatively, KS F 2872 [11] is the rating method for water supply noise based on the NC-curve and A-weighted SPL (sound-pressure level).

Table 2. Criteria and credits in G-SEED for measures to reduce water supply and drainage noises.

Tier	Criteria	Weighting Factors
1	9 points or above	1.0
2	7 to 8 points	0.75
3	5 to 6 points	0.5
4	4 points and below	0.25

- Dwelling-water-supply pressure less than 2.5 kgf/cm^2: 3 points
- Low-flow toilet less than 6 L, single-flush (or 9 L/5 L, dual-flush): 2 points
- Installation of buffer at pipe-crossing slabs: 1 point
- Low-noise drainage pipe: 2 points
- In-floor type for water supply and drainage pipes: 4 points
- Noise-reduction measure for air ducts: 2 points

2.2. ISO and ASHRAE

Recently, researchers involved with the ISO/TC 43/SC 2/WG 29 proposed the 2nd ISO/CD 19488 [12] titled "Acoustic classification of dwellings". The ISO standard is a guideline to facilitate the national implementation of the acoustic classification scheme for residential buildings. The classification scheme specifies the criteria in habitable rooms in dwellings from indoor service equipment producing intermittent noise or irregular noise such as water supply and drainage noises from neighboring spaces, with the six classes described in Table 3. The specified classes are related to in situ measurements, either in the frequency bands in accordance with ISO 16032 [13], or directly in the A-weighted maximum F SPL in accordance with ISO 10052 [14]. The lowest class is F, indicating that the minimum limit is less than 46 dBA in habitable rooms.

Table 3. Class limits for service equipment noise from neighboring spaces (The 2nd ISO/CD 19488).

Type of Space and Sources	Quantity	Class A	Class B	Class C	Class D	Class E	Class F
In habitable rooms in dwellings from service equipment, producing intermittent or irregular noise from neighboring spaces	$L_{AF,max,nT}$ [1]	≤ 26	≤ 30	≤ 34	≤ 38	≤ 42	≤ 46

[1] $L_{AS,max,nT}$ may also be used, provided that 4 dB stricter limits (lower sound levels) are fulfilled, i.e., the same as the $L_{Aeq,nT}$.

The ASHRAE (American Society of Heating, Refrigerating, and Air-Conditioning Engineers, Piscataway, NJ, USA) also suggests a recommended A-weighted SPL as a slow response for various transient plumbing-noise sources in residential buildings, as described in Table 4 [15]. It is evident that the acceptable noise level in the bathroom is less than 45 dBA, while the threshold is 35 dBA in rooms.

Table 4. Recommended maximum A-weighted SPL for various transient plumbing-noise sources in buildings (ASHRAE handbook).

Receiving Room	L_{Amax} (Slow Response) (dB)
Residential bedroom, living room, dining room	35
Residential bathroom, kitchen	45

3. Methodology

3.1. Description of the Studied Housing Units

Field measurements of the water supply and drainage noises from the bathroom were carried out in 14 types of housing units with different floor areas and plans. The floor areas considered in this study are 33 m^2, 36 m^2, 46 m^2, 59 m^2, 74 m^2, and 84 m^2, and they represent the area for exclusive use. Different floor plans with the same floor area were also selected to examine the characteristics of the sound propagation from the bathroom to the adjacent room. The type of housing unit is distinguished by a symbol that indicates the floor area with a number and a plan in an upper-case letter (e.g., 59A = A type of 59 m²). The number of bathrooms in the housing units with a small floor area between 33 m² and 46 m² is one, while the housing units with a large floor area between 59 m² and 84 m² contain two bathrooms that are attached to the living room and bedroom. Figure 1 shows the 14 floor plans of the studied housing units with different floor areas.

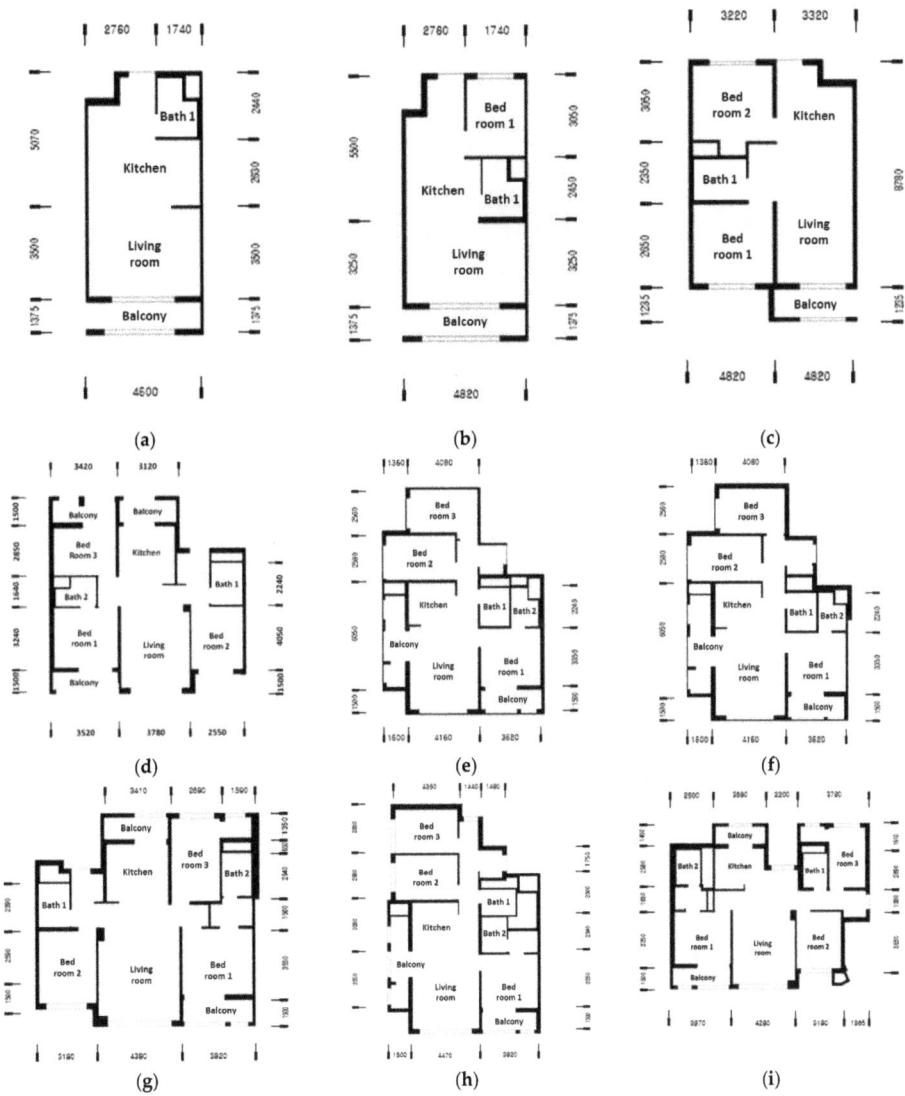

Figure 1. *Cont.*

Figure 1. The 14 floor plans of the studied housing units with different floor areas: (**a**) 33 type; (**b**) 36 type; (**c**) 46 type; (**d**) 59A type; (**e**) 59B type; (**f**) 59C type; (**g**) 74A type; (**h**) 74B type; (**i**) 74C type; (**j**) 84A type; (**k**) 84B1 type; (**l**) 84B3 type; (**m**) 84C type; (**n**) 84D type.

For each type of housing unit, the measurements were also conducted on different floors to examine the fluctuation in noise level due to the altitude of the bathroom in multi-residential buildings with a maximum of 28 floors. The floor in the multi-residential buildings was selected by including the ground, middle, and top floors. Although it depends on the total floors of a multi-residential building, the number of selected properties is between four and six units with a step of the fifth floor. Table 5 lists the numbers of bathrooms and properties that were measured in the buildings. As described in Table 5, the total number of the studied housings where the noise level in the bathroom of the lower floor was measured according to the use of sanitary wares including the water closet, basin, and bath is 64 (113 bathrooms). Additional measurements for the noise level in 11 properties (19 bathrooms) with different floor plans were also carried out on the middle floor of the building, as follows: (1) noise level in the bathroom of the upper floor; and (2) noise level in the adjacent living room and bedroom of the lower floor. Table 6 summarizes the locations for the noise level measurements.

Although the 2nd ISO/CD 19488 suggests a normalization of the RT in the noise level, the RT measurements for the living room and bedroom are omitted here to examine the current situation in situ, which is the method suggested in the Korean standard. It is expected, however, that the influence of the RT in the normalizing of the noise level is approximately from 2.6 dB to 5.8 dB, based on the previous work that shows that the RT in the unoccupied rooms is between 0.9 s and 1.9 s at 500 Hz [16].

Table 5. The number of lower-floor bathrooms (*N* = 113) and properties (*N* = 64) studied.

Type of Housing Unit	No. of Bathrooms (A)	No. of Properties with the Receiving Bathroom (B)	No. of Studied Bathrooms (A × B)
33	1	5 (1st, 5th, **13th**, 16th, 19th floors)	5
36	1	5 (1st, 6th, **13th**, 20th, 27th floors)	5
46	1	5 (1st, 6th, **13th**, 20th, 27th floors)	5
59A	2	5 (3rd, 6th, **10th**, 15th, 20th)	10
59B	2	5 (3rd, 6th, **10th**, 15th, 19th)	10
59C	2	5 (3rd, 6th, **10th**, 15th, 20th)	10
74A	2	4 (1st, 5th, **10th**, 14 floors)	8
74B	2	5 (1st, 5th, **10th**, 15th, 19th floors)	10
74C	2	4 (1st, 5th, 15th, 19th floors)	8
84A	2	3 (**10th**, 15th, 19th floors)	6
84B1	2	4 (1st, 5th, **10th**, 14th floors)	8
84B3	2	4 (1st, 5th, 15th, 19th floors)	8
84C	2	5 (1st, 5th, 16th, 19th, 24th floors)	10
84D	2	5 (3rd, 6th, **12th**, 17th, 25th)	10

* The bold number of floors indicates the floor where additional noise level measurements were conducted as a representative case for each floor plan (11 floor plans except for 74C, 84B3, and 84C).

Table 6. Measured location and number of properties for each measurement parameter.

Measurement Parameter	Location	No. of Properties
Noise level	In the bathroom of the lower floor	64 properties (113 bathrooms)
	In the bathroom of the upper floor	11 properties (19 bathrooms)
	In the adjacent living room and bedroom of the lower floor	

3.2. Description of the Studied Bathrooms

In this study, the measurements were conducted for the bathrooms for which the UBR (unit bathroom) system and wet construction method have been applied. The UBR system is the prefabricated bathroom for which preassembled elements such as finishes, sanitary wares, concealed pipes, conduits, ceiling, bathroom cabinets, and a shower screen are installed. The UBR system is installed in consideration of the advantages in terms of time- and human power-saving, waterproofing, and soundproofing. In spite of the advantages of the UBR system, most multi-residential buildings in Korea have bathrooms using the wet construction method due to the feasibility of the interior design and the high level of impact noise on lightweight walls from the UBR system. Among the studied housing units with 14 different floor plans, the UBR system had been installed in three of the housing units with small floor areas between 33 m^2 and 46 m^2, while 11 housing units with relatively large floor areas above 59 m^2 had been built using the wet construction method. As given in Table 7, the width (W) and depth (D) of the bathrooms are from 2110 mm to 2500 mm and 1600 mm to 1790 mm, respectively, indicating similar sizes, although the floor areas are different. The heights (D) are different according to the construction methods: 2080 mm for the UPR system and 2270 mm for the wet construction method.

Figure 2a,b show the cross-sections of the bathrooms for which the UBR system and wet construction method were applied, respectively. It can be seen that the thickness of the floor slab is 150 mm for both construction methods. The thicknesses of the air cavity between the slab and the ceiling are 455 mm and 255 mm for the UBR system and the wet construction method, respectively. The ceilings of both construction methods are covered by 2.5 mm PVC (polyvinyl chloride) panels without acoustic absorbers, and they hang on lightweight steel frames. The nominal diameter of the PVC pipes connected to the water closet is 100 mm, with a weight of 1737 g/m and a thickness of 3.1 mm. PVC pipes with a 50 mm nominal diameter are used to drain water from the basin and bathtub. The vertical and horizontal pipes for the water closet were connected with 90-degree elbows that are designed to generate low noise levels. The tilting angle of the horizontal pipe is 5 degrees. The water supply pressure is less than 2.5 kgf/m². The water closet installed in the housing units is a siphon type containing a six-liter water cistern. As shown in Figure 2b, the floors of the bathrooms for which the wet construction method was applied have multiple layers consisting of floor tiles, cement mortar, thermal insulator, and waterproofing. The wall of the bathroom facing the living room and bedroom was built with 190 mm thick masonry.

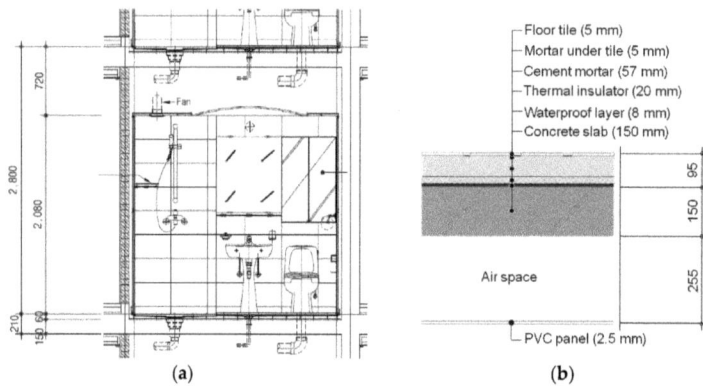

(a)   (b)

Figure 2. Cross-sections of bathrooms for which the (a) UBR system and (b) wet construction method had been applied.

Table 7. Dimensions and construction methods for the bathrooms in each housing unit.

| Type of Housing Unit | Dimension of the Bathroom (W × D × H (mm)) | | Construction Method |
	Bathroom Attached to the Living Room	Bathroom Attached to the Bedroom	
33	2440 × 1740 × 2080 (3.11 m²)	-	UBR system
36	2380 × 1740 × 2080 (3.06 m²)	-	
46	2110 × 1710 × 2080 (3.61 m²)	-	
59A	2240 × 1790 × 2270 (3.62 m²)	2290 × 1640 × 2270 (3.02 m²)	Wet construction
59B	2240 × 1790 × 2270 (3.88 m²)	2240 × 1640 × 2270 (3.07 m²)	
59C	2240 × 1790 × 2270 (3.89 m²)	2480 × 1730 × 2270 (3.00 m²)	
74A	2340 × 1790 × 2270 (3.95 m²)	2340 × 1600 × 2270 (3.56 m²)	
74B	2340 × 1790 × 2270 (3.79 m²)	2230 × 1790 × 2270 (3.83 m²)	
74C	2390 × 1740 × 2270 (4.00 m²)	2340 × 1600 × 2270 (3.58 m²)	
84A	2420 × 1790 × 2270 (3.90 m²)	2390 × 1740 × 2270 (3.99 m²)	
84B1	2420 × 1600 × 2270 (3.87 m²)	2500 × 1620 × 2270 (4.06 m²)	
84B3	2340 × 1590 × 2270 (3.73 m²)	2430 × 1650 × 2270 (4.01 m²)	
84C	2180 × 1740 × 2270 (3.79 m²)	2340 × 1620 × 2270 (3.80 m²)	
84D	2340 × 1790 × 2270 (3.72 m²)	2340 × 1790 × 2270 (4.05 m²)	

3.3. Experimental Setup

The noise levels for the water supply and drainage were measured in the bathroom and adjacent room of the multi-residential buildings. The equipment used for the measurement included a four-channel Harmonie system (0.1 dB) with $\frac{1}{2}$" microphone (G.R.A.S. Type 40AF) and preamplifiers (G.R.A.S. Type 26AG), and the NA-28 portable sound level meter (RION). In the adjacent room including the bedroom and living room, the four-channel Harmonie system and one NA-28 were located at a height of 1.2 m. Four microphones were set up at the corner positions 0.75 m from the room surfaces. One microphone was placed at the center of the room. The noise level in the room was the average value measured over the five microphones. No furniture or other obstacles were in the room. The noise levels in the upper and lower bathrooms were measured using one NA-28 simultaneously located at the center position of each bathroom with a height of 1.2 m. One NA-28 was also located 1 m from the door. In total, eight microphones were used simultaneously for the noise-level measurements for 11 housings with different floor plans, while only one NA-28 was installed in the bathroom of the lower floor for the remaining properties ($N = 53$). Figure 3 shows the experimental setup for the measurements in the bathroom and adjacent rooms of the lower floor. The views of the experimental setups in the bathroom and living room are also shown in Figure 4.

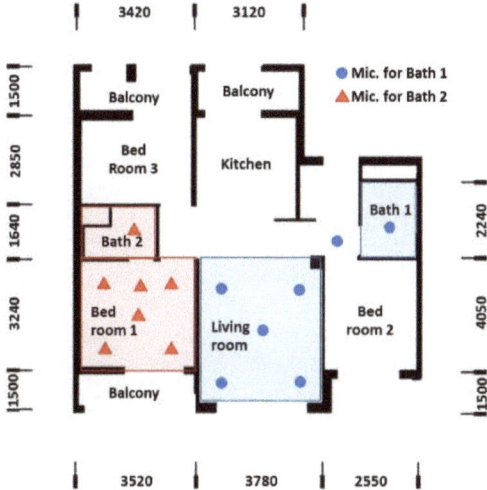

Figure 3. Illustration of the experimental setup for the measurement in the bathroom and adjacent rooms of the lower floor (59A type).

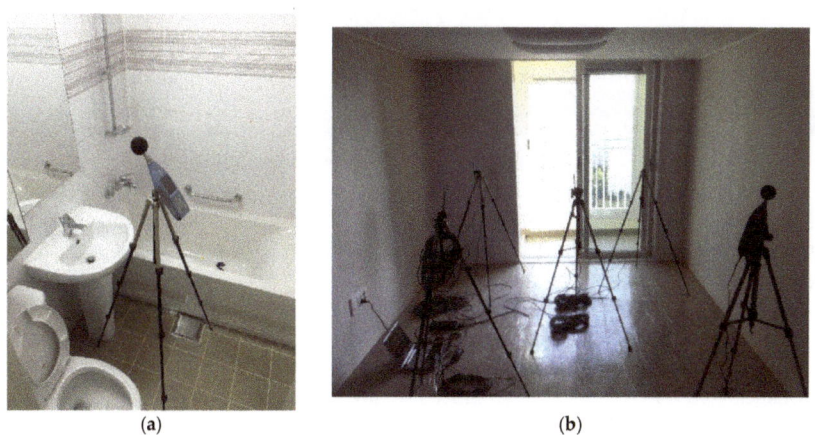

(a)   (b)

Figure 4. Views of the experimental setups in (a) the bathroom and (b) the living room.

The water supply and drainage noises were generated by three consecutive operations of each sanitary ware including the water closet, basin, and bathtub. After the bathtub and basin were filled full of water, the water was drained through the pipe.

The background noises in the bathroom and adjacent rooms are below 25 dBA for the measurements at night-time. This leads to a high S/N (signal-to-noise) ratio over 10 dBA, indicating an insignificant influence of the background noise on the measurement results.

The noise level was measured in L_{AFmax}, as recommended in the 2nd ISO/CD 19488, and in consideration of the fluctuating characteristics of the water supply and drainage noises. The RT in the adjacent rooms was not normalized to examine the noise level in situ.

4. Results

4.1. Time History of Water Supply and Drainage Noises

The use of the sanitary wares in the bathroom of the upper floors generates water supply and drainage noises in the bathroom and adjacent room of the lower floors through structure-borne and airborne transmissions. The time history of the noise generated by the use of each sanitary ware comprises the different characteristics of operation time and fluctuation due to the difference of the amount of used water, the flow velocity, and the diameter and shape of the pipe, among others. In the bathroom, the main sanitary wares include the water closet, basin, and bathtub. Figure 5 shows the time history of the water supply and drainage noises that were measured in different locations simultaneously including in the bathrooms of the upper and lower floors, in front of a closed door, and in the adjacent living room. The time history of the noise from the use of the water closet shows that the water drainage noise generates the peak level during the operation time for about 7 s from the initial usage. After the drainage, water is supplied to the cistern with a low fluctuation of the noise level for approximately 32 s. In all of the measurement locations, the water drainage noise generates the peak noise level due to a siphon, indicating that the maximum noise level is mainly determined during the water drainage. The water supply and drainage noises from the use of the basin and bathtub also generate continuous noise during the water supply, while the noise fluctuates during the water drainage. The difference between the noise levels of the bathrooms of the upper and lower floors is approximately 40 dBA.

Figure 6 shows the time history of the water supply and drainage noises from the use of the water closets installed in 19 bathrooms of 11 housings with different floor plans (11 bathrooms attached to the living room, and eight bathrooms attached to the bedroom). Here, the shortest operation time of the water supply and drainage is approximately 28 s for the bathroom attached to the bedroom of the 84A type, while it is approximately 47 s for the bathroom attached to the living room of the 59A type.

4.2. Noise Level in the Bathroom

The water supply and drainage noises were measured in the bathrooms of the upper ($N = 19$) and lower ($N = 113$) floors according to the use of the sanitary wares including the water closet, basin, and bathtub. Figure 7 shows an example of the frequency spectrum in one octave band for the water supply and drainage noises measured in the bathrooms of the upper and lower floors for the 59A type. The frequency spectrum was analyzed for the noise level measured in L_{AFmax} during the operation time of each sanitary ware. The results show that the use of the water closet generates a relatively high noise level in the bathrooms of the upper and lower floors compared to the basin and bathtub. Generally, the three sanitary wares produced strong sound energies at middle and high frequencies above 500 Hz in the bathroom. It is expected that the high noise levels at the middle and high frequencies cause more sensitive subjective responses due to the use of the sanitary wares.

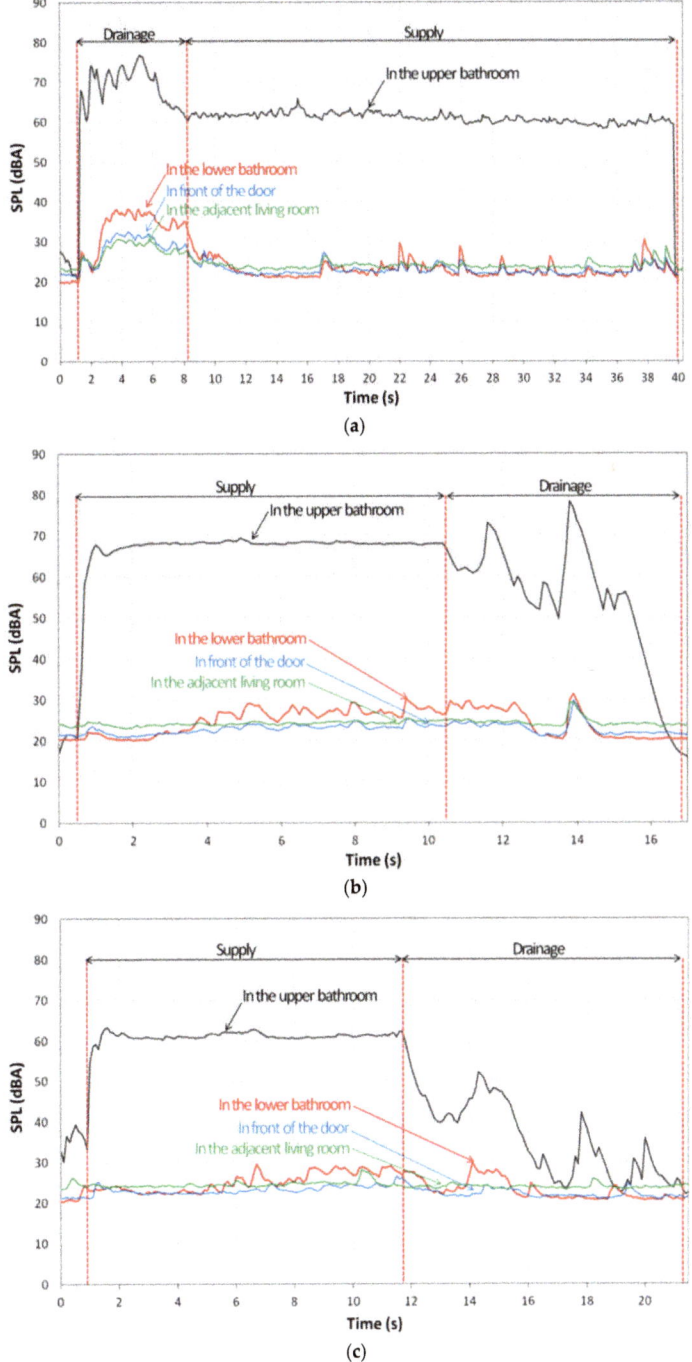

Figure 5. Time history of water supply and drainage noises from the use of sanitary wares including the (**a**) water closet, (**b**) basin, and (**c**) bathtub measured at different locations (only a part of the time history has been shown due to long-time operation).

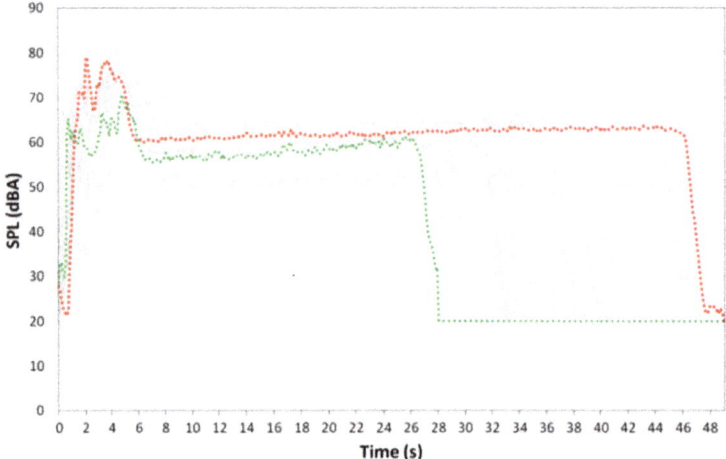

Figure 6. Time history of the noise from the use of the water closet installed in 19 bathrooms of 11 housings with different floor plans (longest time with red dot: bathroom attached to the living room of the 59A type; shortest time with green dot: bathroom attached to the bedroom of the 84A type).

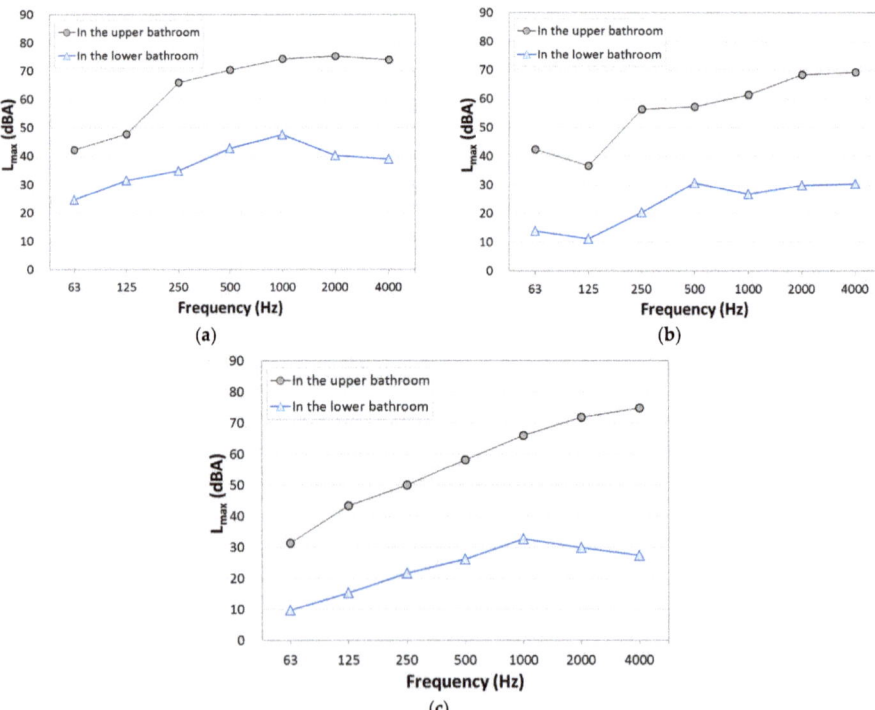

Figure 7. Frequency spectrum of the water supply and drainage noises (L_{AFmax}) from the use of the sanitary wares in the bathrooms attached to the living room of the upper and lower floors for the 59A type: (a) water closet; (b) basin; (c) bathtub.

Figure 8 shows the average noise level from the use of each sanitary ware measured in the bathrooms of the lower floor attached to the living room ($N = 64$) and bedroom ($N = 49$). The results show that the highest noise level is 47.8 dBA for the water drainage from the use of the water closet in the bathroom attached to the bedroom. The noise level of the second ranking is 42.7 dBA for the water drainage from the use of the basin in the bathroom attached to the bedroom. The water supply noise shows similar levels approximately between 33.7 dBA and 37.0 dBA for all of the sanitary wares. The deviation bar indicating the range between the maximum and minimum noise levels implies that the noise level is different according to the studied housings with different plans.

The graph in Figure 9 shows the frequency distribution and cumulative percentage of the maximum noise level in 113 bathrooms of the lower floor according to the water supply and drainage noises of the three sanitary wares. It can be seen that the maximum noise level is concentrated between 46 dBA and 50 dBA. The lowest value of the maximum noise level is 41.3 dBA, whereas the highest value is 60.1 dBA. The average value of the maximum noise levels measured in the 113 bathrooms is 47.7 dBA. The results indicate that most of the residents living in the lower floor can recognize the noise in the bathroom due to the use of the sanitary wares in the upper floor because the S/N ratio is approximately 30 dBA if the background-noise level is assumed to be 20 dBA.

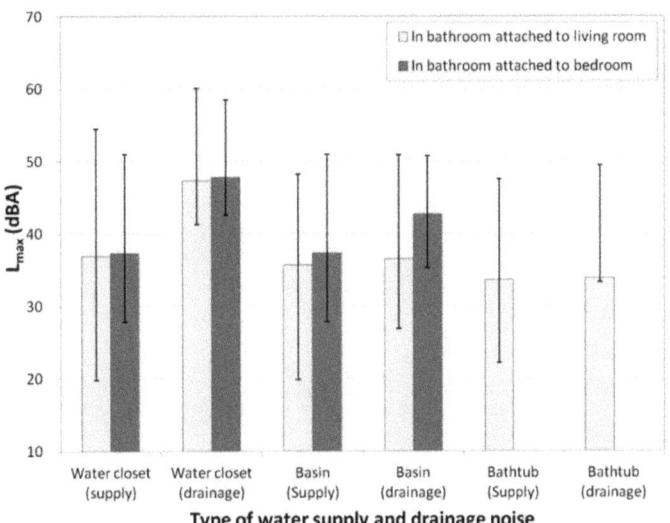

Figure 8. Average noise level for each sanitary ware measured in the bathrooms of the lower floor attached to the living room ($N = 64$) and bedroom ($N = 49$). The deviation bar indicates the range between the maximum and minimum noise levels measured in the different bathrooms.

One of the major factors determining the noise level could be the construction method of the bathroom. In this study, the UBR system has been applied to the floor plans with a small floor area less than 46 m², while the wet-construction method was applied for the larger floor plans. Figure 10 shows the average noise level for the water supply and drainage of each sanitary ware according to the construction methods, including the UBR system ($N = 15$) and the wet-construction method ($N = 97$). The results in Figure 10 indicate that the UBR system generates a noise level that is lower than that of the wet-construction method for all of the operational conditions of each sanitary ware. The highest value of the noise level for the UBR system is 42.8 dBA for the water drainage of the water closet, while it is 48.2 dBA for the wet-construction method. It is also noted that the UBR system has a rather low deviation between the maximum and minimum noise levels compared with the wet-construction method. This implies that the UBR system is advantageous for the management of construction quality in terms of sound insulation.

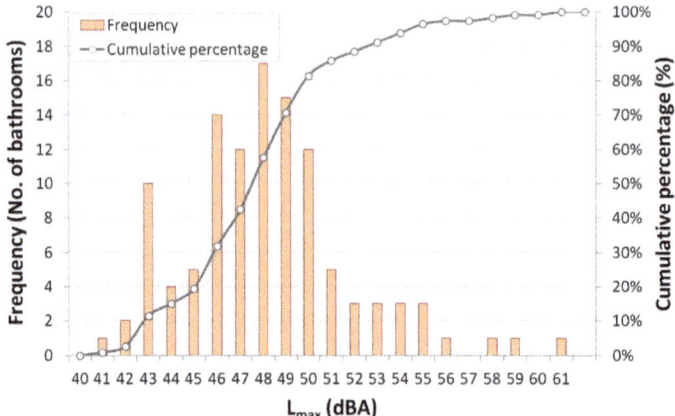

Figure 9. Frequency distribution and cumulative percentages of water supply and drainage noises (L_{AFmax}) in the bathrooms of the lower floor from the use of the sanitary wares ($N = 113$).

In multi-residential buildings, the noise level could change due to the different altitudes of the properties in the multi-residential buildings, thereby affecting the water supply pressure and drainage velocity. The influence of the altitude on the variation of the noise level was therefore examined by dividing the total floors as groups of low (10 floors or fewer, $N = 60$) and high (11 floors or more, $N = 53$) floors, as shown in Figure 11. The results show that the noise levels measured at the low and high floors are similar to each other for all of the operational conditions. This indicates that the altitude of the housing is a manageable design factor affecting the variation of the noise level.

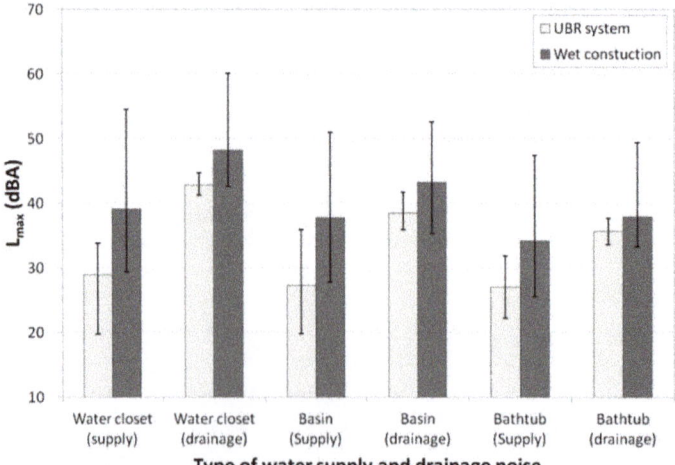

Figure 10. Average noise level for each sanitary ware according to the construction methods including the UBR system ($N = 15$) and wet-construction method ($N = 97$). The deviation bar indicates the range between the maximum and minimum noise levels measured in the different bathrooms.

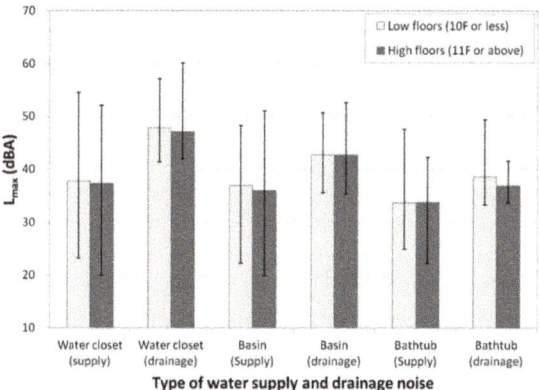

Figure 11. Water supply and drainage noises (L_{AFmax}) according to the groups of low ($N = 60$) and high ($N = 53$) floors.

4.3. Noise Level in the Adjacent Room

The noise levels in the living room and bedroom due to the water supply and drainage in the bathroom form one of the important criteria affecting the indoor environmental quality of multi-residential buildings. Figure 12 shows an example of the frequency spectrum for the water supply and drainage noises from the use of the water closet measured in different locations including the bathroom, in front of the door, and in the adjacent room of the lower floor for the 59B type; here, the door of the bathroom was closed. The results show that the noise levels in both of the adjacent rooms decreased by approximately 10 dBA at the middle frequencies compared with those in the bathroom, while those in front of the door and in the adjacent rooms are similar. It is noted that the overall noise levels in both rooms are strongly determined at 500 Hz and 1000 Hz.

Figure 13 is a graph showing the noise levels measured in the living room ($N = 11$) and bedroom ($N = 8$) of 11 different floor plans according to the different operational conditions of each sanitary ware. The sanitary ware generating the highest noise level is the drainage noise from the water closet for both rooms. The average noise level for the water drainage from the water closet in the bedroom is 39.1 dBA, while it is 34.3 dBA in the living room. Generally, the noise level in front of the door is slightly higher than those in the adjacent rooms.

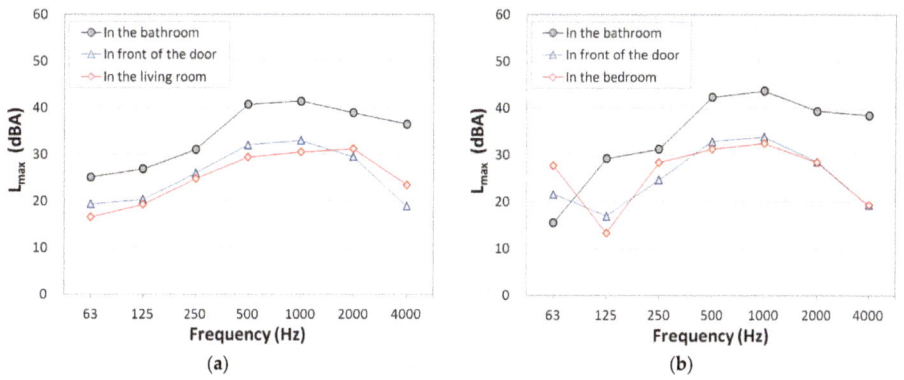

Figure 12. Frequency spectrum of water supply and drainage noises from the use of the water closet measured in the (**a**) living room and (**b**) bedroom of the lower floor for the 59B type.

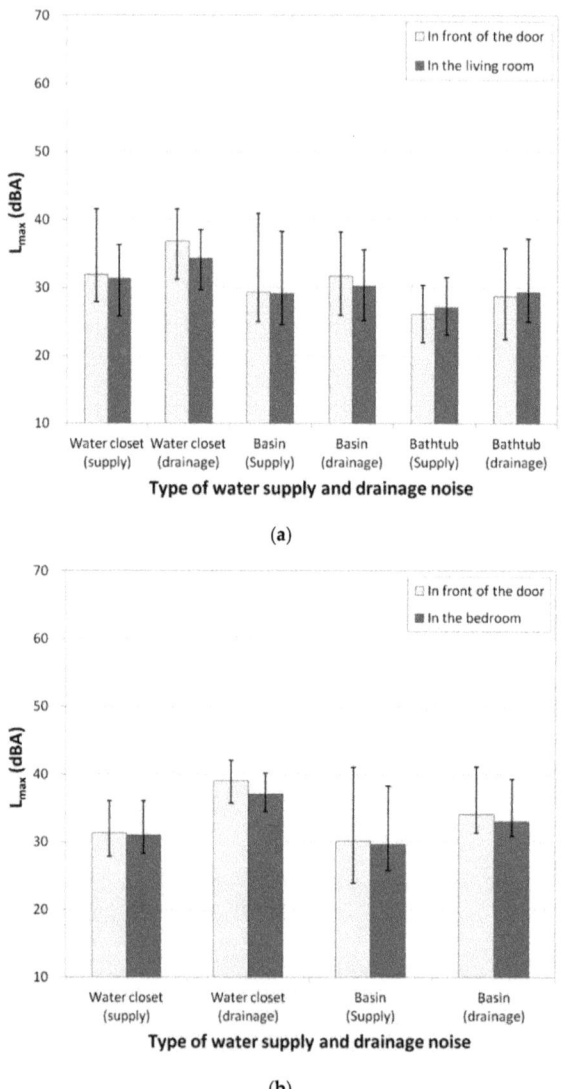

Figure 13. Noise levels measured in the living room (N = 11) and bedroom (N = 8) according to the different operational conditions of each sanitary ware in 11 different floor plans: (**a**) living room; (**b**) bedroom.

Figure 14 shows the frequency distribution and cumulative percentages of the maximum noise levels in the living room and bedroom of the lower floor according to the water supply and drainage noises of the three sanitary wares. The results show that the noise level is concentrated at about 37 dBA, which leads to an average noise level of 37.8 dBA. This result indicates that the water supply and drainage noises could be noticeable, especially at night-time when the background noise is low. Based on the 2nd ISO/CD 19488, it is expected that the average noise level in the rooms meets Class C (living room) and Class D (bedroom) if the RT is normalized.

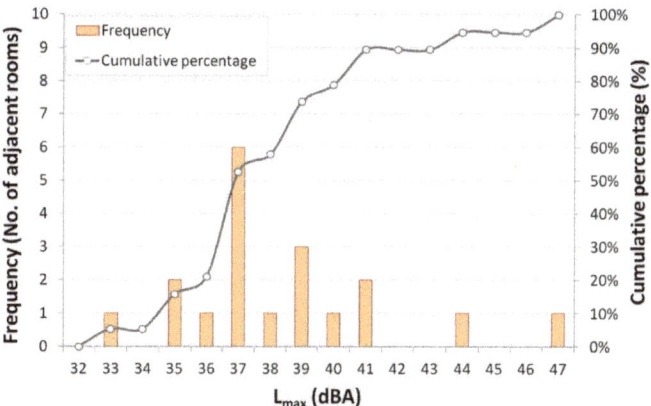

Figure 14. Frequency distribution and cumulative percentages of water supply and drainage noises (L_{AFmax}) in the living room ($N = 11$) and bedroom ($N = 8$) of the lower floor from the use of the sanitary wares.

5. Discussion

Although the focus of this study is the noise levels in situ due to the sanitary wares in the bathroom and adjacent rooms, the final goal of this study is a practical guideline suggestion regarding a way that the noise and vibration transmitted from the bathroom to the adjacent rooms can be controlled to satisfy each class limit described in the 2nd ISO/CD 19488 or the national regulation. Based on the data measured in this study, additional measurements for vibration and sound intensity will be carried out to examine the contribution of the sound energies transmitted through the floor, ceiling, wall, door, and leakages. A laboratory-based experiment is also needed to discover the noise-reduction design factors including the air cavity between the ceiling and floor, the absorber, the sound insulation of the PVC panels covering the ceiling, the vibration isolation of the pipe, the amount of used water, the water pressure, and the lengths and tilting angles of the pipes. Although EN 12354-5 [17] suggests a prediction method of sound levels due to the service equipment, a developed prediction method will also need to be suggested considering the Korean situation. Moreover, a prediction of the sound propagation from the bathroom to the adjacent rooms needs to be carried out in consideration of the various design factors such as the existence of a dressing room, the location of the bathroom, and the distance between the bathroom and the living room.

6. Conclusions

In this study, a series of field measurements were carried out to examine the current situation regarding the water supply and drainage noise in the bathrooms of the multi-residential buildings of Korea. The number of studied housings is 64, and they comprise 14 different floor plans. The water supply and drainage noise were measured in the bathrooms of the lower floor according to the different operations of each sanitary ware including the water closet, basin, and bathtub. The noise levels were also measured in the bathrooms of the upper floor and the adjacent rooms of the lower floor for 11 housing units with different floor plans. The measurement parameters in this study are therefore as follows: (1) noise level in the bathroom of the lower floor ($N = 113$); (2) noise level in the bathroom of the upper floor ($N = 19$); and (3) noise levels in the living room ($N = 11$) and bedroom ($N = 8$) of the lower floor. The time history of the measured SPL from the use of each sanitary ware displayed strongly fluctuating noise levels for the water drainage, while it is rather continuous for the water supply. Also, the water supply and drainage noises produce relatively high SPL values at 500 Hz and 1000 Hz, respectively, compared with the other frequencies.

The measurement results in the bathrooms of the lower floor ($N = 113$) showed that the highest noise level is 47.8 dBA on average for the water drainage noise from the use of the water closet. The second ranking comprises 42.7 dBA for the water drainage noise from the use of the basin, and then 33.9 dBA was measured for the water drainage noise from the use of the bathtub. The water supply noise ranged between 33.7 dBA and 37.0 dBA. The above results suggest that the priority for noise control is in the order of water drainage from the water closet, water drainage from the basin, and water supply to the sanitary wares, as well as water drainage from the bathtub. The frequency distribution and cumulative percentages of the water supply and drainage noises in the bathrooms of the lower floor suggested that the maximum noise level is concentrated between 46 dBA and 50 dBA, thereby deriving the average noise level of 47.7 dBA. The minimum and maximum noise levels ranged between 41.3 dBA and 60.1 dBA. According to the different construction methods of the bathrooms, the UBR system produced a noise level that is lower than that of the wet-construction method for all of the operational conditions of each sanitary ware. The highest noise level for the UBR system is 42.8 dBA, while it is 48.2 dBA for the wet-construction method. The altitude of the housing has an insignificant influence on the variation of the noise level.

The highest noise levels in the living room ($N = 11$) and bedroom ($N = 8$) of the lower floor are 34.3 dBA and 39.1 dBA, respectively, for the water drainage noise from the use of the water closet. The frequency distribution and cumulative percentages of the maximum noise level in the adjacent rooms was concentrated at approximately 37 dBA, thereby deriving the average noise level of 37.8 dBA.

The overall results suggest that the current situation of water supply and drainage noise in the multi-residential buildings of Korea meets Class C (living room) and Class D (bedroom) of the 2nd ISO/CD 19488, although some of the measurement data from the rooms are outside of the minimum limit; however, it is still necessary to develop the acoustic guidelines to satisfy the higher class for the creation of a comfortable residential environment.

Acknowledgments: This work was supported by the 2016 Research Fund of Korea Land and Housing Corporation (R201605003).

Author Contributions: Hong-Seok Yang conceived and designed the experiments; Hong-Seok Yang and Hyun-Min Cho performed the experiments; Hong-Seok Yang and Myung-Jun Kim analyzed the data; and Hong-Seok Yang wrote the paper.

Conflicts of Interest: The authors declare no conflicts of interest.

References

1. G-SEED Green Standard for Energy and Environmental Design. Available online: http://www.g-seed.or.kr/english (accessed on 19 September 2016).
2. Fuchs, H.V. Generation and control of noise in water supply installations: Part 1: Fundamental aspects. *Appl. Acoust.* **1983**, *16*, 325–346. [CrossRef]
3. Fuchs, H.F. Generation and control of noise in water supply installations. Part 2: Sound source mechanisms. *Appl. Acoust.* **1993**, *38*, 59–85. [CrossRef]
4. Fuchs, H.V. Generation and control of noise in water supply installations Part 3: Rating and abating procedures. *Appl. Acoust.* **1993**, *39*, 165–190. [CrossRef]
5. Prek, M. The impact of geometrical parameters on hydrodynamic noise generation. *Appl. Acoust.* **2000**, *60*, 343–351. [CrossRef]
6. Korea Standard (KS). *KS F 2870:2006. Field Measurements of Water Supply Noise in Apartment Bathroom*; Korea Standard (KS): Seoul, Korea, 2006.
7. Korea Standard (KS). *KS F 2871:2006. Field Measurements of Drainage Noise in Apartment Bathroom*; Korea Standard (KS): Seoul, Korea, 2006.
8. The Ministry of Land Infrastructure and Transport. *Criteria for the Interlayer Floor Impact Sound Regulation in Multi-Residential Buildings*; Notification on 2014-446; The Ministry of Land Infrastructure and Transport: Sejong-si, Korea, 2014.

9.   The Ministry of Land Infrastructure and Transport. *Sound Insulation of the Wall Structure and Management Regulation; Notification on 2015-844*; The Ministry of Land Infrastructure and Transport: Sejong-si, Korea, 2015.

10. The Ministry of Land Infrastructure and Transport. *Regulations on Housing Construction Standards*; Notification on 2014; The Ministry of Land Infrastructure and Transport: Sejong-si, Korea, 2014.

11. Korea Standard (KS). *KS F 2872:2008. Rating of Water Supply Noise in Apartment Bathroom*; Korea Standard (KS): Seoul, Korea, 2008.

12. International Organization for Standardization. *ISO/2ndCD 19488:2016. Acoustics—Acoustic Classification of Dwellings*; International Organization for Standardization: Geneva, Switzerland, 2016.

13. International Organization for Standardization. *ISO 16032:2014. Measurement of Sound Pressure Level from Service Equipment in Buildings-Engineering Method*; International Organization for Standardization: Geneva, Switzerland, 2014.

14. International Organization for Standardization. *ISO 10052:2004. Field Measurements of Airborne and Impact Sound Insulation and of Service Equipment Sound-Survey Method*; International Organization for Standardization: Geneva, Switzerland, 2004.

15. American Society of Heating, Refrigerating and Air-Conditioning Engineers, Inc. Chapter 48. Noise and vibration. In *ASHRAE Handbook*; American Society of Heating, Refrigerating and Air-Conditioning Engineers, Inc.: Atlanta, GA, USA, 2011.

16. Kim, M.J.; Lee, B.K. Field measurement and evaluation of the reverberation time in residential buildings. *J. Korean Soc. Living. Environ. Syst.* **2006**, *13*, 213–221.

17. BSI Group. *EN 12354–5:2009. Building Acoustics—Estimation of Acoustic Performance of Building from the Performance of Elements—Part 5: Sounds Levels Due to the Service Equipment*; BSI Group: London, UK, 2009.

Article

Effects of the Distance from a Diffusive Surface on the Objective and Perceptual Evaluation of the Sound Field in a Small Simulated Variable-Acoustics Hall

Louena Shtrepi *, Arianna Astolfi, Giuseppina Emma Puglisi and Marco Carlo Masoero

Energy Department, Politecnico di Torino, Corso Duca Degli Abruzzi 24, Torino 10129, Italy; arianna.astolfi@polito.it (A.A.); giuseppina.puglisi@polito.it (G.E.P.); marco.masoero@polito.it (M.C.M.)
* Correspondence: louena.shtrepi@polito.it; Tel.: +39-011-0904-545

Academic Editor: Gino Iannace
Received: 17 November 2016; Accepted: 23 February 2017; Published: 28 February 2017

Abstract: Simulations of the acoustic effects that diffusive surfaces have on the objective acoustic parameters and on sound perception have not yet been fully understood. To this end, acoustic simulations have been performed in Odeon in the model of a variable-acoustic concert hall. This paper is presented as a follow-up study to a previous paper that dealt with in-field measurements only. As in measurements, a diffusive and a reflective condition of one of the lateral walls have been considered in the room models. Two modeling alternatives of the diffusive condition, that is, (a) a flat surface with high scattering coefficient applied; and (b) a triangular relief modeled including edge diffraction, have been investigated. Objective acoustic parameters, such as early decay time (EDT), reverberation time (T_{30}), clarity (C_{80}), definition (D_{50}), and interaural cross correlation ($IACC$), have been compared between the two conditions. Moreover, an auditory experiment has been performed to determine the maximum distance from a diffusive surface at which the simulated acoustic scattering effects are still audible. Although the simulated objective results showed a good match with measured values, the subjective results showed that the differences between the diffuse and reflective conditions become significant when model (b) is used.

Keywords: room acoustics; simulation; diffuser; scattering; perception

---

1. Introduction

Diffusive surfaces are widely used in performance spaces since they are considered an important design aspect that improves the room's acoustic quality and the listener's enjoyment [1]. Based on this, it has become important to consider their effects on the overall acoustic quality during the early architectural planning stages of a concert hall, usually investigated through geometrical acoustics (GA)-based software. Thus, a lot of effort has been put into the implementation of algorithms that take into account the scattering phenomenon due to diffusive surfaces [2]. However, there is not a clear conclusion as to how the presence, position, and shape of these surfaces influence the acoustic parameters and the subjective perception [3]. Consequently, the correct modeling of these surfaces in GA software is not a trivial task [4]. Therefore, this study aims to investigate the effects of two different modeling alternatives of diffusive surfaces on the reliability and accuracy of the prediction of objective room acoustic parameters and on the perceptual aspects of a concert hall sound field. Furthermore, the surface–distance-dependent sensitivity of the listener has been investigated by comparing the reflective and diffusive configuration of one of the lateral walls. This paper is presented as a follow-up study of the previous paper [5], which dealt with in-field measurements only.

GA-based models have been used as an alternative to both scale-model and in-field measurements after continuous improvements to their accuracy since their first development by Schroeder and

Kuttruff [6]. In particular, additional physical acoustic phenomena have been included such as diffraction and scattering [7–12]. Further interest in auralization has required improvements in the diffusion modeling algorithms, in binaural processing, and in reproduction techniques [2,13,14]. In the last decades, several studies have investigated these aspects based on objective results and on human auditory perception [15,16]. The very demanding field of Virtual Reality has pointed out the need for less computational effort and more realistic auralizations [17,18]. Thus, it becomes important to identify the properties of room acoustics simulation that are perceptually relevant. This affects an important aspect, the modeling level of detail, which in turn might be very time-consuming. The perceptual effects of different surface modeling have not yet been fully investigated. Moreover, the task becomes harder considering that the major drawback, at the actual state of the art of the modeling software, is that the different simulation tools require different input data [19,20]. Thus, the material properties of surfaces or objects, such as absorption and scattering coefficients, have been shown to be aspects that significantly contribute to the uncertainty in simulations and affect their benchmarking [21].

The level of modeling detail is considered a systematic uncertainty factor in GA models and must be decided taking into account the validity of the computational method, which depends on the dimensions of the object or surface irregularities compared to the wavelengths. Practically, this means that objects or surface irregularities that are not large compared to the wavelengths should be considered as flat surfaces with specific properties. No exact guidelines are given regarding this issue, which might lead to significant errors since a GA model might not give accurate results when using either a very detailed model or a very simple one. Several studies have investigated the most appropriate degree of detail in prediction models. Nagy et al. [22] investigated the modeling detail of the audience area in two different kinds of software (Odeon and CATT-Acoustic), while Pelzer, Vorländer, and Maempel [23] assessed the quality of the simulations as function of the model level of detail (LOD). Their preliminary study defined the threshold for the noticeable simplification of the structure size, 70 cm, i.e., there is no need for modeling details beyond this size. Siltanen, Lokki, and Savioja [24] proposed an automatic geometry reduction method, which could simplify the model by reducing irrelevant small details. They concluded that, although this method could be applied in some cases, it needs to be more robust to obtain more reliable results.

The LOD in a GA model affects the generated sound field, which is strongly related to the presence and typology of diffusive surfaces; thus, their acoustical characterization becomes crucial [25–27]. However, general rules are still used to assign the diffusive properties in simulated environments [20,28,29]. As reported in Wang and Rathsam [30], very different scattering coefficient values could produce very different sound fields. They found that models with lower LOD do appear to have greater sensitivity to the scattering coefficient selection, but the changes that have been observed in the parameters did not occur in a consistent manner across all of the halls studied [31]. Wang and Rathsam [30] showed that the scattering coefficient variations do not affect the results of clarity (C_{80}) and lateral fraction (LF_{80}). The most affected parameters are early decay time (EDT) and reverberation time (T_{30}), which exceeded more than two JND-s (Just Noticeable Differences) from the reference model. Lam [20] showed through simulations with different scattering algorithms that the most affected parameter from the scattering coefficient changes was T_{30}. Robinson, Xiang, and Braasch [32] found that the diffusive surfaces applied on the areas of the proscenium splay help to keep stage-to-pit ratios of interaural cross-correlation ($IACC$) high, but, on the other hand, distribute the energy to many reflections over time rather than concentrating it in strong early reflections, leading to decreases in C_{80}. Another variable, which is shown to be influential in determining the model's sensitivity to scattering coefficient, is the listener position [16,30]. A receiver closer to the wall is more sensitive to changes in scattering coefficients than a receiver far from the wall. This sensitivity is particularly related to changes in T_{30}. The contribution of all these variables makes it more challenging to draw a general analytical formula that could relate the scattering coefficient to the acoustic parameters [33]. The correct evaluation of these parameters must also consider the scattering variable, since the realistic environments do not have a perfect diffuse field [34].

Based on these studies, it is evident that the accurate physical simulation of room acoustics is a very complex task. The decision of how much precision should be required from the prediction models relies on our ability to detect differences between reality and simulations. The auditory system seems to be insensitive to many aspects, e.g., small variations in the surface scattering properties [35]. Therefore, the prediction of room acoustical perception needs to take the insensitivity of the auditory system into account. This is linked to the JND of the acoustic objective and subjective parameters, which allows for the characterization of a space and enables numerical comparison between different environments. The simulation using numerical techniques gives clues as to how a performance hall would sound when achieved. Thus, it becomes crucial for the investigation of different alternatives and for the control of the design costs. Acousticians, performers, and architects agree on the need for well-defined objective descriptors that would allow for quantifying specific subjective impressions of the acoustics of the performance space. Especially in enclosed spaces, humans are quite sensitive to the perception of sound in all its temporal, spectral, and spatial aspects, which makes a realistic auralization in room acoustics quite challenging. These three aspects are strongly affected by the presence of diffusive surfaces [36], thus more insight into their use is needed.

In this paper, the model of a variable-acoustics concert hall has been used to investigate, objectively and subjectively, the differences between different modeling techniques of a diffusive surface, as well as the sensitivity of the acoustic parameters to the reflective and diffusive condition of one of the lateral walls. Simulations have been performed in a small shoebox-like concert hall in order to isolate the independent effects of the diffusive surfaces on the acoustic parameters. Two different acoustic configurations of one of the long lateral walls—that is, alternatively reflective or diffusive—have been considered and compared. As reported above, these configurations have been the object of formerly performed acoustic measurements [5]; the measurement setup has been briefly described in this paper (Section 2) in order to aid a better understanding of the investigation. The calibration of the prediction model has been performed based on four acoustic parameters: early decay time (EDT), reverberation time (T_{30}), clarity (C_{80}), and definition (D_{50}). Furthermore, the interaural cross-correlation ($IACC$) has been evaluated based on simulated binaural impulse responses obtained at three different distances from the variable wall. All the acoustic parameters have been obtained and compared for both reflective and diffusive configurations. A perceptual evaluation has been performed through listening tests aimed at determining the maximum distance from the lateral diffusive wall at which the acoustic scattering effects are still audible in the two different modeling alternatives. All the objective and subjective results have been compared to the in-field measurement results.

2. Methods

2.1. Room Model Setup

The model of a variable acoustic concert hall, the *Espace de Projection* at IRCAM in Paris (Figure 1), has been considered in this study. Figure 2 depicts the plan of the hall, which has a rectangular geometry (24 m × 15.5 m × 10 m), and a capacity of 350 seats [37,38]. The geometry and the acoustical properties of the hall can be varied by controlling 172 independently rotating panels (2.3 m × 2.3 m) named *periactes*. Each wall of the hall has four levels of panels. Each panel is made of three triangular prisms (Figure 1), which have three faces with different acoustic properties: reflective, diffusive, and absorptive. The absorptive scheme of all panels has been studied in order to have two different absorption coefficients for adjacent panels. Thus, the total number of panels is divided into two parts: the absorptive side of half of the prisms is filled with a material that absorbs low frequencies (type A), while the other part of the prism has a side that absorbs high frequencies (type B). These two typologies have been obtained by using perforated metal sheets with layers of glass–wool and aluminum sheets inside. The absorptive characteristics of the materials used in the hall are given in Table 1, namely type A and type B [37]. The acoustic characteristics of the walls and ceiling can be modified by changing the properties of the rotating prisms. Six different acoustic conditions of the panels, that is, absorptive, reflective, diffusive, absorptive/reflective, absorptive/diffusive, and diffusive/reflective, can be obtained for the rotating prisms in the second and upper levels, while the first level of the panels can only assume two different configurations: reflective and absorptive.

The two hall configurations, whose in-field measurements results are analyzed and discussed in Shtrepi et al. [5], were chosen in this study so that one of the lateral walls was set at two different acoustic conditions: reflective and reflective/diffusive. The second condition is referred to as diffusive condition for easier understanding throughout the paper. Three CAD models have been created (Figure 1): the reflective condition (RF), which is modeled with flat surfaces, and the diffusive condition, which has diffusive surfaces modeled in two ways, flat (DF) or explicitly modeling the 3D triangular structure (DM).

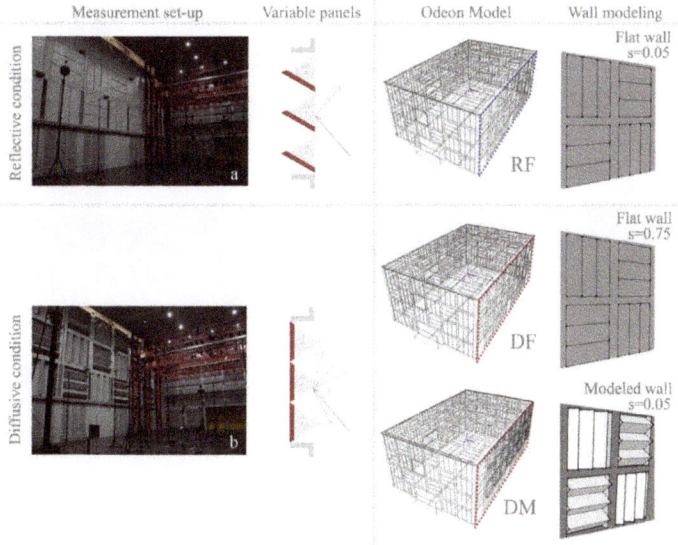

Figure 1. Photos of the two acoustic conditions in the hall: reflective (**a**) and diffusive (**b**). CAD model (RF) for the reflective condition, which is modeled with flat surfaces and s = 0.05. Two CAD models for the diffusive condition: DF (diffusive flat) the prisms have been modeled as a flat surface with s = 0.75, while in the DM (diffusive modeled) the triangular structure has been maintained and s = 0.05 is assigned to each small face.

In the DF model, the prisms have been modeled as a flat surface to which a scattering coefficient equal to the scattering coefficient of the diffusive surface they represent (0.75 at 707 Hz) is assigned. This value was obtained by BEM-based simulations performed with prediction software named AFMG Reflex [39]. Shtrepi et al. [5] gives the results for the frequency-dependent scattering coefficient. Reflex is two-dimensional acoustics simulation software that models the reflection, diffusion, and scattering properties of a sound wave incident upon a defined geometrical structure. Some assumptions are made in these evaluations, namely that the geometry extends infinitely in the third dimension, i.e., into and out of the computer monitor screen. The surface of the sample is assumed to be perfectly rigid and does not absorb sound or allow sound to be transmitted through it. The calculation of the scattering coefficients is based on the ISO 17497-1 [26], while the directivities are evaluated based on the Cox and D'Antonio method [40]. In the DM model, the prisms are modeled as 3D geometries, and to each surface of the prisms a scattering coefficient equal to that of a flat surface (0.05 at 707 Hz) is assigned [41].

The ceiling and the other walls have been fixed to be absorptive in the measurements; thus, they have been assigned absorption coefficients based on type A and type B panels' properties (see Table 1). The absorptive condition was also chosen for the lower level panels in all the measurements in order to avoid the strong reflections from the lower parts of the walls, as this configuration is not usual for an audience in a concert hall. Therefore, the type A and B panel properties have been assigned to these surfaces in the simulations. The floor has been considered as a hard reflective surface.

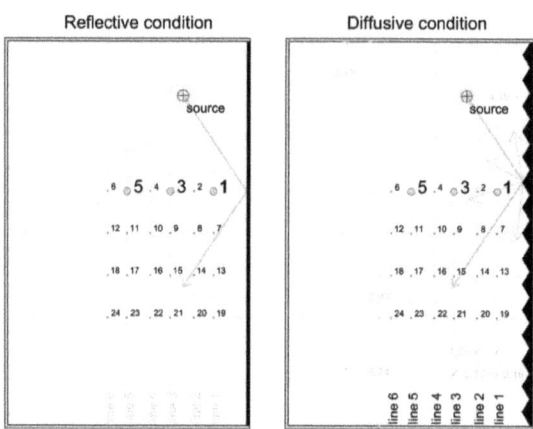

Figure 2. Scheme of the plan for the two acoustic conditions in the hall: reflective and diffusive. The other surfaces in gray were set in an absorptive condition, except for the floor, which was made of a hard reflective surface. The 24 microphone positions are indicated in a crossed array that occupies half of the hall. Positions 1, 3, and 5 were used to perform the binaural simulations and then in the listening test.

2.2. Numerical Method

Odeon 13.00 has been used as a GA software for the simulations. It is based on a hybrid calculation method, which combines an image source method (ISM) and a ray-radiosity method for early reflections (ESR) below a specified transition order (TO) with a ray-tracing/radiosity method (RTM) for late reflections [41]. As in many other types of software, in Odeon the reflected energy can be divided into two parts, namely specular and scattered. Thus, the scattering coefficients should be provided as input data [42]. Usually, the implementation of the scattered energy is different for different kinds of software according to the approximations made for the directional distribution of the scattered reflections [43]. Below, two of these methods, the Hybrid Reflectance Model (HRM) and the vector Mixing (VM), are briefly described.

2.2.1. Scattering Models

The most commonly applied scattering implementations described in [44] are the Hybrid Reflectance Model (HRM) and vector mixing (VM). The HRM is based on the decomposition of the reflected sound into specularly and diffusely deflected parts. In this method, a random number between 0 and 1 is used to determine whether the reflection is specular or scattered. This number is compared with the surface scattering coefficient(s) assigned to the surface. In case it exceeds the value of s, the scattered energy is assumed to be distributed according to Lambert's Law, i.e., the intensity of the reflected ray is independent on the angle of incidence but proportional to the cosine of the angle of reflection [2]. This model complies with the definition of the scattering coefficient based on ISO 17497-1, which defines it in a quantitative way as the fraction of the non-specularly reflected energy.

On the contrary, the VM is based on the linear interpolation of the specular and diffuse reflection [45], i.e., the direction of a reflection vector is calculated by adding the specular vector scaled by a factor (1-s) to a scattered vector following a certain direction that has been scaled by a factor s. This is the basic concept implemented in Odeon [41,46], named "vector-based scattering", where the scattered vector follows a random direction, generated according to the Lambert distribution. Thus, the scattered reflections are also implemented from a qualitative point of view, which makes this model a more realistic approximation of the diffusive surface directivity.

2.2.2. Scattered Sound in Odeon

Odeon considers scattered sound both in the early and in the late part of the calculations. The early scattering is emitted from surface sources that are simulated each time an image source is detected. In this way, at each reflection point of the early scattering rays, a secondary source is created. This process lasts from the current reflection order up to the TO.

The late reflection method is used to treat all reflections that are not considered by the early reflection method. Every time a late ray is reflected on a surface, a small secondary source is generated, similar to a surface source. The secondary sources are assigned a frequency-dependent directionality, which may be a *Uniform, Lambert, or Oblique Lambert directivity* depending on the properties of the reflection as well as the calculation settings chosen by the user. *Oblique Lambert directivity* is a default setting. The Uniform directivity is a simpler model that redirects the scattered reflections uniformly over a hemi-sphere above the incident point. The Lambert directivity is based on the cosine law directivity. These first two options are based on the HRM. A revised version of the Lambert directivity is the oblique Lambert (Figure 3), which uses the concept of "vector-based scattering," i.e., vector mixing. In this model, the orientation of the Lambert sources is obtained by taking into account the "reflection-based scattering coefficient," which combines the scattering due to surface roughness and to surface edge diffraction. If s = 1, the reflected ray will propagate in a scattered direction conforming to the traditional Lambert's law. If s = 0, the reflected ray will propagate in a specular direction, which is obtained from Snell's law, i.e., the angle of incidence is equal to the angle of reflection [2]. The "vector-based scattering" model is used when the scattering coefficient values are between 0 and 1. The resulting direction is determined using s as a weighting between the pure specular direction and the scattered direction, chosen randomly as in HRM (Figure 4a,b). A shadow zone is created between the surface and the incident ray, where no sound reflections can be directed. Intuitively, the shadow zone is small if the scattering is high or if the incident ray is perpendicular to the surface (Figure 3a). Conversely, it is big if scattering is low and the incident ray is oblique (Figure 4b,c). The method is corrected to take into account the fact that for radiation angles different from $0°$, the model leads to energy loss due to the fact that part of the Lambert balloon radiates energy outside the room. The correction factor varies from 1 for a radiation angle of $0°$ to 2 for radiation angles of $90°$.

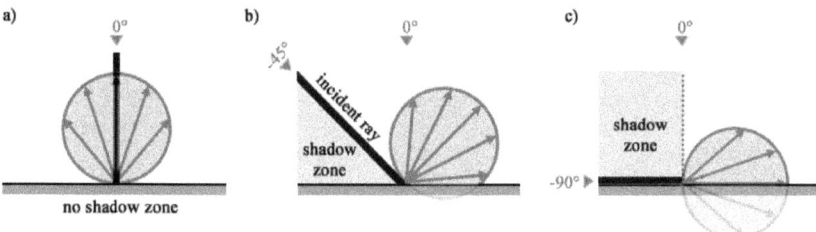

Figure 3. Oblique Lambert model. (**a**) Traditional Lambert directivity is generated when the angle of incidence is $0°$. Correction factor = 1; (**b**) Oblique Lambert directivity is generated when the angle of incidence is within the interval $(0°, \pm 90°)$. Correction factor within the interval (1, 2); (**c**) Oblique Lambert directivity is generated when the angle of incidence is $\pm 90°$. Correction factor = 2 [41].

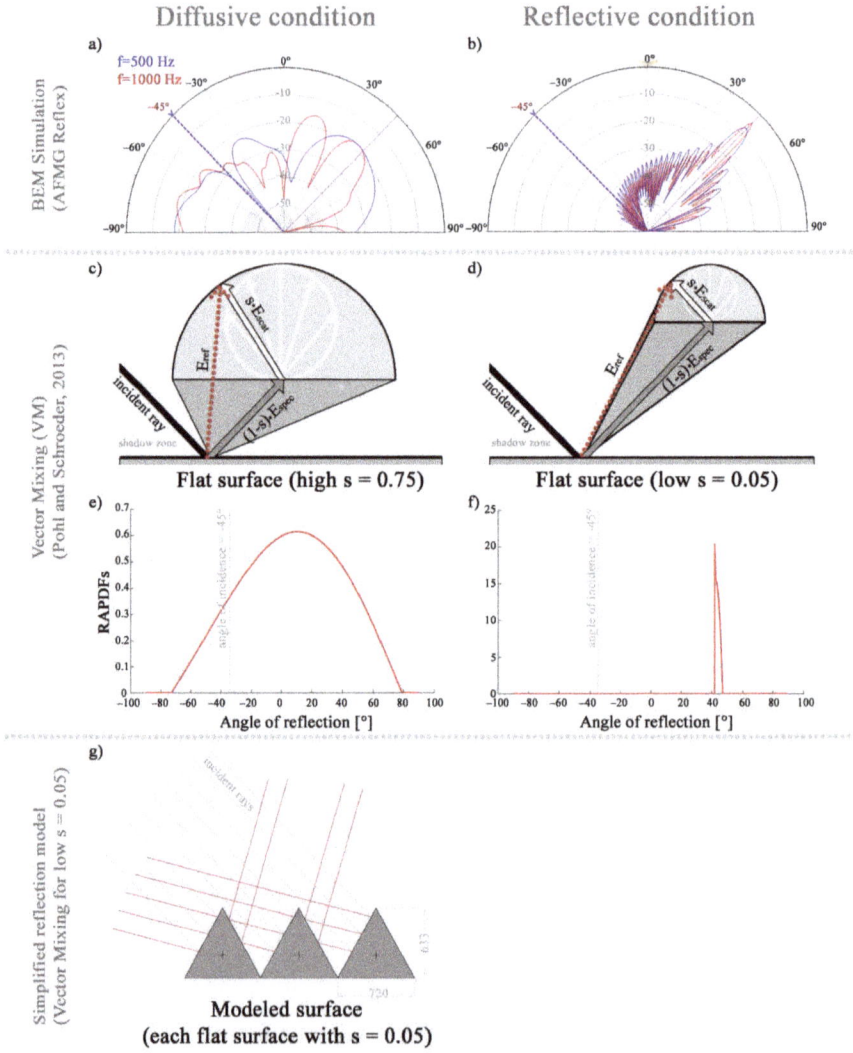

Figure 4. Comparison between diffusion polar plots and different scattered sound models with directional distribution of sound scattered from the *periactes* and a flat surface with sound incidence angle of −45°. (**a**) and (**b**) Polar representation of the pressure amplitude at 500 and 1000 Hz obtained using AFMG Reflex software; (**c**) and (**d**) vector mixing representation for high and low surface scattering value [44]; (**e**) and (**f**) RAPDFs for s = 0.75 and s = 0.05 [44]; (**g**) Simplified reflection model for 3D modeled *periactes*.

2.2.3. Reflection-Based Scattering

The scattered energy in Odeon is a combination of the surface roughness scattering coefficient s_s with the scattering coefficient due to diffraction s_d that is calculated individually for each reflection during the simulations. This combination leads to the "reflection-based scattering coefficient" s_r [41,46], which can be calculated from:

$$s_r = 1 - (1 - s_d)(1 - s_s), \tag{1}$$

where s_d is the fraction of energy scattered due to diffraction and s_s is the fraction of scattering caused by surface roughness.

Surface scattering (s_s) is assumed to appear due to random surface roughness, as defined in ISO17497-1. This type of situation gives rise to scattering that increases with frequency and can be inserted by the user based on scattering coefficient measurement databases, i.e., user-based scattering. In Odeon, typical measured scattering coefficient frequency functions [41,46] are used to expand a mid-frequency scattering coefficient input by the user to all frequency bands. This means that only one input value for the scattering coefficients needs to be specified for a surface at a middle frequency around 707 Hz (average of 500–1000 Hz bands). These coefficients are then expanded into values for each octave band, using interpolation or extrapolation.

Surface edge diffraction (s_d) is scattering due to the surface limited size and surface edges. It is a frequency-dependent phenomenon that affects low frequencies, i.e., frequencies lower than a limiting frequency (f_g). This limiting frequency is evaluated considering the reflection path lengths, surface dimensions and distance from edge of surface, angles between surfaces, offsets, angle of incidence, etc. [41,46]. The s_d is handled automatically by the software since most of the factors affecting its value are not known by the user, and is considered when "reflection-based scattering" is enabled.

2.2.4. Scattering Surface Modeling (IRCAM)

BEM-based simulations have been performed using the AFMG Reflex software in order to obtain the directivities of the triangular structure of the diffusing panels (*periactes*) and compare them to the case of a hard reflective surface. The diffusion polar plots, with a resolution of 1° of the pressure amplitude of the *periactes* and the flat surface, have been depicted in Figure 4a,b for the frequencies 500 and 1000 Hz, and an incidence angle of −45°. These directivities have then been compared to the vector mixing model (Figure 4c,d) adapted after the schemes for high and low scattering values presented in Schröder and Pohl [44], i.e., here high s = 0.75 and low s = 0.05.

Moreover, the Reflection Angle Probability Density Functions (RAPDFs) have been calculated using the open source scripts [47]. These functions describe the angle-wise probability for a striking energy particle/ray to get reflected under a certain angle for a given incidence angle and scattering coefficient. The models shown in Figure 4c,d apply to the IRCAM models DF and RF (diffusive flat and reflective flat models). A simplified reflection model has been built for 3D modeled *periactes* (Figure 4g), which apply to the DM model of the room, i.e., a 3D modeled diffusive wall. In this case the incident rays have been reflected specularly, but the vector mixing model for low scattering values is applied to each reflection in Odeon. The surface edge diffraction is present in all vector mixing models, but it has not been represented in the schemes of Figure 4.

It can be noticed that the more realistic modeling of the triangle structure (*periactes*) of the walls (Figure 4g) in the DM case (including edge diffraction) leads to more realistic directivities than modeling by vector-based scattering, i.e., vector mixing (Figure 4c). In particular, this model does not consider that part of the energy is redirected in the direction of the incidence angle, which can be observed in the BEM simulation and in the simplified reflection model (DM).

2.3. Measurement and Simulation Setup

In the simulations, the 24 receivers have been located in the same positions used in the measurement setup [5] and have been arranged in a crossed array configuration that extended to one of the two halves of the audience area (Figure 2) at a height of around 3.70 m from the floor level. In the measurements, this height was chosen in order to reach the center of the first level of variable panels and to avoid the reflections from the absorptive panels of the lowest level. Additionally, binaural simulations have been performed in three positions (1, 3 and 5), which have been previously used for binaural measurements with an artificial head located at 3.70 m from the floor level.

The sound source was positioned midway between the axis of symmetry of the room and the lateral wall. In the measurements, it consisted of a three-way system of low-, medium-, and high-frequency sources, which were positioned at different heights, that is, at 0.40 m, 3.70 m, and 3.90 m, respectively. The position of the low-frequency source on the floor level has been considered acceptable, since humans are not able to locate the direction of such low frequencies. In the simulations, a single omnidirectional source has been used and located in the same position used in measurements for the mid-frequency omnidirectional loudspeaker.

The main input settings to perform simulations, that is, the number of rays, the maximum reflection order, and the transition order (TO), have to be decided carefully according to the aim of the simulations. First, a reasonable number of rays could be estimated by considering that an expected error of less than 1 JND is regarded as sufficient when estimating the objective acoustic parameters [2]. However, the number of rays has been estimated following the software indication of the minimum number of rays, which is derived by taking into account the aspect ratio of the room as well as the size and number of surfaces in the geometry. This automatic number shown in the settings window was equal to 6161 rays, but a greater number was chosen to avoid artifacts and obtain higher quality in the auralizations used later in the listening tests [18,48]. Thus, this number was set at 100 K rays in all models and the maximum reflection order was set to 10K. A TO = 2 has been chosen based on the literature and frequently used values for similar environments [49]. Run-to-run variations have not been considered here since, based on the literature investigations, the simulator can be considered sufficiently stable [50,51].

Post-processing of both measured and simulated data has been carried out using ITA-Toolbox, an open source toolbox for Matlab [52].

Assumptions and Adjustments

In order to achieve realistic auralizations, it is important to have a well-calibrated GA model. Based on Vorländer [53], a simulation is well calibrated when the difference between simulation and measurement is less than the JND of each objective acoustical parameter. Based upon this statement, the calibration in this study was made by comparing the simulated objective parameters to the measured ones in real conditions of the hall. Furthermore, some of the indications given in the general procedure described in Postma and Katz [50] have been used. The calibration steps can be summarized as follows:

(1) **Assuming diffuse field conditions:** The acoustic conditions used for this study do not represent a diffuse sound field. Since this might influence the correct estimation of the material properties, a different configuration of the hall has been used, and the diffuse field is assumed as an approximation to estimate the absorption coefficients. The model (DM1) used for the material calibration is presented in Figure 6. This model has been chosen since it was considered to have a sufficiently diffuse field based on the achieved spatial uniformity of the reverberation time. Compared to the DM model, it assumes both long lateral walls and ceiling in diffusive condition, while the two short walls are maintained in the absorptive condition. In this configuration a more diffuse sound field is likely to be generated since larger diffusive surfaces have been used and distributed symmetrically in the room. The diffusive surfaces have been modeled as 3D prisms. This was preferred with respect to a flat surface modeling alternative, since it is a closer geometrical representation of the real room. The difference in volume between the two modeling alternatives is ($V_{3D} - V_{flat} = 44.32$ m^3), which could lead to differences in reverberation time of about 1%.

(2) **Preliminary acoustical properties:** As far as the absorption coefficients are concerned, in order to start the calibration process, preliminary acoustical properties (Table 1) have been assigned to the geometrical model's surfaces based on the data reported in the project reports and standard literature [37,38]. Based on the recommendations given in [41], the scattering coefficients were set to 0.05 (707 Hz) for all flat surfaces and for the modeled 3D panels, i.e., in this case each prism surface was set 0.05 (707 Hz). Since no data could be found for the absorption coefficient of the structure and for the diffusive configuration of the panels, the same absorption coefficients

have been used for these three types of surfaces based on the similar construction material (metal sheet).

(3) **Variation of the acoustical properties:** The acoustical properties of type A and B absorptive surfaces, structure, and diffusive panels have been modified since they have the most significant impact on the overall value of the equivalent sound absorption area, due to high absorption coefficients and surface extension, respectively. The variation has been performed manually and step by step until the overall mean differences (for the source and receiver configuration) between measurement and simulated results for EDT, T_{30}, C_{80}, and D_{50} resulted in less than one JND. However, the variation of the absorption coefficient of these surfaces has been restricted in order not to lose the typical acoustic properties of the material they represent (for e.g., a rockwool surface should not vary into a plastered one). Having in mind this constraint, a compromise has been made in order to stop the calibration process when differences between simulated and measured EDT, T_{30}, C_{80}, and D_{50} reached values of about one JND. The results of the material calibration are shown in Table 1 and Figure 5, and the results of the objective acoustic parameters after calibration are depicted in Figure 6. It can be observed that the differences between the simulated and measured results for C_{80} and D_{50} are slightly above one JND. This result was still considered acceptable, based on the restriction of the absorption coefficients variations, and on the fact that the degree of tolerance for the parameters that present values of the spatial standard deviation comparable to the JND should realistically be extended beyond one JND [50].

(4) **Case study models:** The absorptive surface properties obtained after the calibration have been assigned to the respective surfaces (type A and B) in the models of the case study (RF, DF, DM). The same properties have been used in both 3D prisms and flat surface models (DM and DF). This has been considered acceptable since the difference in volume may be considered negligible ($V_{DM} - V_{DF} = 7.77$ m^3). The other surfaces such as doors, floor, and glass windows have remained the same as those used in the calibration model.

Table 1. Absorption coefficients assigned to the different surfaces of the hall. "Fixed materials properties" have not been varied during the calibration process. Materials in the group of "Varied material properties" have been modified starting from the values signed in bold to the gray ones.

		Frequency [Hz]						
	Materials	125	250	500	1000	2000	4000	8000
Fixed material properties	Floor (linoleum on concrete)	0.12	0.10	0.10	0.08	0.05	0.05	0.05
	Doors (hard metallic panels)	0.13	0.11	0.07	0.05	0.05	0.05	0.05
	Windows (single glazing sheet)	0.18	0.06	0.04	0.03	0.02	0.02	0.02
Varied material properties [1]	Diffusive surface (3D panels) and Structure (metallic)	0.10	0.10	0.10	0.10	0.10	0.10	0.10
	Diffusive surface (3D panels) and Structure (metallic), (calib. all models)	0.16	0.16	0.09	0.09	0.14	0.14	0.14
	Type A (Peutz, 1978)	**0.75**	**0.90**	**0.70**	**0.30**	**0.10**	**0.05**	**0.05**
	Type A (Calib. DM1)	1.00	0.95	0.75	0.20	0.10	0.10	0.05
	Type A (Calib. RF)	1.00	0.95	0.75	0.35	0.25	0.20	0.20
	Type A (Calib. DM and DF)	0.80	0.90	0.70	0.20	0.10	0.10	0.05
	Type B (Peutz, 1978)	**0.20**	**0.40**	**0.70**	**0.90**	**0.85**	**0.90**	**0.95**
	Type B (Calib. DM1)	0.45	0.47	0.60	0.70	0.65	0.90	0.95
	Type B (Calib. RF)	0.30	0.50	0.55	0.72	0.68	0.98	1.00
	Type B (Calib. DM and DF)	0.35	0.37	0.50	0.68	0.65	0.90	0.95

[1] Type A and type B material properties have also been plotted in Figure 5 for a clearer visualization of their variation during the calibration process.

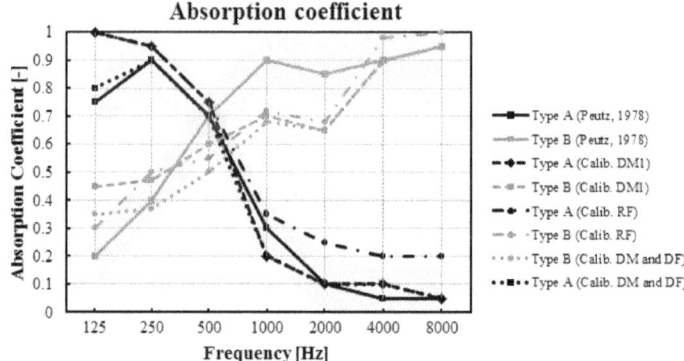

Figure 5. Calibration of the absorption coefficients of type A and type B materials. The gray area shows the lower and upper limit of the acceptable tolerances, as described in the materials' properties in [37].

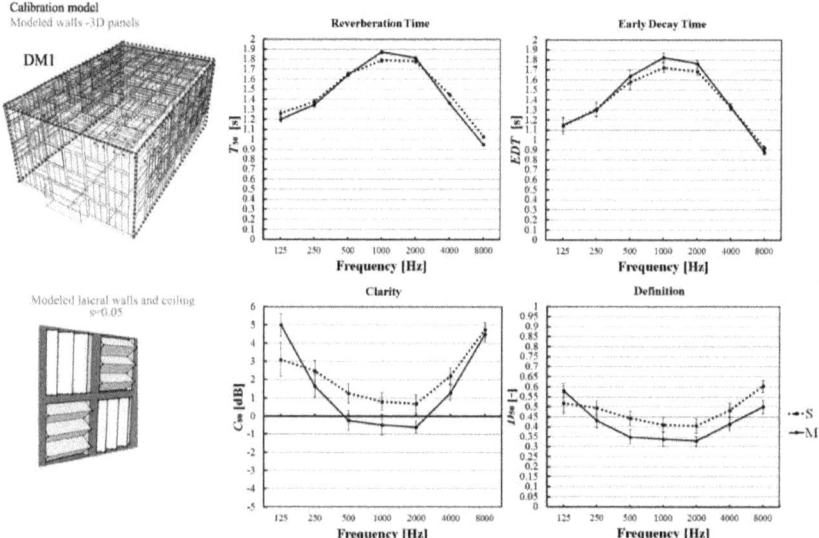

Figure 6. Calibration model (DM1) and objective acoustical parameters obtained after the calibration (Type A and Type B values given for DM1 model materials in Table 1). The diffusive surfaces (3D panels) have been framed in dotted lines. S and M indicate the simulation and measurements results, respectively.

The absorptive materials of type A and type B have been slightly varied in the three models, i.e., different for the three models (RF, DF, and DM) in order to arrive at overall mean differences between measurement and simulated results for *EDT*, T_{30}, C_{80}, and D_{50} of less than one JND. The materials have been modified separately (Figure 5) for the diffusive condition (DM and DF), and for the reflective condition (RF). This difference is due to the fact that the two real conditions present different materials, that is, diffusive and reflective faces of the variable panels, which could have different absorption coefficients. Since no consistent data could be found in the project documentation, it could be considered acceptable that the absorption coefficients of the type A and type B materials are affected by the uncertainty of the other unknown materials' data.

2.4. Room Acoustic Parameters

The sound fields of the reflective condition (RF) and both modeling alternatives of the diffusive conditions (DF and DM) have been investigated on the basis of ISO 3382-1 [54]: reverberation time (T_{30}), early decay time (*EDT*), clarity (C_{80}), definition (D_{50}), and interaural cross-correlation (*IACC*). The values of the first four parameters have been presented in octave bands as mean values over all the receiver positions in order to assess the accuracy of the calibration process.

Since binaural measurements and simulations have been performed in positions 1, 3, and 5, the *IACC* values were evaluated and averaged over 500 Hz, 1000 Hz and 2000 Hz octave band results in each position. The *IACC* has been assessed by considering separately the early-arriving (0–80 ms) and late-arriving (80 ms-inf) sound since they measure different aspects of the sound field.

These parameters have been chosen since they have been used in the measurements [5] and in the main literature concerning the study of diffusive surface effects in room acoustics. The parameters have been evaluated using the functions of ITA-Toolbox, which comply with the ISO 3382-1:2009. This was based on the study performed by Postma and Katz [50], which suggests applying the same objective parameter estimation method for measurements and simulations in order to enable their correct comparison. By using ITA-Toolbox, it was possible to also evaluate *IACC*, which is not included in the Odeon objective parameters results.

As in the calibration process, since the Just-Noticeable Differences (JNDs) report the smallest perceived difference for an objective parameter, they have been used as criteria to judge the significance of the variations induced by changes on the surface properties and surface modeling.

2.5. Subjective Investigation

The perceptual tests aimed to investigate the audible difference threshold between two acoustic reflective conditions by determining the distance threshold at which the listener no longer perceives the presence of a diffusive surface in the sound field of the room under examination. These comparisons have been made between the reflective wall condition (RF) and the diffusive wall condition modeled as flat surface (DF) and as 3D panels (DM), i.e., both RF-DF and RF-DM comparisons have been performed. Furthermore, the thresholds have been compared with the results found with measured impulse responses presented in Shtrepi et al. [5]. Exactly the same method, named the triangular method [55,56], used for the comparison of the measured conditions has been deployed also for the listening test with simulated stimuli. The method implies the use of sets of three stimuli, from each of which the subject has to select the odd stimulus under forced-choice instructions. Stimulus sets ("triangles") are constructed using A and B stimuli, such that all of the six temporal or spatial permutations (AAB, ABA, BAA, and BBA, BAB, and ABB) are used and presented in random order. The triangular method is an undirected protocol since it does not require that the nature of the difference between the A and B stimuli is provided as part of the subject's instructions. The stimulus sets have been presented to the subjects individually through a Matlab routine and later the data have been analyzed by calculating the psychometric functions using Psignifit [57], which is a Matlab toolbox [58,59]. The psychometric function is defined as the relation between a subject's performance, i.e., here the listening test answers, and an independent variable, which is usually some physical quantity of a stimulus in a psychophysical task, i.e., here it is the difference between the reflective and diffusive condition at different distances from the variable wall. The psychometric function is given in the range [0,1] and is limited by a lower limit related to a base rate of performance in absence of stimulus (γ), i.e., the chance threshold, and to an upper limit ($1-\lambda$), where λ corresponds to the miss rate, i.e., it is the rate at which subjects lapse, responding incorrectly regardless of stimulus intensity. The shape of the function between these two limits is given by two parameters α and β, which determine two independent attributes, that is, the displacement of the function along the abscissa and its slope. These are the most important parameters since their values are crucial for the evaluation of the threshold of the psychometric function. Conversely, the upper ($1-\lambda$) and lower bound (γ) parameters are stimulus-independent, based on guessing and lapsing rates, and thus they have very little influence on the threshold estimation.

The method used for variability estimation of the parameters fitted to psychophysical data is based on Efron's parametric bootstrap technique, which is a Monte Carlo resampling technique that relies on a large number of simulated repetitions of the original experiment. This method has been chosen since it needs a small number of data points and is applied to estimate the variability of the parameters, thresholds and slopes of the psychometric functions. The Monte Carlo simulation is based on a system that provides generating probabilities for the simulated dataset, which are the same that are hypothesized to underlie the empirical data set, i.e., the collected psychophysical data. In order to improve this system, the parametric bootstrap is used, which evaluates the maximum-likelihood fit to the real subject's data to determine the simulated subjects underlying probability of success. The maximum-likelihood estimation is made by controlling the parameters of the psychometric function (α and β), which determine its shape based on the best fit to the experimental data.

In the experiment presented here, different triads (triangles) of the test signals have been prepared by convolving anechoic signals with the binaural impulse responses obtained in simulations at positions 1, 3, and 5 (highlighted in Figure 1). Each triad has been built for each anechoic signal and listening position. The triads included two identical signals and one different from the other two in the comparisons RF-DF and RF-DM. These signals have been presented to the listener in a randomized order: comparison of RF with DF (RF-DF-DF, DF-RF-DF, DF-DF-RF, DF-RF-RF, RF-DF-RF, and RF-RF-DF) and comparison of RF with DM (RF-DM-DM, DM-RF-DM, DM-DM-RF, DM-RF-RF, RF-DM-RF, and RF-RF-DM). Also the receiver position and the signal type have been presented in randomized order (Table 2). As in [5], the test has been presented to the subjects via high quality headphones (Sennheiser HD600) without any specific headphone equalization.

Table 2. Listening test scheme. Three different music samples played for three listening positions. Samples "RF" are compared with samples "DF" and "DM", which correspond to the reflective and diffusive condition of the lateral wall, respectively. The order of presentation of the samples has been fully randomized: motif and listening position. Six (3!) permutations of RF and DF or DM order could occur within one triad.

		Choral recording		
	Motifs	Piano solo		
		Orchestra		
Randomized order	Listening positions	1	3	5
	Signals	RF-DF-DF, DF-RF-DF, DF-DF-RF, DF-RF-RF, RF-DF-RF, RF-RF-DF		
		RF-DM-DM, DM-RF-DM, DM-DM-RF, DM-RF-RF, RF-DM-RF, RF-RF-DM		

As explained above, in order to build the psychometric curves, the percentage of correct answers is correlated to the stimulus intensity, which is decreased or increased by a constant step [58,59]. In this study, the stimulus is represented by the difference between the reflective and the diffusive condition compared at each position. Since there is no method to quantify this stimulus intensity variation between the two conditions, the stimulus intensity variation is associated with the distance from the lateral wall, which increased constantly by 2.77 m (at 2.15 m, 4.92 m, and 7.69 m for position 1, 3, and 5, respectively).

Music Samples and Test Subjects

The music stimuli presented to the listeners were created by convolving the simulated binaural impulse responses with samples of anechoic music recordings (5–6 s). Three different anechoic music samples have been chosen based on different style, tempo, and spectral characteristics [5]:

- choral recording ("Alleluia"—Randall Thompson, St. Olaf Cantorei, Anechoic Choral Recordings, Wenger),
- piano solo ("Étude Op. 10 no. 4"—Frédéric Chopin, Renzo Vitale, Digital Recording)
- orchestra ("Water Music Suite"—Handel/Harty, Osaka Philarmonic Orchestra, Anechoic Orchestral Music Recordings, Denon)

The subjects were chosen on a voluntary basis from professors, research assistants, and students at Politecnico di Torino (Italy). They declared their interest in acoustics and music, and all of them had experience in playing a musical instrument or singing in a choir. A total of 38 subjects participated in the listening tests. They were asked to perform an audiometric test by using an iPad-based application named uHear [60] and wearing the same headphones (Sennheiser HD600) subsequently used in the listening test. Only 31 subjects obtained results within the "normal hearing level" and have been considered suitable to perform the perceptual listening test. This sample consisted of subjects aged between 20 and 45 years.

3. Results

3.1. Objective Acoustic Parameters Results

The results have been presented in Figure 7; the plots show the results of each objective room acoustic parameter in octave band frequency as an overall mean value over the receiver positions. It can be noticed that EDT shows a better matching between the simulated and the measured data (<JND). Conversely, T_{30} evaluated for the diffusive condition (gray curves) showed differences higher than the JND at 2000 and 4000 Hz. Also C_{80} and D_{50} showed differences higher than the JND at some frequencies for both diffusive and reflective conditions.

Overall, the simulated results show that the acoustic parameter values are sensitive to the presence of the diffusive or reflective surfaces as in the in-field measured results. The differences higher than one JND have been considered significant (Figure 7). It can be noticed that these differences are more evident at mid frequencies. In Table 3 are shown the differences of the parameter values between the reflective and diffusive conditions and compared to the JND of each parameter. EDT increased from the reflective to the diffusive configuration by more than one JND (JND_{EDT} = 5% of the lowest value of EDT, which in this case is about 0.05 s). Also, T_{30} increased from the reflective to the diffusive configuration by more than two JNDs (JND_{EDT} = 5% of the lowest value of T_{30}, which in this case was about 0.05 s). Conversely, C_{80} decreased by about one JND (JND_{C80} = 1 dB) in position 2 when comparing DM and RF simulations, but no significant difference was obtained in the comparison between DF and RF simulations. D_{50} decreased by more than one JND (JND_{D50} = 0.05) when varying from the reflective (RF) to the diffusive (DM) configuration in positions 3 and 5. While, no significant variations could be found when varying from RF to DF configuration.

Table 3. Differences of the objective acoustic parameters between the DM and RF simulations and DF and RF simulations in position 1, 2, and 3. Differences higher than one JND have been highlighted in bold. The differences are between mean values at 500–1000 Hz (EDT, T_{30}, C_{80}, D_{50}) and 500–2000 Hz ($IACC_{early}$ and $IACC_{late}$).

	Distance [m]		EDT [s]		T_{30} [s]		C_{80} [dB]		D_{50} [-]		$IACC_{early}$ [-]		$IACC_{late}$ [-]	
R	d-S	d-W	DM-RF	DF-RF	DM-RF	DF-RF	DM-RF	DF-RF	DM-RF	DF-RF	DM-RF	DF-RF	DM-RF	DF-RF
1	6.28	2.15	**0.10**	**0.09**	**0.17**	**0.16**	−0.76	−0.61	−0.02	0.00	0.045	**0.109**	0.065	−0.007
3	6.02	4.92	**0.16**	**0.08**	**0.17**	**0.20**	**−1.71**	0.50	**−0.09**	0.02	0.017	**0.097**	−0.038	−0.015
5	6.96	7.69	**0.12**	**0.11**	**0.15**	**0.17**	−0.45	0.17	**−0.06**	−0.03	**−0.091**	−0.011	0.063	0.011
	JND		0.05		0.05		1		0.05				0.075	

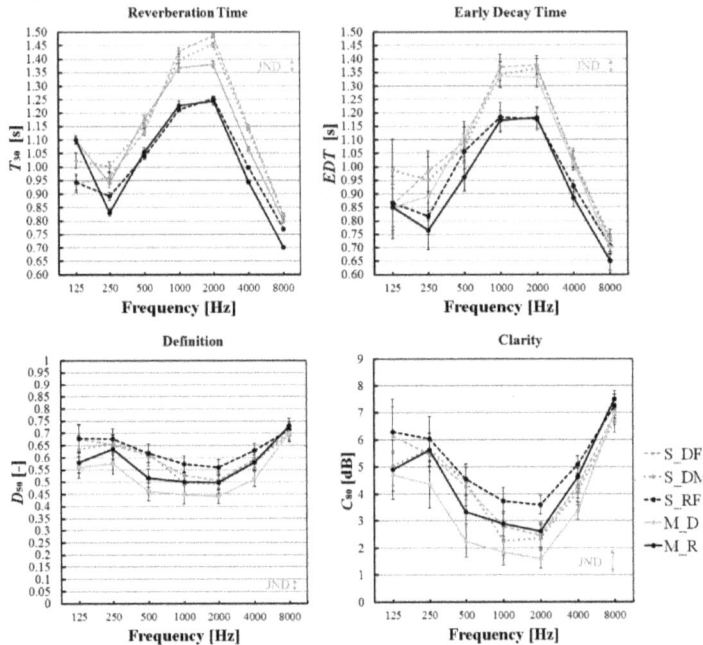

Figure 7. Reverberation time (T_{30}), early decay time (*EDT*), definition (D_{50}) and clarity (C_{80}) simulated and measured values given in octave bands for both reflective (RF) and diffusive (DF and DM) conditions. The step of *y*-axis is equal to 1 JND of each parameter. S and M indicate the simulation and measurements results, respectively.

The results of *IACC* values in receiver positions 1, 3, and 5 have been presented in Figure 8 as a function of the distance from the lateral variable wall. The analyses aimed to highlight the differences in the *IACC*$_{early}$ and *IACC*$_{late}$ values in both configurations of the simulated hall with respect to the measured results. It is shown that differences higher than one JND (JND$_{IACC}$ = 0.075) in *IACC*$_{early}$ occur in receiver positions 1 and 3 between the measured and the simulated results for the reflective condition. The differences between the simulated and measured results for the diffusive condition, are higher for the DF model at the receiver position 1, which was close to the lateral wall. *IACC*$_{late}$ values show differences comparable to one JND in receiver position 3 for the simulated and measured reflective condition, while differences higher than one JND occur in receiver 1 between the measured diffusive condition and simulated results obtained in DM model.

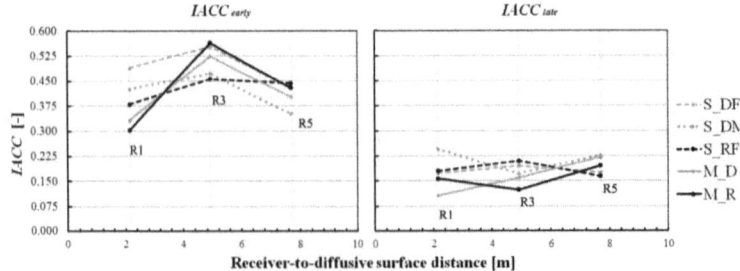

Figure 8. *IACC*$_{early}$ and *IACC*$_{late}$ as a function of the distance from the variable wall.

It can be noticed that there is a peak of $IACC_{early}$ at position 3, which is due to its position in relation to the source, i.e., they are almost aligned. By definition, the sound arriving from the median plane $0°$ makes the value of $IACC$ greater [61].

3.2. Listening Tests Results

Initially a one-way analysis of variance (ANOVA) has been performed in order to determine whether the different types of motifs affect the perception of the differences between the reflective condition and the two diffusive conditions. It showed that the results obtained for the different motifs have no significant influence ($F(1,30) = 1.25$, $p > 0.05$) on the subjective results. Thus, the subject answers have been analyzed considering the overall results independently of the motif. Figure 9 shows the results of the listening tests. The perception of the differences between the two acoustic wall conditions resulted to be more difficult when the signals were played in the DF condition compared to the RF (Figure 9a). The overall correct answer rate in this case is below 50%. Thus, it was not possible to define a threshold. Significant results were obtained when comparing signals between the DM (diffusive modeled) and RF (reflective flat) conditions, which reached an overall correct answer rate above 50% at the different listening positions. Therefore, for this comparison it was possible to build the psychometric function, which was fitted to the experimental data as shown in Figure 9b. The psychometric curve obtained in the previous study [5] with measured impulse responses has been reported in gray. The graph depicts on the *y*-axis the probability of a correct answer, i.e., the performance level as a function of the stimulus, and on the *x*-axis the stimulus intensity associated with the distance from the variable wall. The black circles represent the data collected through the listening tests, i.e., the proportion of correct answers for a given stimulus. The solid line shows the best-fitting psychometric function assigned to the collected experimental data. The horizontal bars depict the confidence intervals, which show the variability of the psychometric function evaluated at 20% (0.20), 50% (0.50) and 80% (0.80) of the interval above the chance threshold (γ), which is equal to 33% (0.33). Since the detection tests presented in this work have been designed according to the forced choice criterion, the threshold must be set to one half of the interval between the guessing (γ) and the lapsing rate $(1-\lambda)$. The threshold is indicated with the dashed vertical line and is the estimated value results of about 7.50 m, which corresponds to listening position at receiver 5. On the other hand, the threshold obtained with the in-field measured impulse responses was estimated at about 2.15 m, which corresponds to the receiver position 1. The value for the cumulative probability estimate (CPE) has been reported in Figure 9b. According to Wichmann and Hill [58,59] a CPE greater than 0.95 denotes that the fit is inappropriate. In this case, the CPE is equal to 0.79 and 0.21 for the simulated and measured signal-based tests, respectively, and thus the psychometric curve correctly fits the data.

During the test, each listener could comment on the differences that guided his/her choice for each single triad. The results of these comments are depicted in Figure 10 as the percentage of listeners that reported the attributes given in the *x*-axis. More than 50% of the subjects could detect differences in reverberation and coloration. Subjects could detect also sound level, spaciousness and source location effects. As in the listening test with measured impulse responses, they declared that they perceived a larger or smaller volume, and closer or a more distant sound source.

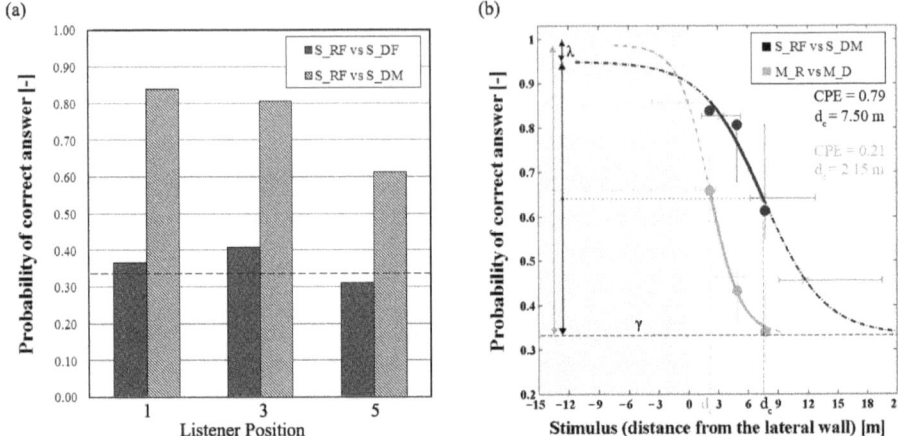

Figure 9. (**a**) Listening test results as the rate of correct answers overall the 31 subjects and three motifs in each listening position. The dark and light gray columns depict the results of the comparisons between the RF and DF conditions, and between the RF and DM conditions, respectively (**b**) Psychometric function for 31 (black) and 44 (gray) subjects and all signals, i.e., simulations and measurements tests, respectively. The black and gray circles represent the collected experimental data, i.e., the proportion of correct answers for a given stimulus intensity, the solid lines show the best-fitting psychometric function assigned to the experimental data, the vertical dashed lines highlight the corresponding threshold distance at which the presence of the diffusive surface is no longer perceived by the listeners.

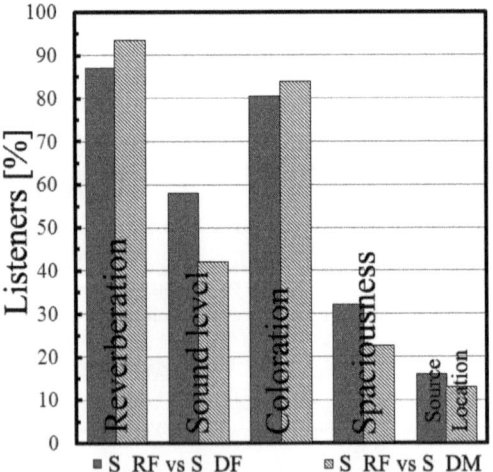

Figure 10. Listeners' subjective evaluations on the perceived differences between the simulated reflective (RF) and diffusive conditions (DF and DM). The *y*-axis depicts the percentage of listeners that reported the attributes given in the *x*-axis.

4. Discussion

Although this study was based on one combination of diffusive surface extension and position in the case of a simple shoebox concert hall, and only one scattering model was used and some assumptions on absorption coefficients were considered, a few useful critical comments can be made on the objective and perceptual results.

The objective results have shown that a good match can be achieved between simulated and measured results. However, the surface modeling and the calibration of the absorptive and diffusive materials require a great effort that is time-consuming. This process might lead to very different material properties compared to laboratory-measured ones. Here, the "measured absorption coefficients" have been estimated using the reverberation room method [37,38], but no data are available to show the degree of confirmation of these values in the application in the real room. It has been shown that laboratory measurements and in-field evaluation of absorption coefficients may differ significantly depending on the characteristics of the environment [62]. Moreover, in our case, materials may have experienced transformations due to aging [63]. Depending on the sound field of the environment under examination, the values of the calibrated absorption coefficients conceal the uncertainties due to initial assumptions: diffuse field, geometrical approximations, uncertainty of material characteristics based on literature, simulation algorithm, etc. As a consequence, such inaccuracies will conduct to possible wrong material choices when evaluating existing environments or newly designed ones.

The early decay time (*EDT*) showed differences between simulations and measurements smaller than one JND independently of the geometric characteristics of the model. Conversely, differences slightly higher than one JND resulted at 2000–4000 Hz for reverberation time (T_{30}) in the diffusive configuration (DF and DM). These were considered acceptable based on the initial constraints: restrictions on the variation of the absorption coefficients and the calibration of other two parameters, that is, clarity (C_{80}) and definition (D_{50}). Moreover, since similar differences can be noticed for simulated models DF and DM, this could not affect the results when these models are compared to the reflective model (RF). Although a great effort was put in the calibration of C_{80} and D_{50}, differences higher than 1 JND resulted at some frequencies. Since the spatial standard deviations of these parameters, i.e., differences between different receiver positions, give results higher than or equal to the JND, the degree of tolerance should realistically be extended beyond 1 JND [45]. In Zeng et al. [28] the predicted C_{80} was larger than the measured ones and the difference was much higher at low frequency bands when using the new method for the detailed model. This was assumed to indicate that more early sound energy is collected because of reflection and diffraction.

The objective acoustic parameters increased (*EDT* and T_{30}) and decreased (C_{80} and D_{50}) with increasing surface scattering as in the measurement results. This shows that in simulations also the diffusive surfaces tend to disperse reflections in space and time leading to a longer reverberation time compared to the reflective condition. In the reflective condition, a more concentrated spatial and temporal reflection is generated and successively absorbed by the absorptive surfaces that cover the ceiling and the other lateral walls. It should be highlighted that this result might change for different combinations of the diffusive and absorptive surfaces as summarized in Shtrepi at al. [35].

The influence of the different modeling alternatives of the diffusive surfaces was more evident at positions close to the variable wall for the *IACC* parameter. The values of this parameter at the positions close to the lateral wall were different for the DM and DF conditions. Robinson et al. [64] showed that the correlation between the impulse responses at two ears at positions close to any surface is lower due to effects of the surface proximity on the impulse response of the ear oriented towards it. In this way, the binaural impulse response is affected asymmetrically on each ear channel (left and right). In the configuration investigated in this study, the right ear is oriented towards the variable wall, while the left ear is oriented towards the other lateral wall, which is absorptive. Thus, the differences in reflections between the two ears are emphasized also by this asymmetric distribution of the material properties, i.e., the correlation between the two ears decreases.

The perceptual investigation highlighted the differences between the scattered sound models shown in Figure 4. Based on the scattering perceptual thresholds [35], a difference in scattering coefficient of 0.70, which is the difference between the scattering coefficient of the diffusive surface modeled flat (0.75) and the reflective surface (0.05), should be easily perceived by the subjects. Despite this, it was not possible to find a distance threshold when the flat modeled diffusive surface (DF) was used. A distance threshold of 7.50 m was found when the DM model was used, i.e., the diffusive surfaces were modeled as 3D panels. As shown in Figure 4g, the more realistic modeling of the diffusive walls in the DM case (including edge diffraction) leads to more realistic directivities than modeling by vector-based scattering, i.e., vector mixing, used in the DF case. In particular, when compared to the BEM simulation polar distribution, it can be noticed that the latter model does not consider the part of the energy that is deflected in the direction of the incidence angle. This might be the reason for the better audibility of diffuse reflections and better agreement with measurements.

The distance threshold is higher than the distance of 2.15 m found by performing the same listening test with measured binaural impulse responses. Such different thresholds might be due to the scattered sound model approximations. As reported in Torres, Rycker, and Kleiner [14], some major limitations of a Lambert-based scattering model are that it neglects phase, thus neglects interference effects between specular and nonspecular scattering, whose sum constitutes the total surface scattering at a receiver position in a room. In the case of the modeled diffusive surface (DM), the scattering algorithm automatically takes into account also edge-diffraction effects, that follow a far-field type of behavior, i.e., are distance dependent [14]. Thus, the differences between the reflective and diffusive condition are evident also at longer distances in simulations with a high degree level of detail.

The comments at the end of each listening test highlighted that the principal effects of the perceptual evaluations within one triad of signals were coloration and reverberation. Some of the listeners claimed to perceive differences in spaciousness, sound level, and source location which might have been further emphasized by the fact that the surfaces of the hall (except for the test surface and the floor) were set in absorptive mode. The reverberation and coloration seem to be more relevant when comparing the RF to the DM model, i.e., in the conditions of 3D modeled diffusive surface. Conversely, the sound level, spaciousness and sound source location were the cues mainly used when comparing the RF to the DF model, i.e., where the diffusive surface was modeled as flat surface. The presence of reverberation might distract the listener from timbral and spatial effects of the early reflections, which were perceived at lower rate [14]. Nevertheless, spectral and reverberation differences seem to be more consistent attributes, since the answers obtained in the RF-DM comparisons lead to correct answers way above the chance threshold.

No correlation between the subjective and the objective parameters results could be found. One possible explanation of the obtained result is that listeners contemporarily rely on different factors to make their decision. Although a multiple regression could be implemented to investigate the relationship between objective parameters and subjective responses [65], there is a need for a single measurable parameter of more practical use.

5. Conclusions

The effects of two modeling alternatives of diffusive surfaces in geometrical acoustics (GA)-based software have been investigated, both objectively and perceptually, in a small variable-acoustics concert hall. This research aimed to isolate the independent effects that a single diffusive surface has on the simulated objective acoustic parameters and perceptual experience based on simulated impulse responses. Thus, two different conditions of the hall, where one of the lateral walls assumed reflective (RF) and diffusive characteristics (DF and DM), have been considered. The two modeling alternatives of the diffusive condition were built based on the simulations state of the art and considering the limits of a possible increase of the modeling level of detail. In the first model (DF) diffusive prisms have been modeled as a flat surface to which a scattering coefficient equal to the scattering coefficient of the diffusive surface they represent (0.75 at 707 Hz) was assigned. In the second model (DM) the diffusive prisms have been modeled as 3D panels with their geometrical characteristics, and to each surface of the prisms a scattering coefficient equal to that of a flat surface (0.05 at 707 Hz) was assigned.

The objective evaluation has been carried out by analyzing the variation of the ISO 3382-1 acoustic parameters T_{30}, EDT, C_{80}, D_{50}, and $IACC$ in each of the three models (RF, DF, and DM). The perceptual evaluation aimed at determining the maximum distance from the wall at which the listeners could no longer perceive the difference between the reflective and diffusive condition. Furthermore, it aimed to investigate if this distance is influenced by the different modeling alternatives of the diffusive surfaces in GA-based software. The psychometric functions have been evaluated and statistically analyzed using the Psignifit toolbox (version 2.5.6).

The main conclusions of this work can be summarized as follows:

- A good match and similar trends can be achieved between simulated and measured results regardless the geometric modeling of the diffusive surfaces. However, this requires different material calibrations with respect to the diffusive properties.
- Listeners in a simulated performance space can perceive the presence of different acoustic scattering properties, and it was found that this perception is related to the distance from the diffusive surface and to their geometric modeling.
- A more realistic geometrical modeling of the diffusive surfaces leads to more realistic reflections directivities than when vector mixing model is used. This might be the reason for the better audibility of diffuse reflections and better agreement with measurements.
- Distance thresholds in simulations (7.50 m) are higher than in real measurements (2.15 m) due to the scattered sound model approximations: reflections and diffraction.
- No correlation between the subjective and the objective parameters results could be found, thus there is a need for further investigation on new single measurable parameter of a more practical use.

Most of the listeners were sensitive to the presence of acoustic scattering also at distant positions from the diffusive surfaces in simulations. Therefore, the use of these surfaces in large concert halls might affect the uniformity distribution of the acoustic quality in a large group of listeners and influence the design goals.

Future work could involve objective and perceptual investigations concerning the comparison of different simulation algorithms, by considering different locations and extensions of the diffusive surfaces in a broader number of hall volumes and shapes.

Many musicians in the stage area are frequently located at distances from the stage walls that are comparable or shorter than the distance threshold found here, thus they are expected to perceive the differences between different modeling alternatives and surface scattering properties assigned in simulations. Based on this, the results of this work become relevant when modeling the surfaces of the stage area and when performing listening tests concerning the acoustics quality of the stage.

Finally, the findings of this study could be useful to further improve the GA-based software guidelines for accurate simulations. Moreover, they might be used in future studies to perform investigations on surface-optimized topology within performance spaces, thus helping to control the design costs.

Acknowledgments: The authors would like to thank Sönke Pelzer for providing the initial accurate room geometry, and Gabriele Rosmino, who provided the necessary modifications to the simulation models. They are grateful to all the listeners who passionately participated in the listening test.

Author Contributions: Louena Shtrepi and Arianna Astolfi conceived and designed the experiments; Louena Shtrepi performed the experiments; Louena Shtrepi and Giuseppina Emma Puglisi analyzed the data; Louena Shtrepi, Arianna Astolfi and Marco Masoero contributed in the analysis and results discussion; Louena Shtrepi wrote the paper.

Conflicts of Interest: The authors declare no conflict of interest.

Appl. Sci. **2017**, *7*, 224

References

1. Beranek, L. *Concert and Opera Halls: How They Sound*; Acoustical Society of America: Woodbury, NY, USA, 1996; pp. 1–643.
2. Vorländer, M. *Auralization: Fundamentals of Acoustics, Modeling, Simulation, Algorithms and Acoustic Virtual Reality*; Springer: Berlin, Germany, 2008.
3. Kim, Y.H.; Kim, J.H.; Jeon, J.Y. Scale model investigations of diffuser application strategies for acoustical design of performance venues. *Acta Acust. United Acust.* **2011**, *97*, 791–799. [CrossRef]
4. Pelzer, S.; Vorländer, M. Frequency- and Time-dependent Geometry for Real-time Auralizations. In Proceedings of the 20th International Congress on Acoustics, ICA 2010, Sydney, Australia, 23–27 August 2010.
5. Shtrepi, L.; Astolfi, A.; D'Antonio, G.; Guski, M. Objective and perceptual evaluation of distance-dependent scattered sound effects in a small variable-acoustics hall. *J. Acoust. Soc. Am.* **2016**, *140*, 3651–3662. [CrossRef] [PubMed]
6. Schroeder, M.R.; Kuttruff, K.H. On Frequency Response Curves in Rooms. Comparison of Experimental, Theoretical, and Monte Carlo Results for the Average Frequency Spacing between Maxima. *J. Acoust. Soc. Am.* **1962**, *34*, 76–80. [CrossRef]
7. Bork, I. Report on the 3rd Round Robin on Room Acoustical Computer Simulation—Part II: Calculations. *Acta Acust. United Acust.* **2005**, *91*, 753–763.
8. Dalenbäck, B.I. The importance of diffuse reflection in computerized room acoustic prediction and Auralization. *Proc. Inst. Acoust.* **1995**, *17*, 27–34.
9. Hodgson, M. On the prediction of sound fields in large empty rooms. *J. Acoust. Soc. Am.* **1988**, *84*, 253–261. [CrossRef]
10. Stephenson, U.M. An Energetic Approach for the Simulation of Diffraction with-in ray tracing based on the Uncertainty Relation. *Acta Acust. United Acust.* **2010**, *96*, 516–535. [CrossRef]
11. Pohl, A.; Stephenson, U.M. A combination of the sound particle simulation method and the radiosity method. *Build. Acoust.* **2011**, *18*, 97–122. [CrossRef]
12. Pohl, A.; Stephenson, U. Extension of the Uncertainty Relation Based Diffraction to Polygonal Holes. In Proceedings of the Forum Acusticum, Krakow, Poland, 7–12 September 2014.
13. Kleiner, M.; Dalenbäck, B.I.; Svensson, P. Auralization—An Overview. *J. Audio Eng. Soc.* **1993**, *41*, 861–875.
14. Torres, R.R.; Rycker, N.; Kleiner, M. Edge diffraction and surface scattering in concert halls: Physical and perceptual aspects. *J. Temporal Des. Archit. Environ.* **2004**, *4*, 52–58.
15. Torres, R.R.; Kleiner, M.; Dalenbäck, B.-I. Audibility of "Diffusion" in Room Acoustics Auralization: An Initial Investigation. *Acta Acust. United Acust.* **2000**, *86*, 919–927.
16. Lokki, T.; Järveläinen, H. Subjective evaluation of auralization of physics-based room acoustics modeling. In Proceedings of the 2001 International Conference on Auditory Display, Espoo, Finland, 29 July–1 August 2001.
17. Blauert, J. *Spatial Hearing. The Psychophysics of Human Sound Localization*; The MIT Press: Cambridge, MA, USA, 1997.
18. Schröder, D. Physically Based Real-Time Auralization of Interactive Virtual Environments. Ph.D. Thesis, RWTH Aachen University, Aachen, Germany, 2011.
19. Vorländer, M.; Schröder, D.; Pelzer, S.; Wefers, W. Virtual reality for architectural acoustics. *J. Build. Perform. Simul.* **2015**, *8*, 15–25. [CrossRef]
20. Lam, Y.W. A comparison of three diffuse reflection modeling methods used in room acoustics computer models. *J. Acoust. Soc. Am* **1996**, *100*, 2181–2192. [CrossRef]
21. Vorländer, M. Computer simulations in room acoustics: Concepts and uncertainties. *J. Acoust. Soc. Am* **2013**, *133*, 1203–1213. [CrossRef] [PubMed]
22. Nagy, A.B.; Kotschy, A.; Gade, A.C.; Johannessen, H. Room acoustical modeling differences and their consequences. In Proceedings of the 39th International Congress and Exposition on Noise Control Engineering, INTERNOISE 2010, Lisbon, Portugal, 13–16 June 2010.
23. Pelzer, S.; Vorländer, M.; Maempel, H.-J. Room Modeling for Acoustic Simulation and Auralization Tasks: Resolution of Structural Detail. In Proceedings of the German Annual Conference on Acoustics, DAGA 2010, Berlin, Germany, 15–18 March 2010.

24. Siltanen, S.; Lokki, T.; Savioja, L. Geometry reduction in room acoustics modeling. *Proc. Inst. Acoust.* **2006**, *28*, 409–416. [CrossRef]

25. International Organization for Standardization (ISO). *354: Acoustics—Measurement of Sound Absorption in a Reverberation Room*; ISO: Geneva, Switzerland, 2003.

26. International Organization for Standardization (ISO). *17497: Acoustics—Sound-Scattering Properties of Surfaces—Part 1: Measurement of the Random-Incidence Scattering Coefficient in a Reverberation Room*; ISO: Geneva, Switzerland, 2004.

27. International Organization for Standardization (ISO). *17497: Acoustics—Sound-Scattering Properties of Surfaces—Part 2: Measurement of the Directional Diffusion Coefficient in a Free Field*; ISO: Geneva, Switzerland, 2012.

28. Zeng, X.; Christensen, C.; Rindel, J. Practical methods to define scattering coefficients in a room acoustics computer model. *Appl. Acoust.* **2006**, *67*, 771–786. [CrossRef]

29. Cammarata, G.; Fichera, A.; Pagano, A.; Rizzo, G. Acoustical prediction in some Italian theatres. *Acoust. Res. Lett. Online* **2001**, *2*, 61–66. [CrossRef]

30. Wang, L.M.; Rathsam, J. The influence of absorption factors on the sensitivity of a virtual room's sound field to scattering coefficients. *Appl. Acoust.* **2008**, *69*, 1249–1257. [CrossRef]

31. Wang, L.M.; Rathsam, J.; Ryherd, S. Interactions of Model Detail Level and Scattering Coefficients in Room Acoustic Computer Simulation. In Proceedings of the International Symposium on Room Acoustics: Design and Science, RADS 2004, Awaji Island, Japan, 11–13 April 2004.

32. Robinson, P.W.; Xiang, N.; Braasch, J. Investigations of architectural configurations and acoustic parameters for multiple sources. In Proceedings of the 20th International Congress on Acoustics, ICA 2010, Sydney, Australia, 23–27 August 2010.

33. Stephenson, U.M. Are there simple reverberation time formulae also for partially diffusely reflecting surfaces? In Proceedings of the 41st International Congress and Exposition on Noise Control Engineering, INTERNOISE 2012, New York, NY, USA, 19–22 August 2012.

34. Embrechts, J.-J. A Geometrical Acoustics Approach Linking Surface Scattering and Reverberation in Room Acoustics. *Acta Acust. United Acust.* **2014**, *100*, 864–879. [CrossRef]

35. Shtrepi, L.; Pelzer, S.; Vitale, R.; Rychtáriková, M.; Astolfi, A. Objective and perceptual assessment of the scattered sound field in a simulated concert hall. *J. Acoust. Soc. Am.* **2015**, *138*, 1485–1497. [CrossRef] [PubMed]

36. Robinson, P.; Walther, A.; Faller, C.; Braasch, J. Echo thresholds for reflections from acoustically diffusive architectural surfaces. *J. Acoust. Soc. Am.* **2013**, *134*, 2755–2764. [CrossRef] [PubMed]

37. Peutz, V.M.A. The variable acoustics of the Espace de Projection of IRCAM (Paris). In Proceedings of the AES 59th Convention, Hamburg, Germany, 28 February–3 March 1978; pp. 1–8, 1310.

38. Peutz, V.M.A. Nouvelle examen des theories de reverberation. *Revue d'Acoustique* **1981**, *57*, 99–109.

39. AFMG Reflex. Available online: http://reflex.afmg.eu/ (accessed on 10 January 2017).

40. Cox, T.J.; D'Antonio, P. *Acoustic Absorbers and Diffusers: Theory, Design and Application*; Spon: New York, NY, USA, 2004; pp. 1–476.

41. Christensen, C.L. *Odeon Room Acoustics Program, Version 13.0, User Manual*; Industrial, Auditorium and Combined Editions: Lyngby, Denmark, 2013.

42. Rindel, J.H. Computer Simulation Techniques for Acoustical Design of Rooms. *Aust. Acoust.* **1995**, *23*, 81–86.

43. Dalenbäck, B.-I.; Kleiner, M.; Svensson, P. A Macroscopic View of Diffuse Reflection. *J. Audio Eng. Soc.* **1994**, *42*, 793–807.

44. Schröder, D.; Pohl, A. Modeling (non-)uniform scattering distributions in geometrical acoustics. In Proceedings of the International Congress on Acoustics, ICA 2013, Montreal, QC, Canada, 2–7 June 2013.

45. Stephenson, U.M. Eine Schallteilchen-Computer-Simulation zur Berechnung der für die Hörsamkeit in Konzertsälen maßgebenden Parameter. *Acta Acust. United Acust.* **1985**, *59*, 1–20.

46. Christensen, C.L.; Rindel, J.H. A new scattering method that combines roughness and diffraction effects. In Proceedings of the Forum Acusticum, Budapest, Hungary, 29 August–2 September 2005.

47. OpenMeasurements. Available online: www.openMeasurements.net (accessed on 15 January 2017).

48. Rindel, J.H.; Christensen, C.L.; Koutsouris, G. Prediction tools in acoustics-Can we trust the PC? In Proceedings of the ACOUSTIS2013NEWDELHI, New Delhi, India, 10–15 November 2013.

49. Rindel, J.H. The Use of Computer Modeling in Room Acoustics. *J. Vibroengineering* **2000**, *3*, 219–224.

50. Postma, B.N.J.; Katz, B.F.G. Creation and calibration method of acoustical models for historic virtual reality auralizations. *Virtual Real.* **2015**, *19*, 161–180. [CrossRef]
51. Dalenbäck, B. Engineering principles and techniques in room acoustics prediction. In Proceedings of the Baltic-Nordic Acoustic Meeting, BNAM 2010, Bergen, Norway, 10–12 May 2010.
52. ITA-Toolbox. Available online: http://ita-toolbox.org/ (accessed on 28 October 2016).
53. Vorländer, M. Prediction tools in acoustics-Can we trust the PC? In Proceedings of the Baltic-Nordic Acoustic Meeting, BNAM 2010, Bergen, Norway, 10–12 May 2010.
54. International Organization for Standardization. *Acoustics—Measurement of Room Acoustic Parameters—Part 1: Performance Spaces*; ISO 3382-1:2009; ISO: Geneva, Switzerland, 2009.
55. Helm, E.; Trolle, B. Selection of a taste panel. *Wallerstein Lab. Commun.* **1946**, *9*, 181–191.
56. Rousseau, B.; Meyer, A.; O'Mahony, M. Power and sensitivity of the same–different test: Comparison with triangle and duo–trio methods. *J. Sens. Stud.* **1998**, *13*, 149–173. [CrossRef]
57. Psignifit. Available online: http://psignifit.sourceforge.net/ (accessed on 20 October 2016).
58. Wichmann, F.A.; Hill, N.J. The psychometric function: I. Fitting, sampling and goodness-of-fit. *Percept. Psychophys.* **2001**, *63*, 1293–1313. [CrossRef]
59. Wichmann, F.A.; Hill, N.J. The psychometric function: II. Bootstrap-based confidence intervals and sampling. *Percept. Psychophys.* **2001**, *63*, 1314–1329. [CrossRef] [PubMed]
60. Szudek, J.; Ostevik, A.; Dziegielewski, P.; Robinson-Anagor, J.; Goma, N.; Hodgetts, B.; Ho, A. Can Uhear me now? Validation of an iPod-based hearing loss screening test. *J. Otolaryngol. Head Neck Surg.* **2012**, *41*, 78–84.
61. Ando, Y. *Architectural Acoustics: Blending Sound Sources, Sound Fields, and Listeners*; AIP Press and Springer: New York, NY, USA, 1998; pp. 1–252.
62. Jeon, J.Y.; Ryu, J.K.; Kim, Y.H.; Sato, S. Influence of absorption properties of materials on the accuracy of simulated acoustical measures in 1:10 scale model test. *Appl. Acoust.* **2009**, *70*, 615–625. [CrossRef]
63. Garcia, F.; Planells, A.; Cerdá, S.; Montell, R.; Giménez, A.; Segura, J.; Barba, A.; Cibrián, R. Archeological acoustics of the venue of the "Misteri d'Elx" oral and intangible cultural heritage (UNESCO): "Basilica de Santa Maria de Elche". In Proceedings of the Forum Acusticum, Krakow, Poland, 7–12 September 2014.
64. Robinson, P.; Pätynen, J.; Lokki, T. The role of diffusive architectural surfaces on auditory spatial discrimination in performance venues. *J. Acoust. Soc. Am.* **2013**, *133*, 3940–3950. [CrossRef] [PubMed]
65. Ryu, J.K.; Jeon, J.Y. Subjective and objective evaluations of a scattered sound field in a scale model opera house. *J. Acoust. Soc. Am.* **2008**, *124*, 1538–1549. [CrossRef] [PubMed]

MDPI AG

St. Alban-Anlage 66

4052 Basel, Switzerland

Tel. +41 61 683 77 34

Fax +41 61 302 89 18

http://www.mdpi.com

Applied Sciences Editorial Office

E-mail: applsci@mdpi.com

http://www.mdpi.com/journal/applsci